PSYCHODIAGNOSIS

Galton

Binet

Freud

Rorschach

FRANCIS GALTON (1822–1911): British scientist and pioneer in methods, psychologic and statistical, for measuring and comparing the traits of individuals; inventor of the word association technic.

ALFRED BINET (1857–1911): French psychologist; constructor—with Simon—of the first widely and successfully used test of general intelligence.

SIGMUND FREUD (1856–1939): Austrian psychiatrist; founder of psychoanalysis and of psychodynamic dream-interpretation from which the various projective methods of psychodiagnosis are largely derived.

HERMANN RORSCHACH (1884–1922): Swiss psychiatrist who adapted the ink-blot method for diagnostic application in a psychodynamic setting, thus introducing the technic that bears his name.

PSYCHODIAGNOSIS

An Introduction to the Integration of Tests in Dynamic Clinical Practice

BY

SAUL ROSENZWEIG, Ph.D.

Associate Professor, Departments of Psychology and Neuropsychiatry, Washington University, St. Louis, Mo. Formerly Chief Psychologist, Western State Psychiatric Institute and Clinic, Pittsburgh, Pa.

WITH THE COLLABORATION OF

KATE LEVINE KOGAN, Ph.D.

Formerly Senior Clinical Psychologist, Western State Psychiatric Institute and Clinic, Pittsburgh, Pa.

GRUNE & STRATTON
NEW YORK
1949

Printed by Boyd Printing Co., Inc., Albany
Bound by MOORE & CO., INC., Baltimore,
in pyroxylin-impregnated cloth
water-repellent and verminproof

A man's individuality is his fate.

Herakleitos of Ephesos

Preface

About twenty years ago F. L. Wells (20)* in a memorable volume, "Mental Tests in Clinical Practice," presented a methodology that has grown since then very largely in the directions that he envisaged. Even now his book can be read and reread with profit since its essential philosophy is still fresh and modern. In the intervening years, however, there has been notable progress in the field of experimental psychodynamics and—more relevant to clinical practice—in that of the projective methods. Of these latter instruments Wells's book discussed only the "free association experiment." In contrast, the volume by Murray (10) and his co-workers, "Explorations in Personality," which appeared in 1938—a decade ago—is replete with examples of this more evolved approach to the understanding of the individual case. The Thematic Apperception Test, the Rorschach and other projective technics are there liberally employed. The present book may be said to combine in its orientation the contribution of Wells with that of Murray in a form that represents the cumulative and progressive use of tests in psychodiagnosis today.

Experience with beginning students of professional psychology, as well as with those in the allied fields of medicine, nursing, occupational therapy, and social work, has revealed a clear need for an up-to-date introduction to psychodiagnosis that could be read in a short time and understood without extensive background. Such a text would have to be written in untechnical language and could well avoid the more usually discussed aspects of test standardization that are

---

* It should be pointed out in explanation of the practice regarding references in the text that articles and books of general interest have been numerically listed in one section at the end of the volume. Numbers in parentheses beside an author's name anywhere in the text refer to this bibliography. References for the individual tests described in Chaps. 3 through 7 are indicated at the end of each of these chapters.

described in many psychologic works. Its chief function would be to explain the purpose, materials, instructions, obtained data, scoring methods, and interpretation of a representative group of psychologic tests as these are currently applied. In order to illustrate the integration and interpretation of test findings sample reports would be required. To fulfill the design thus sketched is one of the purposes of this volume.

In 1944 an attempt was made minimally to satisfy the need for an introductory text in psychodiagnosis through the publication of "An Elementary Syllabus of Psychological Tests" (16). It is from this germ that the book before the reader has developed. The aim throughout has been to offer a concrete demonstration of the operations performed by the clinical psychologist in his diagnostic role. Abstract formulations as to method and theory occupy a far less prominent place here, partly because it has seemed premature to state baldly principles that are as yet largely implicit and tentative in the work of the psychodiagnostician. Nevertheless, the advanced student and the professional worker will find in these pages a consistent application of dynamic postulates intended to knit together the older psychometric and the newer projective technics. The array of personality studies in Parts III and IV demonstrates the cogency of this approach. Several new contributions to procedure are also included, notably in respect to the analysis of the Thematic Apperception Test, the use of the Picture-Frustration Study, and the development of the Photoscope technic for evaluating psychosexual status.

The division of responsibility in the preparation of the present work should be indicated. The senior author wrote the entire manuscript, except as presently to be noted, and is responsible for the organization and execution of the book. The collaborating author, in addition to being continually available for consultation, contributed first draft write-ups for about half the manuscript including, in particular, some of the individual test descriptions and most of the protocols in Part II, the case materials in Part III and similar portions of three chapters in Part IV.

Earlier versions of several chapters have appeared as journal articles, some of them in collaboration with former colleagues, as follows: S. Rosenzweig, J. Personality, 1946, 15, 94–100 (Chap. 1); S. Rosenzweig and R. A. Clark, J. abnorm. soc. Psychol., 1945, 40, 195–204 (Chap. 13); H. J. Clarke, J. Personality, 1946, 15, 105–112 (Chap. 15); K. L. Kogan, ibid, 113–120 (Chap. 16); S. Rosenzweig, ibid, 121–142 (Chap. 19); S. Rosenzweig, B. Simon and M. Ballou (Dolkart), Amer. J. Orthopsychiat., 1942, 12, 283–293 (Chap. 20); S. Rosenzweig, J. abnorm. soc. Psychol., 1949, 44, in press (Chap. 21). Thanks are extended to authors and journals for permission to adapt and rewrite these papers for inclusion here. Grateful acknowledgment is made to Mrs. Gayle Kelly Lumry for administering the tests and writing a draft of the report incorporated as World Test Protocol 2 (Chap. 7).

With one or two exceptions (in particular, the content of Chapter 20), the described cases have been drawn from the files of the Psychology Laboratory at the Western State Psychiatric Institute and Clinic, Pittsburgh. The testing was carried out by the authors with substantial collaboration from the various members of the Laboratory during 1943–1948, while the senior author served as Chief Psychologist. In a sense this book is thus a fruit of the practical operations of this unit and is based upon its experience. Other clinics, no doubt, have other emphases and aims, but in the main outlines of what is described, it is expected that the selection here involved will not in any major aspect prejudice the picture of the psychodiagnostician's work conveyed to the reader. Moreover, as is explained in the text, the fact that nearly all the reports are derived from studies of mental patients—rather than "normals"—is not considered to obscure in any significant way the portrayal of what is essential in the dynamic approach to psychodiagnosis.

The bounty of the Institute under its Director Grosvenor B. Pearson, M.D., has been great during the period in which the data for this book were gathered and the writing completed. Acknowledgment is made with thanks.

The secretarial services of Miss Betty Busche were an indispensable aid in the completion of the book; her skill and patience contributed in significant measure to such accuracy and formal attractiveness as it possesses. Mrs. Edith E. Fleming rendered important assistance in the work of preparing the illustrations, reading the proofs, and compiling the index. To Mrs. Louise Rosenzweig a debt of gratitude is owed for unfailing encouragement and help at every stage of the writing.

Thanks are extended to Mr. Thomas M. Jarrett, official photographer of the University of Pittsburgh, for the photography in the frontispiece. Three of the portraits in that plate are reproduced by permission and with acknowledgment as follows: to Professor E. S. Pearson for the photograph of Francis Galton from Karl Pearson's *The Life, Letters and Labours of Francis Galton,* Cambridge University Press, 1930, Vol. III[A]; to Doctor Henry H. Goddard for the picture of Alfred Binet from Binet and Simon's *The Development of Intelligence in Children,* Williams and Wilkins Company (Baltimore), 1916; to Doctor Olga Rorschach for the previously unpublished photograph of her late husband.

Professor Arthur M. Young of the Department of Classics at the University of Pittsburgh kindly supplied the exact translation of the pre-Socratic fragment (number 119 in Vol. I of *Die Fragmente der Vorsokratiker* by H. Diels) which appears as the epigraph of the book.

S. R.

December, 1948.

CONTENTS

xi

PART FIVE: THE FUTURE

Part One

INTRODUCTION

Chapter 1

Clinical Psychology as a Psychodiagnostic Art

A S A PSYCHODIAGNOSTIC art clinical psychology derives historically from two chief sources—the psychometric and the psychodynamic. It is from the pioneer work of Francis Galton, who was interested in the measurement of individual differences as a basis for the eugenic advancement of the race, and from that of Alfred Binet, who was attempting to improve educational practices in the elementary grades, that psychometric devices for the interindividual assessment of intelligence and other capacities arose. There thus emerged a group of psychometricians who were versed in the use of these instruments and in the related statistical methods and who worked characteristically in educational settings. The psychodynamic origins of clinical psychology are found in the contributions of the nineteenth-century French psychopathologists and, even more typically, in the work of Freud and his associates. Psychoanalysis developed an approach to the individual from the standpoint not of intellectual capacities but of drives and conflicts within the person and assumed that the individual must be understood primarily in his own terms rather than in comparison with some normative population. The projective methods of psychodiagnosis, e.g., the Rorschach, evolved largely from this medically oriented matrix and represent currently a major experimental frontier of clinical psychology.

It is, of course, easily possible to overdraw the distinction between the old and the new. Those clinical psychologists who have had adequate training and experience in the past, with or without the psychodynamic orientation, have always discharged their responsibilities in a fashion that distinguished them signally from the sheer psychometrician. The significant differentiation today lies in emphasis either upon test devices that lend themselves by their limited nature to careful statistical standardization or upon technics that subserve the understanding of the whole man. In other words, the dynamic clinical psychologist now aspires to the role of an explorer who uses whatever objective instruments are available but relies also upon interview procedures that are largely qualitative and upon projective technics that are not statistically standardized in the strict sense of the intelligence tests. Conceptually he takes his stand upon an interpretation of the individual's adjustment as understood in terms of capacities and limitations, past history, and present environmental relationships. With this approach the psychologist naturally needs to draw upon every available avenue of knowledge. Though he uses what he can from the experimental and clinical psychology of the past, he also leans heavily upon the formulations of psychoanalysis, psychobiology, and psychosomatic medicine as well as upon the older psychiatric knowledge and upon such contributions to the understanding of behavior as may be had from anthropology and the social sciences.

It is desirable to define the connotations of the term *psychodiagnosis* as its usage is gradually beginning to warrant and as, at any rate, it is employed in the present book. Convinced of the inadequacy of phenotypical diagnostic signs and symptoms, psychologists are turning with increasing frequency to underlying or genotypical dynamics for the more stable variables upon which to build personality theory and clinical practice. At the same time it is recognized that empirical signs can alone provide a basis for scientifically investigating and predicting behavior. It thus becomes the task of psychodiagnosis to bridge the gap between diagnostic indications and implicit psychodynamic forces

—an objective that must depend largely upon new knowledge of the systematic relationships between the various levels of the personality. From this standpoint *psychodiagnosis* may be regarded as a portmanteau word signifying the reconciliation of *psychodynamics* and *diagnosis*.

There is, of course, no one exclusive approach to psychodiagnosis. Even the psychologist uses a considerable variety and his colleagues in related professions have their own methods that obviously lie outside the scope of this volume. What distinguishes the work of the psychologist as psychodiagnostician is his reliance upon "tests" that even in the case of the projective methods have been *standardized*. This greater objectivity of the psychologist's tools is what recommends his work to colleagues in other disciplines.

The problems that the clinical psychologist can help his co-workers to solve are almost coextensive with the whole field of adjustment. To aid in *differential diagnosis*—whether in the sense of the psychiatric label or of more functional differentiations—the psychologist has a repertoire of procedures that delve into various aspects of the patient's capacities. The well-known intelligence tests belong here, as do also memory tests, measures of intellectual inefficiency and deterioration, and the newer procedures for studying concept formation. In relation to *treatment* there are technics that help not only to determine whether a particular patient is likely to benefit from a contemplated therapy but aid also in evaluating the effects of a method which has already been employed. Both the capacity tests already mentioned and the personality devices yet to be described are relevant in this context. As related to problems of vocational and social *rehabilitation* there are available a large number of aptitude and achievement tests that supplement in important respects the more general tests of intellectual level and efficiency. Finally, there is the increasingly important area of *personality dynamics* in connection with which the psychiatrist may be given assistance in the better understanding of the patient as well as in the planning and conduct of psychotherapy. The procedures available here comprise not only the *subjective* approaches represented by the well-known questionnaires and inventories but also the *objective* miniature life-situation tests (which are somewhat harder to institute in a clinical setting) and—currently most significant of all—the *projective* technics.

The projective methods occupy a unique place in the new orientation of the clinical psychologist. More than any other of the available psychodiagnostic devices they embody the psychodynamic point of view. They differ in fundamental respects from the psychometric tests upon which the clinical psychologist had to depend previously. While the latter could with seeming success be administered by a technician, scored by a clerk, and interpreted by anyone who could read a percentile chart, the projective technics represent a means, supplementary to the psychometric, for comprehending the total personality in psychodynamic terms. In the proper hands, these technics are an application of experimental methodology. In so far as they are employed merely to elicit "signs" pointing invariably to one or another "diagnosis," they will do considerable harm. There is obviously much room for important research that will make it possible to use these procedures more reliably and consistently, but they are intrinsically disposed against any over-simplified form of interpretation and it is doubtful whether they can ever attain a high degree of independence from the skill of the psychologist who employs them.

The fact should, however, be recognized that all psychologic tests can be administered and interpreted on a broad psychodynamic basis. The mechanical practice of psychometrics is no longer considered adequate. Even from the ordinary test of intelligence the qualified examiner may glean important information about the personality by observing not only the rightness or wrongness of the answers according to the test key, but by noting the nature and process of "erroneous" responses. Incidental verbalizations, physical behavior, and changes in rapport are similarly significant to the skilled observer. In other words, the interpretation of any psychologic test involves, in addition to the statistical comparison of the subject's results with those of other persons, an understanding of the intra-individual patterning of his reactions.

In like fashion the use of many overlapping instruments, instead of reliance upon one alone, makes it possible to approach the interrelated capacities, traits, and drives of the individual from diverse directions. It thus becomes feasible by a discriminative study of convergence and discrepancy to arrive at a more valid interpretation of the total personality.

Not only are all the available psychologic tests potentially psychodynamic in application but every person, patient or so-called normal, exemplifies the principles of psychodynamics and is to be understood accordingly. This statement is not equivalent to the truism that everyone is a little abnormal but represents instead the position that, from the psychobiologic orientation, every individual is "normal." Normality here becomes equivalent to "lawful" or "understandable." In his own terms and from the standpoint of his efforts to adapt to his environment and to himself with his particular drives, capacities, and handicaps, every individual is psychodynamically intelligible. Such a view contrasts sharply with that according to which the normal is set off against the abnormal by appeal to group standards statistically determined in measurably descriptive terms. The psychodynamic orientation does not exclude such statistical standards but goes beyond them in attempting to account for the various positions of the individual in his group according to the interrelationships within his particular unity as a person. In the light of these postulates it should be apparent that even though the great majority of the cases discussed in this volume are those of mental patients, the diagnostic labels are clearly secondary to psychodynamic considerations. The latter hold not only for these so-called abnormal individuals but for so-called normal ones as well. The essential methods and principles of psychodiagnosis as exhibited in this work are thus presented as having a more or less universal validity.

Since the art of psychodiagnosis thus clearly involves skills of a high order, a question naturally arises as to the nature of the "artist" or "artisan" who is qualified to practice. It would extend beyond the scope of the present discussion to consider the necessary training of the clinical psychologist but a few comments may be in order concerning the personality characteristics of the potential psycho-diagnostician. In clinical psychology, as in every other field devoted to the understanding and treatment of behavior, the personality of the practitioner is crucially important. We do not yet have more than a glimmering of the criteria for proper selection, though the problem is broadly recognized and with it the obligation to study it. The clinical psychologist is most fortunately situated for conducting such an investigation though he has, in fact, probably done much less about systematic selection than have other professional groups, and certainly less than many industries. The obvious explanation for this paradoxical difference lies, of course, in the recency of clinical psychology as a profession.

The personality criteria that appear, on the basis of experience in various centers, to be especially important for potential clinical psychologists are not only those that are relevant generally in psychiatry, social work and other fields devoted to the study and treatment of man, but those which bear more particularly on the psychodynamic point of view above sketched. This point of view implies a certain outlook upon human nature in general without which the practice of psychodiagnosis becomes difficult if not impossible. Among the relevant personality criteria in such a context are the following: (1) A keen interest in people and in human relations without the morbid type of curiosity that indicates unresolved aggressive or sexual drives. (2) A capacity for empathy with others. (3) Aptitude for appreciating meaningful interrelationships in personal experience, based upon a keen sensitivity to certain emotional details and a broad cultural background. (4) Greater verbal than mechanical ability but with the qualification that the verbal ability should be more "ability" and less "verbal." (5) Freedom from such guilt or anxiety as would impede a natural expression of aggressiveness necessary for objectifying relationships. (6) Tolerance in the best sense of the term—more interest in the understanding of drives, habits, and attitudes than in the making of moral or other valuative judgments.

PLAN OF THE BOOK

As has already been indicated, the method of presentation adopted for this volume emphasizes the concrete materials and operations of the clinical psychologist rather than the abstract principles that are implicit in his tools and in his work.* The conventional discussion of test standardization is accordingly omitted. The chief subdivisions of the book represent the effort to demonstrate in steps of increasing complexity the manner in which tests are used in psychodiagnosis. Thus a series of available instruments are first described one at a time in Part II and each of these is illustrated by one or more representative protocols from actual subjects. The protocols here in question are recognizably incomplete and in a certain sense fail to represent the function of the individual test in a battery. It is for this reason that in some instances the same subject has served for illustration not only of the individual tests but, at a later stage of the volume, to exemplify the results obtainable from a group of related instruments used with the same individual. The careful student will profit from the comparison of the individual test protocols with the report of the full battery in these instances.

In Part III the integration of psychologic findings from several test procedures is illustrated. In the three cases covered, the concrete responses from each of the several tests employed are presented, test by test. The tentative conclusions drawn from each test are described and an effort is made to state the hypotheses on which the selection of the succeeding instruments was made. The findings from the other tests are similarly presented and, as far as the circumstances permit, the evolution of the picture is sketched *in statu nascendi*.

* Some of these principles remain still to be formulated. The older and well-recognized ones, concerned mainly with the psychometric approach, have been frequently presented. The manner in which psychologic tests *sample* behavior experimentally and the way in which they achieve *objectivity* (as compared with the subjective impressions derived from interviews, etc.) by the statistical determination of *reliability* and *validity* are described with unusual clarity and brevity by Darley (4), Chap. 3, and more comprehensively by Greene (6).

At the end the psychologic report as it would be offered to a professional colleague is given. In selecting the three cases thus treated, the objective was to include patients differing widely in type.

Part IV carries the reader another step forward. In order to make available a broader exhibit of cases than could be offered in Part III, a representative series of reports from patients with a variety of problems is here presented. Moreover, the aim now becomes one of combining with the test approach other essential data for adequate diagnosis, especially social history and psychiatric interviews. To some extent this same objective is followed in the reports based on individual tests in Part II and in the evolutionary reports that are offered in Part III. In Part IV, however, the step is not incidental but occupies a place of almost correlative importance with the presentation of the test findings. At the same time, the contribution made by the psychologic tests remains focal.

Part V briefly reviews the past relationships of clinical psychology to general or experimental psychology and considers the most fruitful future orientation of the one to the other. In this context psychodiagnosis emerges as both art and science.

Part Two
THE RANGE OF AVAILABLE INSTRUMENTS

Chapter 2

Scope

THE SCORE of tests to be outlined and illustrated in these pages have been selected from the hundreds available to exemplify the chief types employed in present-day clinical psychology. The descriptions are in every instance faithful to the source materials. The first group of procedures discussed is concerned with the measurement of intelligence. Instruments for both adults and children are covered. Some which depend mainly on the use of words and some relying chiefly on performance with the hands are included. A second array of tests deals with loss of mental efficiency, i.e., intellectual deterioration. Some of the best devices for the detection of deficit and inefficiency are discussed. A third group of procedures is concerned with vocational aptitudes and interests. One of these instruments is a measure of mechanical ability, a second attempts to gage musical talent, and a third surveys vocational interests in general. Tests of personality constitute the final category presented, though here a division into two sections has been made. The first section includes certain of the more conventional approaches to personality, particularly the questionnaire or inventory now often used merely to elicit the subject's *opinions* of his behavior as a measure of insight. The second section comprises the projective approaches to psychodynamics

—procedures that permit the subject to reveal himself by the way in which he organizes relatively neutral stimulus material. These devices probe the deeper, implicit and sometimes even unconscious foundations of the total personality and represent the newest and the boldest devices in the armamentarium of the psychologist.*

The range of tests covered in this text testifies to the rapid strides which have been made in clinical psychology during recent years. The psychologist in hospital, clinic, or school is no longer limited to the technics available for the measurement of intelligence alone. The personality of the whole man, emotional as well as intellectual, in its various interrelationships becomes more and more his province. Even where intellectual functions are studied, the emphasis has been shifted from the numerical intelligence quotient to the more intimate analysis of the components in mental ability, as reflected in the various subtests; and less stress is laid upon the momentary status than upon the dynamic growth and decline of intellectual capacities. Equally, if not even more, significant are the various projective procedures that have been developed in the past few years to supplement the rather superficial personality inventories. That important area of personality which includes the basic needs, attitudes, goals, and habit patterns involved in every major life adjustment may now thus be approached.

Needless to say, increasingly greater skill is required of the clinical psychologist in proportion to the greater responsibilities laid upon him by these improved instruments. Not least among these demands is that for research in those important regions where vital clinical problems, on the one hand, and methods of laboratory experimentation, on the other, are seen more and more to converge. From this standpoint the tests here outlined often disclose problems for fundamental research into the nature of personality as well as into the characteristics of the instruments themselves. It may reasonably be expected that progress in both these directions will be mutual and coincident.

* For a survey of certain educational and achievement tests not covered in this volume the reader is referred to J. G. Darley (4), Chap. 4.

Well-trained clinical psychologists in mental hospital, child guidance center, school, personnel unit of factory or store, or in the various social agencies are prepared to give most of the tests here described and many others. Facilities for carrying out a psychologic examination naturally differ from clinic to clinic. Time is always a consideration and, though most of the devices discussed below take from 30 minutes to an hour and a quarter for their administration, a period as long, if not longer, is apt to be required for scoring. When, finally, the interpretation of results is reached, not only is further time required but the relatively highest order of skill, based on varied experience, is demanded. The clinical psychologist must be capable of evaluating the representativeness of the findings in terms of the subject's cooperation and general mental state at the time of examination. An intimate knowledge of both the objectives and limitations of the particular procedures is essential if naive misinterpretation of results is to be avoided. The qualitative interrelationships among items or subtests are often more important than the final numerical score of a scale, and far more skill is required for the understanding of the former than for the computation of the latter. Since reliance is, moreover, practically never placed on one test alone, the most exacting task for the psychologist consists in collating the results of various tests. By noting the way in which the different procedures complement or even contradict each other, it is possible to build up a fairly dependable picture of the living individual.

Before a combination of instruments can be understood, however, each must be met singly and recognized for what it has to contribute to the whole. The five succeeding chapters present such treatment of a score of separate tests.

Chapter 3

Tests of General Intelligence

IN THIS SECTION are included tests that are variously divisible. Some of these headings are: (a) for use with *adults* or with *children* primarily, though sometimes the same test has one form for each of these large age groups; (b) for administration to *individuals* or to *groups*—sometimes both; (c) *verbal* in respect to the content of the problems presented and the form in which the answers are prescribed, or *performance* (manipulative) in that the tasks are solved by judgment expressed through eye-hand coordination. An effort will be made to present samples of all these categories.

The role of the intelligence test in psychodiagnosis naturally depends upon the particular problem presented. Where a question of mental deficiency is involved, the introduction of such a test needs no justification. Sometimes, however, the value of such a measure is less obvious but equally important. For example, in instances where mental disorganization that accompanies certain psychotic conditions must be evaluated for a complete understanding of the disorder, the intelligence test may provide invaluable clues both quantitative and qualitative. In this context the intelligence rating may illuminate the course of the patient's mental disorder by affording a measure for comparison with his educational or occupational achievement in the past. While such study is apt to be diagnostic in its primary purpose, the results help also in determining whether designated treatment methods or plans for placement or vocational education are justified. There are, by and large, standards of intellectual capacity required for success in different occupations and professions. So, too, certain forms of psychotherapy demand a degree of cooperation and insight from the subject that would not be possible without a certain minimal intellectual level.

A normal growth curve has been described as follows: intelligence increases rapidly from birth, reaches its maximum between 14 and 20 years of age, stays at a fairly constant level for a period of time, declines gradually as middle age is approached, and then more sharply with the oncoming of old age. The evaluation of deterioration is a problem in itself, important not only in senile conditions but also in certain extreme forms of mental disturbance, including organic brain disease. Though scales of general intelligence, when properly analyzed, are of help in this connection, a number of tests, as illustrated in the next chapter, have been constructed for this special purpose.

It is more and more being emphasized by clinical psychologists that the I. Q. or mental age alone tells only a very small part of the story with reference to the patient's intellectual capacities. In fact, some psychodiagnosticians refuse to report such figures lest they be abused by over-simplified interpretation. To supplement the gross quantitative total of an intelligence test, the clinician introduces findings based upon the separate components of the subject's performance. Many intelligence scales, e.g., the Wechsler-Bellevue discussed below, make it possible to study the relative efficiency of the subject in different sorts of intellectual tasks. When such an approach is employed, it becomes feasible to investigate characteristic patterns of intellectual efficiency. Thus, in the various mental disorders particular combinations of items may tend to be lowered in score, others to be raised. Systematic studies from this point of view have been directed of late to the effects of advancing age, organic brain disease, and the several neuroses and psychoses.

The analysis of subtest patterns in intelligence scales like the Wechsler-Bellevue has been long anticipated by studies of so-called "scatter." It is expected that mental development will, in the case of the healthy individual, proceed more or less constantly in respect to the various aspects of ability. The subject who performs at grossly different levels of efficiency in the tasks included in the usual composite scale is apt to be internally disorganized in a way that corresponds with the disorganization presented in the test results. The degree of scatter thus becomes a criterion of arrested or otherwise impeded function. On such a basis it then becomes possible to analyze further the qualitative patterns of efficiency that may distinguish one mental disorder from another.

In the present chapter the tests presented are concerned primarily with evaluating the general level of intelligence as well as the several components usually comprised under that heading. More specialized deviations as, for example, in conceptual thinking or memory are considered in Chapter 4. In practice, where a question of intellectual disorganization or deterioration needs to be carefully evaluated, both the ordinary intelligence tests and the specific measures of intellectual efficiency need to be employed.

1. REVISED STANFORD-BINET INTELLIGENCE SCALE *

a. *Purpose.* In 1901 a French educational commission recognized the need for separating mentally defective from normal children in order that the former might receive more adequate instruction. In response to this need Alfred Binet published his first scale for measuring intelligence in 1905. After his death in 1911, the fundamentals of his work were made the basis of a number of revisions and extensions in this and other countries. The form which came into most general use was that of Terman, known as the Stanford Revision of the Binet Tests. This first Stanford Revision was published in 1916 and was replaced after 20 years of very wide application by the revision of Terman and Merrill, which appeared in 1937. The latter revision, known as the Revised Stanford-Binet Intelligence Scale, is the form most widely used at the present time. Its purpose is to determine the level of general mental ability.

b. *Materials and Instructions.* The scale consists of a large number of items ranging in difficulty from the Two-Year (II) level to the Superior Adult level. For the younger children such tasks as putting wooden beads on a string, building block towers, naming small objects, etc., are given. Tests of immediate memory span for words and numbers are found throughout the scale.

* References for the individual tests described in Chaps. 3 through 7 are indicated at the end of each of these chapters.

At the higher levels items are given which involve abstract verbal and numerical reasoning. For example, absurd situations are described and the subject is asked to pick out the incongruous features. Other test items require the subject to define abstract terms, give similarities and differences, or draw designs.

Simple instructions are given orally to the individual subject for each test item.

The Revised Stanford-Binet Scale provides two forms, designated as *Form L* and *Form M,* which differ in content but are mutually equivalent with respect to difficulty, range, reliability, and validity. The alternate form is available for use in retesting.

c. *Data and Scoring.* Representative samples of responses are given in the manual as criteria for scoring each response. The test items in the scale are arranged in year groups. The year group in which the individual can pass all the test items is known as his *basal year.* Testing is continued until the subject can pass none of the items in a year group. Each successful completion of a test item in a year group earns the subject a certain number of months credit. The sum of the credits in terms of months is known as the *mental age.* This expression of the test results in terms of age norms means that the ability of a given subject corresponds to the average ability of subjects of that age. The ratio of the mental age to the chronological or actual life age multiplied by 100 is known as the *Intelligence Quotient* or I. Q. For example, if a child received a mental age of 10 years and had a chronological age of 10 years, the I. Q. would be 100. However, if he had a mental age of 8 years and a chronological age of 10 years, the I. Q. would be 80. On the other hand, if the subject had a mental age of 12 years and a chronological age of 10 years, the I. Q. would be 120.

d. *Interpretation.* Results in terms of I. Q., if valid, may be classified into rough groups as follows:

Above 120	Superior intelligence
110–120	High average
90–109	Average
80–89	Dull normal
65–79	Borderline
Below 65	Mentally defective

The present test is designed primarily for use with children. With this end in view, the standardization was almost entirely based on children, and the content is directed toward children's interests. For these reasons, the use of the instrument with adults, except those of inferior level, is questionable and its interpretation doubtful.

Illustrative Protocol 1

A girl 9 years and 11 months old was referred to an out-patient psychiatric clinic for advice regarding home placement. She was the next to the youngest of ten children. After the mother's death, when the patient was three years old, the father had made futile attempts to maintain a home with the aid of housekeepers, and by placing the younger children in the homes of various relatives. At the time of referral the child was living with the family of a married brother under extremely crowded conditions; six persons were housed in three rooms. Here she was creating a problem because of masturbation and sex-play with her four year-old niece. A sympathetic aunt had expressed willingness to give her a foster home, provided that better understanding of the child's difficulties and of her potentialities could be gained.

The psychologic examination was therefore planned in order to investigate both her intelligence and her personality endowment. The Revised Stanford-Binet Examination, Form L, was chosen as a means of evaluating intellectual capacity since it is one of the most satisfactory technics for use with children and since its results provide especially good prediction of school progress. The following observations were made during the course of the examination.

The child was able to pass all the year VII tests, and the assumption was made that she would thus be able to pass all items which were easier than these; she was credited with a *basal age* of 7 years. At year VIII she was able to recall the main facts from a brief story which had been read to her, and she successfully reproduced a sentence from immediate memory. She recognized the practical absurdities of some verbal statements and analyzed correctly the similarities and differences between certain concrete concepts, such as a baseball and an orange, and an ocean and a river. Her vocabulary, as measured by the number of words adequately defined, was below the standard for this age level. She also failed certain questions of social and practical comprehension, stating that the water made a sailboat move, and that if she found a three year-old baby who was lost, she would take it to the Lost and Found in a department store. Of the six tests at this age level she succeeded in four and was, therefore, given additional age-credits of 8 months.

Of the year IX tests she failed only one out of six—that requiring the reproduction from memory of simple visual designs which had been exposed for ten seconds. She was able to resolve the absurd statements presented at this level, could supply rhymes for given words, computed simple change mentally, and repeated four digits reversed. She successfully visualized and represented the result of cutting a folded piece of paper. These successes earned her 10 months credit.

At year X the only credit she lost was on the vocabulary subtest. She read a short paragraph quickly and accurately, with good recall of its content. She demonstrated normal richness and fluidity of associations by naming more than 28 words in one minute and gave acceptable reasons for simple social values. The practical absurdity of a pictured scene was adequately analyzed by her. She also demonstrated immediate memory for six digits. Another 10 months age-credit was added to her total.

When year XI was reached she began failing more markedly. She gave correctly in simple form the meanings of abstract words, repeated a fairly long sentence by rote, and again detected the absurdity of certain statements. She again failed in reproduction of visual designs. She could not successfully analyze the similarity between three concepts, such as a snake, a cow, and a sparrow, or a book, a teacher, and a newspaper, although her efforts were better than complete failure. She failed to grasp the logical significance of a social problem situation. She thus passed only half of the items at this age standard, and was credited with 6 months more.

At years XII and XIII, respectively, she passed only one task, each dependent almost entirely on rote memory and concentration. She was able to repeat five digits in reversed order and to reproduce a series of isolated words lacking logical connection. All other attempts at these levels were failures. She earned, then, 4 additional months credit, 2 each at year XII and year XIII.

All year XIV tests were failed and the examination was terminated on the assumption that she could do no tasks more difficult than these. Her accumulated credits were then tabulated as follows:

Basal Age	7 years
VIII	8 months
IX	10 months
X	10 months
XI	6 months
XII	2 months
XIII	2 months
XIV	0 months

Total: 7 years, 38 months
or 10 years, 2 months

With a chronological age of 9 years, 11 months, her I. Q. was thus 103.

The results of the scale warranted the conclusion that the child was to be rated at the average standard for her age, and that, according to some of the indications, her potential capacity might be even a little higher. She read adequately at her age norms and displayed especially good attention and concentration so that in at least some spheres she evidenced better than average skills. On the other hand, social comprehension and vocabulary range were notably limited. These findings indicated that she had not learned as readily from her interpersonal and social relationships as she had from more impersonal experiences; hence she had assimilated less knowledge and judgment from her environment than she should have since she seemed to have the mental capacity to handle fairly complex concepts. This kind of pattern frequently means that there have been emotional problems of long standing with the result that the child is tense and anxious in affectively-toned situations and becomes detrimentally selective about the type of problem which he handles effectively.

Consideration of the personality findings in conjunction with the Stanford-Binet Scale confirmed the final conclusion that this child's environment had failed to give her the acceptance she needed for adequate personality development. It was, however, judged that she had the potential capacity for adjustment if the right combination of environmental conditions and psychotherapy could be instituted.

Illustrative Protocol 2

This 12 year, 3 month-old girl had become the ward of the county authorities as a result of her mother's severe epilepsy, which made it impossible for a suitable home to be maintained. The patient was an only child whose father had deserted the family when she was two. The grandparents had made a home for the mother and child as long as the mother was able to do a certain amount of house work and care for herself and the child. After the mother was of necessity hospitalized because of the frequency and severity of her attacks, the grandparents maintained that they were unable to keep the little girl. They supported that assertion by claiming that she was stubborn, untruthful, dull, and did not get along well in school. The child was in the fourth grade at the time of referral. Psychologic examination was requested as an aid in determining whether the grandparents' complaints had any basis in fact and whether institutionalization or foster home placement would be the more appropriate.

In the complete psychologic examination both verbal and performance measures of intelligence were included in order to evaluate the subject's educational and vocational potentialities. The Revised Stanford-Binet was employed as part of this test battery, and the following observations were noted.

The child was friendly and talkative throughout the examination but rambled quickly from one topic to another. Sometimes she forgot before completing a task what she had started out to accomplish. She became restless and fidgeted after a short period at any concentrated activity although she said that she liked the tests and seemed eager to comply with requests in order to make a good impression. She stated that music was the only one of her school subjects that she enjoyed, and that she especially disliked arithmetic.

On the Stanford-Binet Scale she had complete success only at year VI, and was accordingly credited with a *basal age* of 6 years. At year VII she recognized the absurdity of pictured situations, and was able to state the similarity between simple concrete concepts, such as an apple and a peach, and a ship and an automobile. She knew and described the acceptable form of behavior in a situation in which she had broken something belonging to someone else, or in which another girl hit her without meaning to do it. However, she could not repeat five digits in any of three trials and was unable to supply opposite analogies in incomplete sentences such as: "The point of a cane is blunt, the point of a knife is ————." In this example the subject responded "long." She likewise failed in copying a simple diamond form and thus revealed retardation in the sphere of visual-motor development. (Her attempts at this task are shown in Figure 1.) These responses gave her credit for three of the six tests at this level, and added 6 months to her total mental age.

Her vocabulary was just above year VIII so that she received credit here but not at higher levels. She was familiar with the first nine words on the list, but said she had never heard *muzzle* or *Mars,* that *lecture* meant to mix something in a bowl, and that *juggler* was a jug for holding wine or something. She adequately recalled the essential facts of a story which was read to her but could not repeat a sentence verbatim. Good social comprehension was again demonstrated by her correct responses to problem situations. She continued to generalize in a simple way by giving both similarities and differences between a baseball and an orange, an airplane and a kite, and an ocean and a river. Absurdities in verbal statements were not detected by her. Thus, there were four successes and two failures at this level; she earned 8 months additional credit.

FIG. 1. Attempted Copy of Diamond in Stanford-Binet Scale, *Protocol* 2.

At year IX she continued to display poor visual-motor skill by being able neither to reproduce designs from memory nor to visualize how a folded and cut square of paper might look if it were unfolded. She could not supply rhymes for given words, and failed to repeat four digits in reverse order. She was able, however, to compute simple change rapidly and succeeded also in detecting absurdities in verbal statements considered to be more difficult than the ones she had previously failed. She thus earned 4 months credit at this level.

She was credited with only one success at year X—for her ability to name 34 words in one minute. Her rambling, distractible manner of thinking seemed to make this task especially easy for her. There were no other successes either at this or at higher levels.

Her accumulated mental age credits above the year VI basal age amounted to 20 months, the total mental age thus being 7 years, 8 months, and the I. Q., 63. It was noted that except for speed of verbal free association, her highest level of success was three full years below the norms for her age. There seemed to be no special disturbances in one type of activity or situation but, instead, a general retardation in all aspects of her development. Her inferior visual-motor skills were interpreted as strong evidence of poor potential capacity since such abilities are least likely to be affected by emotional or personality difficulties.

Since the other tests used confirmed the results of the Stanford-Binet, it was concluded that the girl was mentally retarded and best classified in the moron group. No specific personality disturbances, other than those related to her intellectual limitations, were observed. It was predicted that she did not have the mental ability for successful accomplishment even in her present fourth-grade placement, and that she would require either special-class instruction or automatic placement according to age and size. It was finally noted that if her environment could be adapted to meet her limitations so as not to make undue demands upon her, there was reason to believe that she could make an adequate adjustment outside an institution.

Illustrative Protocol 3

A 17 year-old girl was admitted to the psychiatric hospital with an illness of sudden onset. She had reached her last year of high school with the reputation of being a good student. Her illness began with a fainting spell which was followed by a period of disturbed behavior—screaming, crying and mental confusion. There was a history of much familial instability. A sister had committed suicide six years earlier. After her admission to the hospital several convulsive seizures of *grand mal* type occurred but she reacted well to medication. She was first examined during her early weeks of hospitalization, at which time she achieved a low average rating on the Wechsler-Bellevue Scale; there was, however, considerable evidence of temporary inefficiency in her test performance. Six months later her behavior had shown certain definite changes and she was much less tense and anxious. Re-examination was requested to help in evaluating whether this alteration represented an improvement in her actual condition or merely another phase of her illness.

On the occasion of the second examination, the Revised Stanford-Binet was employed since the alternate form of the Wechsler-Bellevue Scale had not yet been published. The patient appeared cheerful and friendly but her interest in the tests themselves was somewhat apathetic. Her successes were erratic and variable and covered a very wide range. The general results were very similar to those of the earlier examination. She achieved a mental age rating of 16 years, 7 months and an I. Q. of 94.

In order for her to achieve complete success on a test series and thus establish a basal level, it was necessary to continue testing with progressively easier materials until year IX was reached. She showed marked inability in sizing up problems and in educing relationships and hence failed to detect the inappropriate aspects of situations usually grasped by children of ten, eleven, and twelve. She was likewise unable to reproduce the essential facts of a short paragraph that had been read to her. Though she apparently recalled a few isolated details, she reorganized them in a context quite different from that in which they had appeared.

It sometimes happens that a subject, especially if mentally disturbed, will give two basal ages. Such was the case with this girl. After the basal year IX had been determined, it turned out that she also passed the full set of tests for year XIII. The unpredictable and disorganized nature of her performance is thus demonstrated. Above year XIII successes were again scattered.

She seemed to do best in tasks requiring familiarity with verbal material that was to be reproduced in the same form in which it was originally learned. Vocabulary, for example, met the norms for the second Superior Adult level, and she could make logical sentences involving quite abstract words. However, she could not adapt what she knew to new situations and gave indications of interference in concentration and reasoning. She was, therefore, unable to perform at lower levels certain tasks which she was able to pass at superior ones.

It was accordingly inferred that her level of intellectual function was still considerably lower than it must have been before her acute disturbance. It seemed that she had retained the use of familiar concepts and symbols at a much higher level than she had maintained her ability to apply this knowledge adaptively to new problems or situations. The wide range of discrepancy (scatter) in the skills she displayed and the inconsistency in the quality of her responses were taken as confirmatory qualitative evidence that her illness had persisted and was reflected in her pattern of intellectual function.

2. WECHSLER-BELLEVUE INTELLIGENCE SCALE

a. *Purpose.* This test was constructed to measure the intelligence of *adults* and *adolescents* on both verbal and performance materials.

b. *Materials and Instructions.* It is administered orally to the individual subject, and consists of ten subtests, five of which are described as Verbal and five as Performance. The verbal tests depend upon language for the giving of directions and for the responses of the subject. They are relatively more abstract than the performance tests. The latter are usually concrete, practical, and rest upon little or no use of words other than the simple directions given by the examiner. The performance tests require the subject to do something such as copying a design in blocks or arranging pictures in a story-telling sequence.

Two parallel forms of the scale have been provided, Form I and Form II. The same types of subtests, consisting of different but equated content, are included in both forms. The alternate form is especially useful for retest purposes.

A brief description of each subtest and its function follows:

1. *Information:* consists of questions formulated to tap the subject's range of information on material that the average person with average opportunity should be able to obtain for himself.

2. *Comprehension:* measures the use of "common sense" and judgment in situations described to the subject. Success on this test depends upon the possession of a certain amount of practical information and the ability to use past experience.

3. *Arithmetical Reasoning:* measures mental alertness as well as ability to handle practical calculations.

4. *Memory Span for Digits:* measures immediate memory for digits, forward and backward.

5. *Similarities:* measures ability to discriminate between essential and superficial likenesses; to generalize and think in abstract terms.

6. *Picture Arrangement:* measures ability to comprehend or "size up" a total situation.

7. *Picture Completion:* measures ability to differentiate essential from unessential details.

8. *Block Design:* a test of general intellectual functioning, involving both synthetic and analytic ability, but influenced considerably by the capacity to solve problems in spatial relations.

9. *Object Assembly:* measures insight into spatial relationships of familiar objects.

10. *Digit Symbol:* measures speed and accuracy of learning new associations.

Alternate Test—Vocabulary: Its excellence as a test of intelligence is probably derived from the fact that the number of words a person knows is at once a measure of his past learning ability, his fund of verbal information, and the general range of his ideas.

c. *Data and Scoring.* Subtests are variously scored on the basis of speed, accuracy, comprehension, ability to discriminate and analyze, according to the nature of the task. The points accumulated for each subtest are weighted and totaled to obtain the Full Scale Intelligence Quotient. Verbal and Performance Scale I. Q.'s are separately computed, but these are always considered in relation to the Full Scale I. Q. The Vocabulary test may be scored as an alternate for one of the five verbal subtests.

d. *Interpretation.* This is an excellent scale for adults and adolescents because, unlike many tests of intelligence in the past, it has been standardized on older subjects rather than on children. Furthermore, the material is genuinely interesting to older subjects. Analysis of the scores on the subtests may disclose patterns pointing to temporary loss of efficiency, deterioration due to normal decline with advancing age, or impairment resulting from mental illness. Diagnostic patterns have been described for several types of mental disorder and some progress has been made in delineating the differentiating characteristics from one type of impairment to another.

Illustrative Protocol 1

A 32 year-old married male had been arrested on charges of arson and malicious mischief to the railroads. The court inquiry revealed that he had left school at the age of 14, having reached only fourth grade. He had held many simple laborer's jobs. This record suggested that mental deficiency might be an important factor, and a psychologic examination was requested to investigate this possibility.

The Wechsler-Bellevue Scale was selected as the most appropriate measure. His total score yielded a Full Scale I. Q. of 94. This result, by and large, indicates average intelligence. He was slightly more adept in nonverbal tasks than in verbal ones, so that his I. Q. on the Verbal Scale was 89, on the Performance Scale, 99. It was noted,

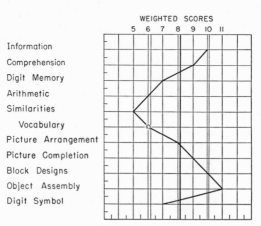

Fig. 2. Scattergram for Wechsler-Bellevue Scale, *Protocol 1.*

also, that he responded quite slowly to verbal questions as though he had difficulty in expressing himself. That this characteristic was not the result of generalized motor retardation was attested by his normal pace in manipulative tasks.

The pattern of his scores on the separate subtests is represented in the accompanying "scattergram" (Figure 2). His weighted scores, as read from the tables in the manual, range from 5 to 11. The heavy line at 8.2 represents the average of his scores on the ten subtests. The lighter lines which enclose the range from 6.2 to 10.2 indicate the expected variability in a person of this level, or what might be called the *normal deviation range.*

If his results on the separate items are examined, the data from which the above figures are derived will be better understood. On the *verbal* part of the scale, he knew 14 of the questions on Information, and though he could not tell who invented the airplane, nor who wrote "Hamlet," he gave the approximate population of the United States and knew that Egypt was in Africa. His responses to the questions on the Comprehension test tended to be on a simple factual level, and indicated that he thought in concrete terms rather than in abstract ones. On Digit Memory he was able to repeat six digits forward and to reverse four. He succeeded in the first five problems on Arithmetic —a result presumably commensurate with his schooling—but he could do none of the more difficult ones. It was noted, further, that he could not read the printed problems correctly. He had extreme difficulty in analyzing the concepts in the Similarities test and in those few cases in which he did succeed his responses were in very concrete terms of use or function. His successes in Vocabulary—an additional test—were limited to a very simple level.

If attention is turned to the *performance* portion of the scale, it may be noted that he was able to put several of the series included under Picture Arrangement in logical sequence and received credit for the first four items. The more difficult series were apparently beyond his level of comprehension, and he did not achieve even partial success. He recognized the essential omissions in the Picture Completion test without undue difficulty, and again displayed an even level of competence within the limits of his capacity. He performed Block Design with relative ease and succeeded in all items, although he received the additional credits for speed only on the simplest pattern of the series. He successfully assembled all the disarranged forms in Object Assembly and in this instance received a time-bonus on the most difficult item. This subtest yielded his highest score and, as may be noted on the scattergram, the only weighted score which falls above his normal deviation range. In the Digit Symbol test he supplied the correct symbol for each number in a laborious fashion so that he had very few spaces filled at the end of the time limit and obtained his lowest performance subtest score. It is a question whether this difficulty in forming an association between a symbol and a familiar concept is not related to his recognized reading disability.

In reviewing and synthesizing these results several conclusions seem warranted. It is clear that this man is not of limited mental endowment. His poor school progress must have been due to factors other than intellectual ones. He was noted as having a reading disability which, uncorrected during his early schooling, could well have impeded general progress. He also exhibited difficulty with other types of material usually learned in school (arithmetic and vocabulary). His success on nonverbal tasks was clearly of average level—a result supporting the view that his apparent dullness is related to educational rather than to natural deficiency. Finally, the relative evenness of his separate scores ruled out temporary inefficiency or other essential disturbance of mental function. The test results were therefore accepted as being representative of his native capacity, and he was judged as having average intelligence.

Illustrative Protocol 2

A 23 year-old girl was transferred to a mental hospital from another (state) hospital after the acute phase of a psychotic episode was past. She was a high-school graduate and had been an honor student.

She had been employed as a clerical worker after completing her education. Her illness began at the age of 20 and was characterized by frequent temper tantrums and occasional physical abuse of her family. She became progressively withdrawn, careless of her personal appearance and hygiene, and expressed delusions of persecution. Later she could recall none of these manifestations of her illness. At the time of examination she appeared to be extremely bashful and shy but she responded fully to direct questioning.

The first test of the routine psychologic examination, which was administered several weeks after her transfer, was the Wechsler-Bellevue Scale. Her scores indicated that she was functioning at the low average standard, the Full Scale I. Q. being 92. Her I. Q. on the Verbal Scale was 96, on the Performance Scale, 89. These levels were considerably below the expected standard for a high-school graduate who had been an honor student.

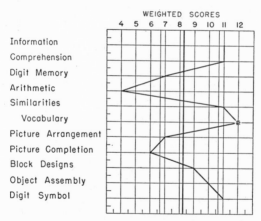

FIG. 3. Scattergram for Wechsler-Bellevue Scale, *Protocol 2*.

It was noted further that there was a wide scatter among her scores on various types of tasks (see Figure 3). In problems closely dependent on the reproduction of familiar information or verbal concepts, without the requirement of logical resynthesis to meet a new situation, she did very well. Thus in Vocabulary, which is often considered the best single indicator of pre-illness level, she did best (weighted score of 12). Information, Comprehension and Similarities were also high (weighted scores of 11). Even in these spheres, however, she introduced much personalized material into her responses. She said, for example, that if she were the first person to discover a fire in a theater, she would tell the usher "and if he was too dumb, I'd go to the drugstore and have them help me call the fire department, and if they were dumbfounded, I'd call myself." Again, she explained the similarity between air and water by stating that "both are substances which cannot be destroyed; God gave them to us, and they are here forever."

Other evidence bore out the interpretation that it was not so much her ability to adapt to new problems that was impaired as it was her ability to detach herself from personal preoccupations in assessing new situations. For example, on the Digit Symbol test, where impersonal or neutral content is involved, she also had a high score (weighted score 11), comparable to her achievement in familiar reproductive tasks. However, on Picture Arrangement, where the test items readily suggest everyday experiences and relationships, her weighted score was only 7. Furthermore, her absorption in her own thoughts appeared to interfere with effective attention and concentration, a disturbance reflected in her low scores on Arithmetic (weighted score 4), Digit Memory (weighted score 7), and Picture Completion (weighted score 6).

These results, in conjunction with those obtained from other tests in the battery, led to the conclusion that, although the patient's overt behavior had lost its bizarre qualities, a marked intellectual and personality disturbance was still present. Her pattern of function was considered to be both quantitatively and qualitatively altered from what for her would be normal; features characteristically associated with unrealistic withdrawal of a schizoid type were evident.

Illustrative Protocol 3

The subject was a 25 year-old woman whose husband had been hospitalized as a result of many neurotic complaints and obviously depressed behavior. He attributed his "breakdown" to his excessively long hours of work as a railroad clerk, and to the fact that he had had to assume the responsibility for a variety of household duties during his leisure time. He stated that his wife seemed unable to run the house, and he therefore had to do the marketing, cleaning, and cooking after his regular work. The patient's physician requested that a psychologic examination be administered to the wife as an aid in determining whether her incompetence was a matter of fact or a reflection of the patient's distorting emotionality.

The Wechsler-Bellevue Scale was employed for this purpose. Her I. Q. on the Full Scale was 63; her Verbal I. Q. was also 63, her Performance I. Q., 68. Her responses in all the subtests were quantitatively and qualitatively those expected of a person with limited endowment. For example, she stated that a thermometer tells you where to go and that London is in the United States. She did not know where rubber came from and could not tell the number of weeks in a year. Similarly, she responded correctly only to the simplest of the arithmetic problems. Her verbalizations were all on a primitive, concrete level, without any evidence of capacity for abstract thinking. She said, for example, that a coat and a dress were alike in that "you wear both," and that air and water were similar "because they're both cool." She was equally handicapped in the manipulative, or performance, subtests and displayed poor judgment and planning ability in them. She succeeded only on the simplest items.

The scattergram of the patient's scores is shown in Figure 4. Since none of the results was at, or even near, the average level, a fundamental lack of intellectual capacity appeared to exist. Moreover, the fact that her highest scores were on some of the items most apt to be lowered by emotional disturbance precluded the interpretation that her poor performance might be the result of transient personality disorder (weighted scores of 7 on Digit Memory, Picture Arrangement, and Object Assembly). It was therefore concluded that the subject must provisionally be considered mentally deficient and that she did not have the intellectual capacity to establish or follow out an organized household routine without rather close supervision. The husband was, in this instance, apparently right.

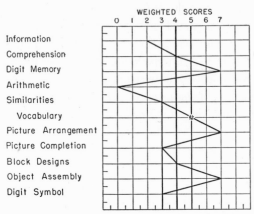

FIG. 4. Scattergram for Wechsler-Bellevue Scale, *Protocol 3.**

3. OTIS SELF-ADMINISTERING TESTS OF MENTAL ABILITY

a. *Purpose.* This short, convenient intelligence scale is used to obtain a rough estimate of an individual's mental level. This is a self-administering paper-and-pencil test applicable either to individuals or to groups.

b. *Materials and Instructions.* The Intermediate Examination is designed for grades four to nine, the Higher Examination, for high-school students and adults. There are four alternate forms (A, B, C and D) for each of these two levels. Each test form consists of 75 problems involving matters of information, arithmetic, number-series completion, recognition of opposites, analogies, understanding of proverbs, logical inference, and practical judgment. The items are arranged in chance sequence for content but roughly in order of increasing difficulty.

c. *Data and Scoring.* The subject may be allowed either 30 or 20 minutes (with different score expectations), and must write the answers to as many of the problems as he can within that time.

* In this figure, the limits of the range happen to coincide with the ordinates for Weighted Scores 3 and 5 and hence appear as heavy lines—dissimilar to the corresponding lines in Figures 2 and 3.

d. *Interpretation.* From the raw score, the corresponding standard score, percentile rank, Otis I. Q. or Binet mental age equivalent may be determined with the aid of tables.

For screening purposes the results are reasonably reliable. In the higher ranges of ability the test is a better measure of speed and alertness than of power. Extremely low scores may make advisable further testing with more adequate measures such as the Stanford-Binet or Wechsler-Bellevue Scales.

Illustrative Protocols 1 and 2

In the selection of a stenographer the Otis Self-Administering Test was used to supplement a stenographic test, the Picture-Frustration Study (see p. 167), and an evaluation on the basis of personal interview. There were two final applicants, aged 21 and 23, of whom one was to be chosen. The Intermediate Examination with a 30-minute time limit was employed.

The first of these girls went through all the items but left 6 of them blank. Of those she completed, 25 were incorrect. She was thus credited with 44 correct responses. According to the tables provided in the manual, this score is equivalent to a mental age of 12 years, 10 months on the Stanford-Binet and an Otis I. Q. of 85. Qualitatively the candidate appeared to be a fast and careless worker.

The second applicant completed 74 of the 75 items, there being 1 omission. She gave 11 incorrect answers and received credit for 63 correct ones. This score is equivalent to a Stanford-Binet mental age of 16 years, 3 months, and an Otis I. Q. of 104.

On the basis of these results, the second applicant was favored for the position. Since the other sources of information confirmed the impression that she was well suited for the type of work involved, she was accepted. Had the employer had further responsibility to the first applicant, an individual intelligence examination would have been important in determining the reliability of the inferior Otis score.

4. A POINT SCALE OF PERFORMANCE TESTS
(Grace Arthur Scale)

a. *Purpose.* This test is designed to serve as a nonverbal (performance) scale for measuring intellectual capacity. Its primary value lies in supplementing results from verbal intelligence tests. Such tests fail to give an adequate picture of certain individuals in whom verbal and nonverbal abilities are markedly unequal in their development. The present scale is used also in cases where verbal tests are inadequate because of (a) foreign language handicap or (b) speech or hearing defects. Though the test can be used satisfactorily with subjects of all ages, it is in practice employed mainly with children and adolescents.

b. *Materials and Instructions.* There are available two forms of the scale of which the second was designed especially for retest purposes. Form I consists of the following subtests:

1. *Knox Cube Test.* This consists of five one-inch cubes. Four of the cubes are placed in a row two inches apart; with the fifth cube the examiner taps the four cubes in a certain order. The subject is required to copy the performance. Twelve different tapping patterns are given.

2. *Seguin Form Board.* This consists of a board containing ten variously shaped recesses into which correspondingly shaped blocks are to be fitted. The subject is given three trials in which to place the blocks in the correct holes as quickly as possible.

3. *Two-Figure Form Board.* This test is not scored; it is used only for practice. It consists of a form board in which there are a cross and a square. Nine blocks are to be fitted into the board.

4. *Casuist Form Board.* This board consists of four figures, three circles varying in size, and a stadium. Twelve odd-shaped pieces fit together to form the four figures.

5a. *Manikin.* This consists of six pieces (two arms, two legs, a head and a body) which fit together to form a man.

5b. *Feature-Profile.* Four pieces forming an ear and three pieces forming a profile fit together on a head-piece to form a complete face.

6. *Mare and Foal.* This consists of a board on which is pictured a farm scene. Seven pieces, varying in shape, have been removed. These pieces are placed above the board and the subject is required to fit them in the board as quickly as possible.

7. *Healy Picture Completion I.* This is a board on which is depicted a scene of people doing various things. Parts of the picture, nine squares of the same size, are left out and the subject is instructed to put in from a group of 50 possible squares the most sensible solution for each of the omissions.

8. *Porteus Maze Test.* This consists of 11 different mazes on paper. They are of increasing difficulty. The subject starts at the beginning of each maze and tries to find his way out. He marks his progress with a pencil. No retracings are allowed. The number of trials permitted depends upon the difficulty of the maze.

9. *Kohs Block Design Test.* This consists of 16 similarly colored blocks with different colors on the various sides. Designs of increasing difficulty, beginning with a 4-block and ending with a 16-block pattern, are to be constructed.

In Form II of the scale there are only five subtests. The Knox Cube Test, the Seguin Form Board, and the Porteus Maze Test are used again with instructions modified to help counteract practice effects. The Healy Picture Completion II board is substituted for the similar one described above. There is, finally, the Arthur Stencil Design Test which consists of 18 stencils cut from colored paper. The subject is required to reproduce colored designs that can be made from various combinations of from two to seven stencils. This subtest serves as an equivalent for the Block Designs of Form I.

c. *Data and Scoring.* Raw scores are obtained for each of the tests in terms of the time taken to complete the task, the number of correct performances, or a combination of both criteria. With the aid of tables the raw scores may be converted into points and into approximate mental ages.

d. *Interpretation.* The mental age on this scale largely indicates the subject's level of capacity for manipulating concrete materials. The mental age on verbal intelligence tests is often lower, particularly where individuals of limited ability are concerned.

Illustrative Protocol 1

A six year-old boy was brought to an out-patient clinic by his mother. His difficulties included temper tantrums, fights with his younger brother, and enuresis. He was also noted as being fearful; for example, he refused to go to sleep at night without company. A complete psychologic examination was included as part of the necessary work-up in evaluating the case.

The patient had first been given the Revised Stanford-Binet, on which he earned a mental age of 7 years and an I. Q. of 108. To measure his capacity in more concrete tasks he was also given the Arthur Scale. It was observed during this test that his movements were awkward and uncoordinated. His scores on the separate items ranged from year IV to year VI, and in no situation did he succeed beyond the norms for his age. His total point score was equivalent to a mental age of 6 years, 1 month; his I. Q. was 94.

His behavior in the various subtests is instructive. On the Knox Cubes his performance was variable and gave the impression of fluctuating attention. He successfully reproduced six patterns, the 1st, 3d, 5th, 6th, 7th and 10th, making errors in the intermediate ones. When the entire series was repeated at the end of the examination, he was able to reproduce the first five patterns correctly but failed some of the more difficult ones which he had solved previously. The average of his two trials was thus 5.5 patterns correctly reproduced— a result that agrees with the norms for year VI. In doing the Seguin Form Board he appeared to have considerable difficulty in perceiving which shape belonged in a given recess. He had to try a piece in several positions before it slipped into place. Whereas most children are able to increase their speed with additional practice on the second and third trials, this boy's first attempt was his shortest; he seemed to "go to pieces" with increasing exposure to the task. Each succeeding trial required a longer time and was characterized by a greater amount of random activity. He scored at year V. In the Casuist Form Board, he displayed similar difficulty and had managed to complete only two of the four forms at the end of five minutes. He was again credited at year V. He assembled the Manikin with the arms in reversed position but was well satisfied with his production. He required 75 seconds to place the seven pieces in the Mare and Foal picture. Both these performances fell at year V. He was more adept at the Healy Picture Completion Test. He was given at least partial credit for eight of his nine choices; i.e., they were relevant in some degree to the depicted situation though not always fully adequate. For example, he inserted a picture of a baseball where the position of the boy's foot would suggest a football instead. His total points gave him credit at year VI. His greatest difficulty in the entire scale was experienced on the Porteus Mazes. He was unable to select the correct open pathway (year V) though he had two trials. He scored at year IV. In the last subtest, the Kohs Block Designs, he was able to execute only the first pattern, a simple one constructed from four blocks with fully-colored sides. This performance gave him credit at year V.

These results did not indicate any serious intellectual deficiency though they were interpreted as showing some retardation in motor development and visual-motor coordination as compared to more abstract verbal capacities. It was pointed out that he might experience initial difficulty in certain school subjects, such as writing and reading, and it was recommended, especially in view of the emotional tension and anxiety he so readily displayed, that he not be pushed too hard in his early efforts.

Illustrative Protocol 2

A nine year-old boy, who was not doing acceptable schoolwork even though he was repeating the second grade, was recommended by the school authorities for a psychologic examination that might be helpful in evaluating his capacity and in making plans for him. The father had deserted the family when the boy was two months old. Shortly afterward the mother left the baby with her parents and went to a neighboring state to work. He had been reared by the grandparents and was recognized as being unduly dependent upon them and as lacking in social or emotional maturity. His speech and other behavior was obviously infantile.

In the psychologic examination he was first given the Stanford-Binet Scale. His I. Q. of 94 indicated that he should be doing acceptable second-grade work though he might not be capable of meeting in full the standards for his age. His scores were rather scattered, however, and he exhibited some successes several years above his age level. Since, in addition, he was obviously not at his best in speech expression, the Arthur Scale was chosen to supplement the more highly verbal Stanford-Binet.

His scores on the Arthur items also covered a wide range—from the sixth to the twelfth year. Four of his eight ratings were at the higher level mentioned, so that his total score was equivalent to a mental age of 11 years, 4 months, and an I. Q. of 125. He was therefore classified in the superior group for the type of material involved in this scale.

If one examines his test performance in detail, it is found that his lowest score was on the Knox Cubes, a task involving rote memory. He reproduced only six patterns on both the initial and final trials and was thus rated at year VI. His next poorest result was on the Mare and Foal test, on which he took 34 seconds to place the missing pieces in the picture—a result corresponding to the level for year VIII. His solution for the Healy Picture Completion Test was exactly at his age level, with at least partially relevant selections for all the pictures. On the remaining items he scored above the expectation for his age—at year XI on one, and at year XII on the others. These were the tasks most closely dependent on reactions to visual forms and spatial interrelationships in impersonal, constructive situations. Qualitatively his responses to these items exhibited excellent judgment, analysis, and planful reasoning. He was able to replace the pieces of the Seguin Form Board in 13 seconds, to assemble all four forms of the Casuist Board in 52 seconds, and to complete the Feature Profile in 97 seconds. He succeeded in all but the most difficult of the Porteus Mazes, and although he required two trials on some of them, he always found the correct exit, at least on his second attempt. He also did exceptionally well on the Kohs Block Designs. He was able to reproduce 10 of the 17 patterns, including several of the rather complex ones that consist of 16 blocks.

The discrepancy between the Arthur and the Stanford-Binet results suggested that the boy may not have been natively as skilled in verbal as in other abilities and that, more probably, his social and emotional problems had impeded his learning. The Arthur Scale score was accepted as being more nearly representative of his potential level of development. It was evident that his problem was one primarily not of intellectual capacity but of emotional involvement.

5. GOODENOUGH DRAW-A-MAN TEST

a. *Purpose.* This test serves as a measure of intellectual development in children between the ages of 3½ and 13½ years. It is based on the observation of Goodenough and other investigators that the number of elements included in the drawing tends to increase with age and with intelligence. The method has also recently been adapted as a projective personality technic, with either children or adults.

b. *Materials and Instructions.* The child is given a blank sheet of paper and is asked to make a picture of a man—the best picture that he can draw. Drawings can thus be obtained either from a single child or from a group. In some of the projective adaptations of the method, the subject is requested to make drawings of both a man and a woman.

c. *Data and Scoring.* The drawing is scored according to a system which assigns credits for the various elements present (e.g., head, eyes, ears, clothing) or for the correct proportions and relationships among parts (e.g., arms attached to trunk at correct points, area of head not more than one-half or less than one-tenth that of trunk). The total number of credits is then converted into a mental age equivalent. There are 51 separate points that may be scored. For personality interpretation more qualitative features of the drawing are scrutinized.

d. *Interpretation.* The test is useful as an additional or confirmatory indication of mental ability level. It is not to be depended upon as a sole measure of intelligence since factors other than purely intellectual ones may affect the drawing. It has been observed, for example, that the child who is poorly adjusted socially has a less mature concept of people and that his production may therefore score below his general level on other tests.

Qualitative aspects of the drawing may also be of importance. Occasionally the concept may be superior to its representation in the drawing—a discrepancy that may reflect neurologically determined defects of a visual-motor nature. A "stick-figure" or a "snow man" is often an evasion, more common in rather clever adults than in children. A tiny figure in a corner of a large sheet of paper will sometimes be produced by a timid, anxious child. Other insecure children may draw with short, sketchy strokes. The child who is concerned with his physical condition may draw a nude figure instead of a clothed one as most children do. Adults with a sexual problem may reflect this maladjustment in the concepts of man or woman that they project in the test.

Illustrative Protocol 1

This was a nine year-old girl whose psychologic examination is presented in detail in Chapter 10. Both verbal and performance scales of intelligence were employed; the Goodenough Test was included because the purpose of the examination was to evaluate the possible interplay of neurologic and emotional factors.

The patient's drawing of a man is reproduced in Figure 5. In executing it she made a number of erasures and seemed to be confused about her concept and its representation. She proceeded in the following manner. She made the schematic outline for the head, in which she placed eyes, eyebrows, a crude nose, and a mouth. Then she added hair along the outside edge. Next she drew the shoulder line and put a collar, tie and row of buttons down the center. She made several attempts at representing the trunk but finally left it without any side outlines; she proceeded to attach arms at the top and legs at the bottom of the trunk-space.

FIG. 5. Drawing of a Man in Goodenough Test, *Protocol 1.*

Her drawing was assigned credit for the following 14 points: head, legs, arms, shoulders, eyes, nose, mouth, nostrils, hair, clothing, fingers, and eyebrow present; limbs represented as two-dimensional and eye-shape given in correct proportions. The total point-score of 14 is equivalent to a mental age of 6 years, 6 months.

These results will be considered more fully in the detailed report given below. It may be noted here, however, that the Goodenough intellectual level, being lower than her ratings on the more elaborate scales, was considered to have been affected by emotional aspects of this test situation. There was no evidence of that type of asymmetry and distorted proportional relationships which suggests an organic brain defect.

Illustrative Protocol 2

The case of this patient, like that of the foregoing, is discussed in greater detail in a succeeding portion of the book (Chapter 19). He is a 24 year-old male portrayed as an "amnesic personality." It seemed likely that his difficulties stemmed, in part at least, from his family and other social relationships, and that his concepts of the masculine and feminine roles were confused.

In this instance the patient's drawings of a man and a woman were intended as projective data for personality evaluation. No attempt is made in such circumstances to score the figures for the elements contained as a basis for appraising intellectual level. Chief importance is attached to the concepts of the male and the female projected in the drawings.

Fig. 6. Drawings of a Man and Woman in Goodenough Test, *Protocol 2*

The pictures executed by the patient are shown in Figure 6. The lines of his drawings, it should first be pointed out, were so lightly executed that it was considered advisable to reinforce them for photographic purposes. This light drawing pressure is perhaps an indication of his uncertain approach to the task. A comparison of the male and female drawings brings out a considerable difference. In general, the figure of the man is less detailed and more tentative than that of the woman. The man is portrayed as a rather ineffectual and weak figure; the woman as large, bejeweled, and possibly domineering. Of particular interest is the fact that though the hands and fingers of the male figure are not included and the feet are inadequately portrayed, the figure of the woman includes a hand with prominent fingers and feet that are normally depicted. The drawing of the woman extended on the left to the edge of the paper, a circumstance that truncated the arm on that side. The one arm included is almost withered in appearance. The head of the male figure is unusually small for the body whereas that of the female is well proportioned, if not disproportionately large.

These results suggested a problem of sexual identification and led to further consideration of the patient's generalized psychologic pictures of men and women. It was found that he had been exposed to a family constellation in which roles were played by a somewhat ineffectual father and an overdominant mother. The ways in which these influences were interwoven with his whole pattern of reactions to the world are discussed at length in Chapter 19.

REFERENCES

General

Mursell, J. L. Psychological Testing. New York: Longmans, Green, 1947.

Sherman, M. Intelligence and its Deviates. New York: Ronald Press, 1945.

Stoddard, G. D. The Meaning of Intelligence. New York: Macmillan, 1943.

Revised Stanford-Binet Intelligence Scale
Terman, L. M., and Merrill, M. A. Measuring Intelligence. Boston: Houghton, Mifflin, 1937.

Wechsler-Bellevue Intelligence Scale
*Rapaport, D., et al. Diagnostic Psychological Testing. Vol. 1. Chicago: Year Book Publishers, 1945.
*Wechsler, D. The Measurement of Adult Intelligence. 3d ed. Baltimore: Williams and Wilkins, 1944.

Otis Self-Administering Tests of Mental Ability
Otis, A. S. Otis Self-Administering Tests of Mental Ability. Yonkers-On-Hudson: World Book, 1922.

Grace Arthur Point Scale of Performance Tests
Arthur, G. A Point Scale of Performance Tests. Vol. I. Clinical Manual. New York: Commonwealth Fund, 1943.
Arthur, G. A Point Scale of Performance Tests. Revised Form II. New York: Psychological Corporation, 1947.

Goodenough Draw-A-Man Test
Goodenough, F. The Measurement of Intelligence in Drawings. Yonkers-On-Hudson: World Book, 1926.

* Asterisk indicates that the reference in question includes a fairly extensive bibliography related to its subject matter.

Chapter 4

Measures of Intellectual Deviation

"DETERIORATION," "loss of efficiency" and "intellectual impairment" are concepts used to describe the processes with which the present group of tests deals. These concepts refer to the fact that there are individuals who are not as capable mentally as they are believed to have been at an earlier time. There are, for example, patients who have sustained head injuries or have suffered from a psychotic illness for a long period and who appear to have lost ground intellectually either in a general sense or in some specific function. Such tests as belong in this group may therefore be addressed either to the study of deterioration in all spheres by sampling the individual's capacity in a variety of test situations or to the investigation of some one or another special capacity. The most commonly appraised functions of this latter sort are memory and conceptual thinking.

Occasionally the need for a special study of deterioration is recognized from the results obtained with a test of general intelligence. If the findings demonstrate a discrepancy between the subject's measured intellectual ability and the level of attainment expected on the basis of education or vocation, the use of a test for intellectual deviation is indicated. Sometimes the same sort of further study is pointed up by a broad scatter of abilities in the various subtests. The devices discussed in this chapter are thus, in part, an elaboration of those features that inhere in the tests of general intelligence when patterns of subtest scores are scrutinized. The common basis resides in the premise that disproportionate difficulty with one or another specific type of mental performance is a symptom of qualitative intellectual deviation.

Present medical knowledge about deteriorative processes is still incomplete and controversial. It is generally accepted that the mental impairment associated with known structural damage to cerebral tissue is likely to produce a permanent loss. If a psychologic examination should indicate quantitative and qualitative inconsistencies in a subject's pattern of test scores, and if in the physical examination or personal history there is evidence of brain trauma, the interpretation of "organic defect" is usually warranted. Even in such instances, however, the burden of proof rests ordinarily upon laboratory procedures, such as the electroencephalograph and pneumoencephalograph, or upon postmortem findings. It has similarly been found that prolonged psychotic illness, especially if of schizophrenic type, is frequently accompanied by a progressive decline of intellectual capacity. In most cases these changes are classified as deterioration of an irreversible character since neither the illness as a whole nor the intellectual defect which is a part of it improve in the course of time. There are, however, recorded cases of exceptional and unpredictable remission after a lengthy illness with marked improvement in intellectual function as well as in other aspects of the personality. Such findings warrant considerable caution in the interpretation of findings in this psychodiagnostic field.

Test results alone cannot be relied upon to indicate whether negative intellectual changes are permanent and irreversible or whether they will be manifest only as long as illness persists. These measures provide primarily an indication of intellectual status at the time of examination, secondarily a basis for comparing present efficiency with the level expected according to the person's educational and vocational backgrounds. Some instruments are characterized by internal measures of discrepancy that purport to indicate change in status, but even in the interpretation of such results, it is clinically advisable to weigh carefully the intellectual history of the subject.

1. Babcock-Levy Revised Examination for the Measurement of Efficiency of Mental Functioning

a. Purpose. It is known that intellectual efficiency declines to some extent in normal old age and much earlier in some cases of mental illness. Studies of such decline have shown that it occurs more slowly in certain abilities than in others. The abilities involved in vocabulary tests (definitions of words) hold up much better than do those called for by tests of functions like immediate memory, the learning of new associations, adaptive response to complex situations, etc. A person's score on a vocabulary test may, therefore, be used as one estimate of his original or maximum ability while results from other tests may serve to indicate the present level of intellectual functioning. Comparison of the vocabulary score with the other scores reveals the degree to which the individual's present functioning level coincides with his original level; i.e., it yields an index of efficiency. For example, a person may have a vocabulary rating indicative of superior adult intelligence, but his ability to recall the content of a simple paragraph may be equivalent to that of an average eight year-old child. The Babcock-Levy Examination for Efficiency of Mental Functioning is a test involving such comparisons.

b. Materials and Instructions. The Vocabulary test from the Revised Stanford-Binet Intelligence Scale (with special norms) is used. The other 33 subtests in this examination are grouped for analysis into six divisions named as follows: Easy Questions (including information), Initial Learning, Learning, Repetition (rote memory), Motor (visual-motor directions), and Easy Continuous (symbol-association). Simple oral instructions are given to the individual subject. For example, when naming common objects is required, the examiner says, "See how quickly you can tell me the names of these things as I hold them up."

c. Data and Scoring. Some subtests, like that involving vocabulary, are scored according to correctness of response. Others are scored on the basis of both speed and accuracy. The subject's total obtained score for each division of the examination is compared with the expected score for an individual of his vocabulary level, and the degree to which his score falls below expectation is regarded as a measure of efficiency loss in specific areas. The total (average) efficiency score for the test is similarly compared with the expected level to obtain an *Efficiency Index*.

d. Interpretation. Because there is a general lowering in efficiency of all abilities (including those measured by the Vocabulary test) in old age, in cases of severe mental illness, and in mental deficiency, this examination must be interpreted in relation to other information concerning the subject. In general, however, a marked discrepancy between vocabulary rating and other test scores suggests loss of efficiency. Such loss may be the result of organic deterioration, as in cases of brain disease, or may be a reflection of either temporary or chronic emotional disorders.

Illustrative Protocol 1

A 29 year-old veteran was admitted to a psychiatric hospital for an illness which had its onset while he was still in military service. He was the third of five children, and had made slow progress in school, finally leaving the sixth grade when he was 16. He had been employed as a common laborer, loader for a coal company, until the time of his induction. Little was reported of his adjustment to the army, but after a short time in it he began to drink heavily. The acute onset of symptoms followed several months later. When he was transferred to the civilian hospital with a diagnosis of Dementia Praecox, Hebephrenic Type, he was quiet and cooperative, and had no recall of the events during the disturbed phase of his illness. The prolonged period of alcoholism in conjunction with his "amnesia" indicated that a test of mental deterioration might be appropriate. Accordingly, the Babcock-Levy was included in the battery of psychologic tests administered.

The Wechsler-Bellevue Scale was given first, and he was rated by it at the average level of intelligence with a Full Scale I. Q. of 96. The items of the Babcock-Levy scale were then introduced. He was able to define 17 of the words in the Vocabulary test correctly—a result that placed him at year XIII. His performance on the other six test divisions will be described in detail.

In the section Easy Questions, he provided all the data of personal identification accurately (name, age, birth year, siblings, etc.) but his responses were occasionally delayed and thus earned him only partial credit. He named the days of the week correctly in 5½ seconds, the months in 7 seconds. He counted backward from 20 to 1 without error in 14½ seconds. He named familiar objects, except for a thimble, fairly rapidly. He wrote his full name in 7½ seconds. He was able to repeat the days of the week in reversed order with only one error, but became completely confused in reversing the months of the year. He was slow but accurate in selecting from a list of 24 words 12 that had been read to him earlier. His weighted score on these items, as read from the tables provided, was 12.3. The norm for subjects with a year XIII vocabulary is 14.5. Hence, a difference of —2.2 was recorded.

His greatest discrepancy occurred in the tests of Initial Learning. He reproduced only two ideas from the paragraph which was read him and for which 22 countable memories are possible. (Immediately following this poor performance the paragraph was read to him again in preparation for a later recall.) After a first presentation of 10 pairs of word-associates, he was able to recall only 5. His reproduction of simple designs, which he was permitted to study for 10 seconds each, was only partially correct. His weighted score of 9 was 5 points below the expected standard.

The Learning section consists of three items, each involving recall of material exposed for study considerably earlier in the test session: remote recall of the paragraph mentioned above, completion of the paired word-associates after a delay, and memory, similarly, for the members of a Turkish-English vocabulary list exposed earlier. The patient's score of 11.3 fell below his expected score of 15.0, and a difference of —3.7 was recorded.

The Repetition items include memory for digits forward and backward, verbatim repetition of sentences of increasing complexity, and the Knox Cubes. The last test requires the subject to reproduce sequential patterns by tapping different combinations of four blocks in the same order in which the examiner has tapped them. The subject scored only 1.8 points below his expected score on these items.

In the Motor tasks, he accomplished readily the symbol-digit test, in which the subject is required to insert code numbers into each of five geometric forms printed in randomly repeated order, the key remaining available. Next he wrote easily the words "United States of America," and the sentence "I hope to leave here very soon." He traced, as instructed, between the parallel lines of a double-lined cross for two trials. His responses in this section were, however, a little slow so that his weighted score was 1.6 points below standard.

On the final division, Easy Continuous tasks, he earned his best score. This total was based on his scores for the five lines of the already described symbol-digit associations, a similar test in which colors and numbers are associated, his ability to count backward by 3's from 64, and his display of proficiency on the Turkish-English vocabulary with the key still present. His score of 12.5 was only 1.1 points below the norm for the year XIII vocabulary.

The average of his six efficiency ratings gave the patient a total efficiency score of 11.3. The norm for his vocabulary level was 14.0. His *Efficiency Index* was therefore —2.7. (According to Babcock and Levy, only indices of —3 or greater "definitely indicate abnormally poor functioning.") Since the patient similarly failed to give evidence of impairment in other tests that he took, it was concluded that, though he displayed some difficulty in new learning, he was not suffering from any generalized intellectual deterioration. The interpretation was made that his tendency toward preoccupation and withdrawal was responsible for his failure to assimilate new material more readily, and that this tendency was merely a secondary symptom of his illness.

Illustrative Protocol 2

A married woman of 39 exhibited symptoms of slurred speech, memory defect, difficulty in walking and somewhat fixed facial expression shortly after a fall in which she sustained a mild head injury. Her problem became severe within a short time, and careful examination revealed that syphilis of the central nervous system was present. She was admitted to the hospital about a year after the illness was first noted; the psychologic examination was performed two months later.

Her I. Q. on the Wechsler-Bellevue Scale was 65—a mental defective rating incompatible with her history of having completed two years of high school and having been employed as a supervisor by a telephone company. It was therefore apparent that some deterioration had occurred and the Babcock-Levy Examination was employed as a means of evaluating the extent and nature of the impairment.

The Vocabulary test placed the patient at year XV—a result judged to be a fairly reliable indicator of her pre-illness level. Her scores on the various sections of the Babcock-Levy scale may be tabulated as follows:

	Patient's Weighted Score
Easy Questions	10.3
Learning	9.6
Repetition	9.5
Motor	7.7
Initial Learning	4.6
Easy Continuous	5.7
Total (Average) Efficiency Score	7.9
Expected Level for Year XV Vocabulary	14.6
Efficiency Index	—6.7

The large discrepancy between the patient's actual attainment and the level commensurate with her vocabulary standard falls within the range for individuals with marked disturbance of mental efficiency. This finding served to confirm the view that her moron I. Q. classification represented a significant drop from her original endowment.

Observation of the qualitative features of her behavior as she worked on the tests substantiated this interpretation. She followed directions poorly, was impulsive, and plunged into the tasks before she fully understood what was expected of her. She was cheerful and talkative but continually digressed into irrelevant discussion of her own current activities and tended to relate most of her responses to personal experiences. At certain times she appeared to be concentrating and exerting a fair degree of effort; at others she gave the impression of being more or less out of contact. Her physical appearance was slovenly and unattractive. The previously mentioned slurring of speech and difficulty in gait were readily observed.

In this instance, then, evidence of lowered intellectual capacity occurred in conjunction with demonstrable damage to the central nervous system. It was therefore concluded that an interpretation of "organic deterioration" was justified.

2. Shipley-Hartford Retreat Scale for Measuring Intellectual Impairment

a. Purpose. This instrument is useful for detecting mild degrees of intellectual impairment in individuals who were originally of normal intelligence. It is not intended for very deteriorated or confused subjects, intellectual subnormals, or persons with language or educational handicaps. It rests, like the Babcock-Levy scale, on the premise that a comparison of vocabulary with other scores permits evaluation of mental efficiency.

b. Materials and Instructions. The test consists of two sections—Vocabulary and Abstraction subtests—printed on a single-sheet blank, and may be administered either to individuals or to groups. A ten-minute time limit is allotted each section. The Vocabulary test, which is given first, consists of 40 multiple-choice items of increasing difficulty. The Abstraction test consists of 20 series-completion items, e.g., numbers in a certain progression which the subject must analyze in order to supply the final item of the series.

c. Data and Scoring. Each correct vocabulary item earns credit for one point, each correct abstraction item, for two, the maximum score for each part being 40. A Conceptual Quotient (C. Q.) is obtained from the ratio of the subject's abstraction score to that expected for a "normal person" with the same vocabulary score as his. The scale also yields Vocabulary Age, Abstraction Age and Mental Age ratings.

d. Interpretation. The Conceptual Quotient rests on the observation that in conditions affecting intellectual efficiency, vocabulary is relatively unaffected while the capacity for abstract (conceptual) thinking declines rapidly. The C. Q. is thus an index of impairment, quotients below 100 representing various degrees of inefficiency. With a normal C. Q. the mental age rating provided by the scale may be considered a valid indicator of approximate intellectual level; with a very low quotient, the obtained mental age is taken to represent a level midway between the patient's best and least preserved capacities.

Illustrative Protocol 1

A 39 year-old mother of nine living children was admitted to a psychiatric hospital with both somatic and mental complaints. The relationship of husband and wife was poor in the extreme. She attributed the source of her difficulties to her "shiftless, irresponsible" husband whose employment as a laborer failed to provide adequately for the large family. He, in turn, expressed the view that his wife would be forced to stay with him if they continued to have children. The patient's depressive and seclusive behavior was seen in retrospect to have developed gradually over a period of several years; visual hallucinations and ideas of persecution made their appearance suddenly after an attack of pneumonia a month before hospitalization. The admission diagnosis was Schizophrenia.

The initial psychologic examination yielded an I. Q. of 92. Since the patient had completed the third year of high school at 15, with better than average grades, it was assumed that her native endowment must have been well above the low average level indicated by the intelligence test. To investigate the presence and extent of impairment the Shipley-Hartford Retreat Scale was accordingly administered.

The patient was able to select the correct synonym for 24 of the 40 words in the Vocabulary test. She marked only two words incorrectly, omitting the other items. Since the test directions state, "If you don't know, guess" the subject is automatically credited with one point for each four items omitted to compensate for the number of successes obtainable by chance guessing alone. Thus her total vocabulary score was 27, with a corresponding Vocabulary Age of 15.9 years. When, however, she was confronted with the Abstraction test, she was able to give only four responses in the ten-minute period allowed. Three of her answers were correct. Her total abstraction score was therefore 6, and her Abstraction Age 9.4 years. The Conceptual Quotient, representing the ratio of abstraction to vocabulary scores, was 59. Since so low a quotient is found in less than 1 per cent of normal individuals, it was concluded that the patient gave evidence of impairment presumably attributable to her mental illness. To establish such an interpretation other tests and observations were obviously needed.

Illustrative Protocol 2

A student nurse, aged 18 and in her second year of training, was referred for psychiatric help because certain family adjustments were apparently making difficult for her the interpersonal relationships involved in her work. It was noted that her scholastic achievement had not suffered and that she was most free of tension and anxiety while actually engaged in nursing procedures. The psychologic examination was in this case mainly devoted to the evaluation of emotional and personality reaction patterns, but in order that no important factors be overlooked, the Shipley-Hartford Retreat Scale was employed as a rapid means of evaluating intellectual inefficiency.

The subject defined correctly 30 of the words on the Vocabulary test. She omitted only one item, the word *denizen,* and selected incorrect synonyms for the remaining nine items. Her Vocabulary Age was found to be 17.0 years. The Abstraction test was handled with considerable deftness. She filled in the correct numbers or letters for the first 15 items speedily and accurately. She puzzled over the last five items, finally completing two of them correctly and leaving the others unanswered. Her Abstraction Age was 18.1 years on the basis of this performance. Her Conceptual Quotient was 106. It was in addition found that, according to this scale, her Mental Age was 17.8 years.

These results ruled out any important intellectual inefficiency and classified her further as of better than average endowment. Since these findings were compatible with the program of professional study in which she was already engaged, the remainder of the examination was directed to the investigation of her emotional life.

3. OBJECT-SORTING TEST

a. Purpose. This instrument is one of a group designed to evaluate "conceptual thinking ability" or "the capacity to adopt a categorical or abstract attitude." It was first used experimentally in describing and defining the qualitatively abnormal approach to problem-solving employed by patients with cerebral pathology. Later applications have shown that it could also provide information about the thought processes in neurotic and psychotic functional disorders. Relatively little has thus far been accomplished toward establishing a quantitative scoring system or setting up norms.

b. Materials and Instructions. The test material consists of approximately 30 objects which may logically be subdivided into various groups on the basis of *use* (smoking objects, eating utensils, tools), *size* (usable objects or miniatures), *color* (red, white), *material* (paper, rubber, metal), *shape* (round, rectangular), etc. The task to be performed is twofold. In Part I the objects are placed on the table before the subject in random order. After a demonstration trial, an object is selected by the examiner and set to one side of the group. The subject is then asked to pick out all the other objects that might belong with this one in some way. Six such groupings are made, the objects used in each previous sorting being returned to the main pile each time. Record is made both of the objects included in each grouping, and of the subject's exact verbalization of "the reason they belong together." In Part II the examiner forms certain groupings of objects for the subject who is then asked to state the principle of sorting involved. If his explanation is inadequate, the correct one is given him and his response to this statement is noted. Twelve such test situations are presented.

c. Data and Scoring. Part I is designed to measure and evaluate the subject's spontaneous or active approach—the type of conceptualization that he employs by preference. The sortings are scored under three headings. First, they are inspected for *conceptual level* as follows: (1) *abstract, conceptual,* e.g., all tools, including toy tools. (2) *functional,* e.g., all eating utensils that can be used, but not miniatures because too small for use. (3) *concrete,* e.g., matches specifically grouped with pipe so that the former may be used to light the latter. Secondly, the sortings are scored for *adequacy,* i.e., the efficiency, accuracy, and completeness with which the particular level of conceptualization is applied. Finally, the groupings are evaluated for *looseness or narrowness* according to any deviation from the normal pattern in the direction of over-rigid or over-flexible application of the principle involved.

Part II of the test evaluates the capacity of the subject to comprehend abstract principles of categorization when the situation demands their use. As compared to Part I, a more passive form of conceptualization is considered to be here involved.

d. Interpretation. It has been observed that normal individuals take with equal facility to both the "concrete" and "abstract" approaches and are able to shift to the more complex conceptual level without difficulty when the situation requires. In many patients with cerebral pathology the ability to apply abstract or conceptual principles is impaired, and their performance is characterized by "concrete" solutions. Milder forms of organic disorder, especially those based on diffuse rather than focal lesions, may not exhibit this defect. Certain deteriorated psychotics (e.g., schizophrenics) have almost as much difficulty with the test as do organic patients. Other patterns of performance, involving discrepancies between active and passive concept formation or between success on object-sorting and on more purely verbal application of concepts, have been described in a variety of psychiatric disorders. Developmental differences in normal individuals have also been reported.

Illustrative Protocol 1

A man of 42 was admitted to a mental hospital with a history of extreme alcoholism over a period of 15 years. His wife, who had been his drinking companion, died about four months previous to his hospitalization, and his already excessive drinking then increased. At the time of admission there was considerable evidence of neurologic disturbance, including tremors, ataxia, nystagmus, intellectual disorientation and memory defect. A provisional diagnosis of Korsakoff Syndrome was made with a view to further study. A psychologic examination was requested to investigate especially any defects in conceptual thinking that might indicate cerebral damage.

A test of general intelligence (the Wechsler-Bellevue Scale) was first given. It rated the patient in the bright normal group, and presented no evidence that his level of function was materially different from what was to be expected on the basis of his educational and vocational histories. In other words, there seemed to be no indications of generalized deterioration. Attention was then turned to those specific areas in which brain damage most frequently effects a qualitative change or causes the individual to adopt an altered mode of approach; namely, memory, perception of space-form relationships, and conceptual thinking. To study the last area the Object-Sorting Test was employed. The patient's responses are given in detail as follows:

PART I. ACTIVE CONCEPT FORMATION

Object presented	Selected to go with it	Reason given	Scoring
1. Large fork	Large knife, large spoon.	They're to eat with; to help at a meal.	Concrete level, adequate, narrow.
2. Pipe	Book of matches.	Can't smoke pipe without matches to light tobacco.	Concrete level, adequate, normal span.
3. Bicycle bell	Large screwdriver.	Use screwdriver to take bracket off and on.	Concrete level, adequate, narrow.
4. Red cardboard circle	Nothing.	I don't know what it is; I don't know what should go with it.	Failure.
5. Toy pliers	Toy hammer, toy hatchet.	Looks like a small tool chest.	Conceptual level, inadequate, narrow.
6. Rubber ball	Nothing.	Just play ball. Don't need anything.	Failure.

PART II. PASSIVE ACCEPTANCE OF ABSTRACT CATEGORIES

Group	Patient's response	Reaction to correct explanation	Scoring
1. Red	For someone who has a hobby.	One is light red or pink. Could say 'red or pink.' That would be close.	Failure.
2. Metal	All made of a type of metal.		Full credit.
3. Round	All serve their own purpose.	Yes, all round.	Failure.

PART II. PASSIVE ACCEPTANCE OF ABSTRACT CATEGORIES *(Continued)*

Group	Patient's Response	Reaction to correct explanation	Scoring
4. Tools	Same for useful purpose, like carpentry.		Partial credit (functional rather than conceptual statement).
5. Paper	Something like to start a fire with.	No. Matches aren't 100 per cent paper.	Failure.
6. Pairs	Both sort of alike, a large and a small. Two alike.		Full credit.
7. White	Color is all the same, white.		Full credit.
8. Rubber	All rubber.		Full credit.
9. Smoking	All a smoke, for relaxation, all for enjoyment.		Full credit.
10. Silverware	Alike for eating purposes, only different sizes.		Partial credit (functional rather than conceptual statement).
11. Toys	For hobby or enjoyment, use every day.	Not necessarily.	Failure.
12. Rectangles	All used for individual purposes.	Yes, all have four corners.	Failure.

Analysis of the responses in Part I revealed that they were based largely on the patient's concepts of the objects as related to specific, concrete situations. Silverware was associated with a table set for eating, and he therefore omitted the miniature objects which were not concretely useful. Similarly, the only object he related to a pipe was a book of matches. Thus items 1, 2, and 3 were scored for adequate application of a concrete principle, with resultant narrowness in two of the three instances. He could find no objects to group with the red cardboard circle or the rubber ball because he could not identify either of them with a concrete situation in which they were associated with other things. He rejected several of the sortings offered by the examiner in Part II because he could not overlook small concrete or sensory differentiations (see especially groups 1 and 5).

The general approach just described has been found empirically to be characteristic of patients with organic brain disease. Experience has shown that in most such cases some residual capacity to apply abstract principles is present; the extent of the limitation is probably related to the extent (and location) of the pathology. Even the normal individual will fall back on concrete and functional descriptions from time to time, but he is not so prone to do so, and he rarely has difficulty in accepting broader and more abstract categories.

Comparison of the present patient's reactions with those recorded in the next case will clarify the distinction between impaired and unimpaired conceptual capacity.

Illustrative Protocol 2

This patient's history is very similar to that of the man just discussed. He, too, was admitted to the hospital after a prolonged period of heavy drinking. However, his breakdown was characterized more by psychotic manifestations than by indications of neurologic disorder. He had been periodically alcoholic for about 25 years previous to his hospitalization at the age of 44. The psychologic examination was designed to investigate the possibility of encephalopathy, resulting from excessive use of alcohol, as well as to evaluate his personality patterns. At the time of examination acute symptoms were no longer present, and he was cooperative in all procedures.

On the Wechsler-Bellevue Intelligence Scale he earned a Full Scale I. Q. of 113, with very close agreement between verbal and performance ratings. Although no evidence of generalized deterioration was found, additional tests were employed to investigate the specific disabilities frequently associated with cerebral damage. For the area of conceptual thinking the Object-Sorting Test was used. His responses in it are tabulated in detail below.

PART I. ACTIVE CONCEPT FORMATION

Object presented	Selected to go with it	Reason given	Scoring
1. Large fork	Large spoon, large knife, all toy silverware.	All of table use.	Conceptual level, adequate, normal span.
2. Pipe	Cigarette, book of matches, loose matches, cigar, rubber cigar, toy pipe.	For smoking.	Conceptual level, adequate, normal span.
3. Bicycle bell	Toy screwdriver, large screwdriver.	Have to clamp this on some part of the wheel.	Concrete level, adequate, narrow.
4. Red cardboard circle	File card, green square.	Paper.	Conceptual level, adequate, narrow.
5. Toy pliers	Large pliers, large screwdriver, toy screwdriver, toy hammer.	Tools.	Conceptual level, adequate, normal span.
6. Rubber ball	Cigar, toy pliers, toy hammer, toy silverware.	For youngsters' use.	Functional level, adequate, normal span.

PART II. PASSIVE ACCEPTANCE OF ABSTRACT CATEGORIES

Group	Patient's response	Reaction to correct explanation	Scoring
1. Red	Color, red.		Full credit.
2. Metal	Metal.		Full credit.
3. Round	Could be used as toys.	Accepts.	Partial credit (inadequate conceptual definition).
4. Tools	For carpentry.		Full credit.
5. Paper	Paper.		Full credit.
6. Pairs	Display. Not all same.	Accepts.	Failure.
7. White	White.		Full credit.
8. Rubber	Rubber.		Full credit.
9. Smoking	Smoking utensils.		Full credit.
10. Silverware	Table use and metal.		Full credit.
11. Toys	Toys.		Full credit.
12. Rectangles	Squares.		Full credit.

The responses in Part I may be considered to be representative of the kind and quality characteristically found among normal subjects. Although the attributes assigned as the basis for sorting were sometimes related to use or function, the reactions as a whole demonstrated the capacity to overlook concrete dissimilarities and to adopt a categorizing approach. In Part II there was little evidence of difficulty in grasping the abstract principles involved; in those instances in which the patient could not give the solution by himself, he exhibited good comprehension of the underlying principle when it was stated for him.

The results thus indicated that the patient's illness had caused no demonstrable disturbance in his conceptual thinking ability. The examination was then directed toward other specific functions often affected by cerebral damage. (See Wechsler Memory Scale, Illustrative Protocol 2, p. 72.)

Illustrative Protocol 3

A 38 year-old female patient had had several hospitalizations for psychotic episodes. Her periods of illness were becoming progressively longer and the free intervals correspondingly shorter. Though she remained in good contact with the environment and was able to carry on some routine clerical work effectively, her mental content showed increasing preoccupation with ideas of reference and other peculiar thoughts.

An intelligence test rated her at the bright normal level. The Object-Sorting Test was employed to clarify the quality and nature of her thinking processes. Her selections of objects in Part I are illustrated in Figure 7. The bizarre and erratic manner of thinking upon which her responses depended is clear even without detailed analysis. It is apparent that while she was able to conceptualize, she did not employ abstract principles in their usual significance and that she tended especially to make inaccurate over-generalizations. Thus items 2, 3, 4, and 5 were scored as inadequate although she employed all three conceptual levels in these responses.

The patient's ability to comprehend the conventional sorting categories of Part II gave further evidence that her thinking disorder was not typical of an "organic" subject. Instead her responses, tabulated below, indicated her highly individualized manner of thinking —an approach likely to predominate over a more adaptive type of adjustment in most situations. The interpretation made was that a thinking disorder characteristic of a functional psychosis was present.

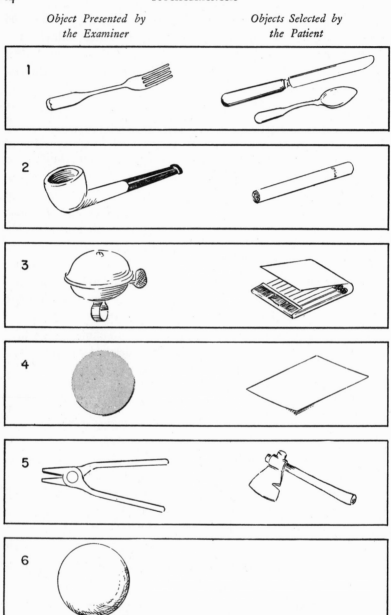

FIG. 7. Arrangement of Objects in Sorting Test, *Protocol 3*.

Part I. Active Concept Formation

Object presented	Selected to go with it	Reason given	Scoring
1. Large fork	Knife, spoon.	Table service.	Concrete level, adequate, normal span.
2. Pipe	Cigarette.	Prince Albert and a cigarette. A twosome. The party of the second part doesn't smoke a pipe.	Functional level, inadequate, loose.
3. Bicycle bell	Match book.	That means a messenger boy. I'm looking for a messenger boy. One of the messenger boys at the Hotel Roosevelt wouldn't be busy.	Concrete level, inadequate, loose.
4. Red cardboard circle	White card.	Does this (white file card) contain cellulose? Paper derivative.	Conceptual level, inadequate, loose.
5. Toy pliers	Toy hatchet.	Two tools of the building trade.	Functional level, inadequate, narrow.
6. Rubber ball	Nothing.	Patient places nothing with it, verbalizing as follows: "Is there a doctor in the house, or a child? Swollen hemoglobin. Go with it? Decrease in activity. That would lower the blood pressure."	Failure.

PART II. PASSIVE ACCEPTANCE OF ABSTRACT CATEGORIES

Group	Patient's response	Reaction to correct explanation	Scoring
1. Red	Same basic color, red.		Full credit.
2. Metal	All contain metal component.		Full credit.
3. Round	I don't know.	Accepts.	Failure.
4. Tools	Builders' equipment.		Full credit.
5. Paper	Paper products.		Full credit.
6. Pairs	I don't know.	Accepts.	Failure.
7. White	Colorless. White.		Full credit.
8. Rubber	Rubber.		Full credit.
9. Smoking	Pleasure of smoking. Until recent years man's diversion. Masculine *and* feminine.		Full credit.
10. Silverware	Miniature and standard size table service.		Partial credit (functional rather than conceptual statement).
11. Toys	Basic materials are represented.	Accepts.	Failure.
12. Rectangles	Squares.		Full credit.

4. VIGOTSKY BLOCKS

a. Purpose. This technic is another designed for the assessment of an individual's ability to solve problems involving the application of abstract concepts. It sheds light upon the dynamic process of thinking rather than upon the static products of intelligence. The test is a difficult one for the subject and is therefore not very useful with persons of limited intelligence. For the same reason, however, it frequently reveals thinking disturbances in very intelligent individuals who otherwise manage to mask their handicaps by fluent verbalizations.

b. Materials and Instructions. The subject is shown a group of 22 small blocks representing five different colors and a variety of shapes. He is told that on the basis of certain principles to be discovered by him the blocks can be classified into four clearly separated groups, and that each of the four kinds has a name. These names—nonsense syllable designations, e.g., *bik*—are, in fact, printed on the under-side of the blocks and divide them according to the combined criteria of height and top area as follows: tall-small, tall-large, flat-small and flat-large groups. As a beginning the subject is offered a sample block, which the examiner turns over to display its name, and is instructed to find all the others that belong with it. Errors are demonstrated throughout the procedure by similarly turning over other blocks one at a time and leaving their names displayed. Additional conceptual clues are thus provided at intervals as the subject works until he has arrived at the correct sorting. He is then required to state the principles of classification involved. The examiner reinforces the criteria by repeating them for him. Finally, the subject is asked to re-sort the blocks and restate the principles of classification.

c. Data and Scoring. In the form here described this test is not scored quantitatively. Careful record is made of the subject's behavior and verbalizations as he proceeds. He is encouraged to state aloud the plans he has in mind. It is thus possible to observe such features as planfulness (attempts to employ a definite principle of sorting, e.g., shape or color), resourcefulness (numbers of alternative hypotheses exhibited), flexibility (willingness to give up an unsuccessful basis of sorting), and other aspects of procedure. Note is taken of the subject's ability to recognize the correct solution when he has achieved it and to state the classification scheme. Finally, the ability to repeat the solution serves as a guarantee of its mastery.

d. Interpretation. Even the normal individual may take a long time and may need many demonstrations of error before he can solve the test problem, but he does not offer bizarre or confused reasons for his attempts and he is usually able to accept and to re-employ the correct principles with ease. Patients with demonstrated impairment in abstract capacity, on the other hand, tend to deny the legitimacy of the four correctly sorted sets of blocks by pointing out the concrete differences of shape, color, etc., within each group. Moreover, they can almost never repeat the solution or adequately state the basis of classification. Some patients whose thinking is disturbed on an emotional basis exhibit various qualitative peculiarities: they may lose themselves in making patterns of the blocks or sort on the basis of some obscure symbolism or, failing to hold the goal idea, they may group some blocks for color, some for shape, and some for size. They may also tend to believe that the scheme of classification is an arbitrary one imposed by the examiner. In general, the unfamiliarity of the task makes conventional verbal explanations inapplicable so that bizarre reasoning may become qualitatively more apparent here than it does in other, less complex tasks.

Illustrative Protocol 1

The patient was an adolescent boy whose case is discussed in detail in Chapter 18. He had shown a tendency toward individualized responses in other tests and it was therefore decided to employ the Vigotsky Blocks for studying any latent peculiarities of his thinking processes. His running comments as he worked with the blocks are here reproduced. The replies of the examiner are to be understood as repetitions of the instructions or, unless otherwise stated, as noncommittal comments.

1. After giving the general instructions, Examiner (E.) starts Subject (S.) by selecting a tall, triangular block, turning it over to display its name, and requesting S. to pick out the blocks that go with this sample. S. asks, "How many times are you supposed to sort them?" S. works aimlessly a while, then starts to sort by shape, selecting various

triangles. "You can take them out once you get them in, can't you?
Shift them around." E. replies in the affirmative.

2. E. indicates that a flat triangle does not belong in the group by
turning it over and showing that it has a different name. "Height,"
S. says, peering at the blocks from an angle. "Kind of crowded, too."
Smiles, looks perplexed. "You can't put this there, can you?" E.
responds that S. may do anything he likes. "I don't like to guess.
I'll try color. It sounds too easy, but I'll try anyhow." Does so.
"That's out, too many colors. White isn't a color though, is it? This
is awful!"

3. A tall, small block is now turned up by E. "It's complicated."
S. works a while longer. "This is probably so simple it's right under
my nose and I can't see it. The trouble is too many shapes. I'll make
a circle and a square." S. begins to sort blocks into two shapes and
two heights.

4. He is shown that a circle and a square belong in the same group.
S. looks surprised and says, "Is there a reason for them going together?"

5. S. turns up another tall, small block by accidentally knocking it
over. "The more that show, the less I get." Soon, however, S. appears
to be approaching the correct solution. Abruptly he decides that he is
wrong and stops. Appears "stuck."

6. E. makes another demonstration. "They look like opposite things
to me."

7. Additional block turned up by E. "I'll start on this; it looks
easier." Turns attention to another group of blocks. "But I don't
know about these. This is a guessing game the way I'm doing it."

8. Additional demonstration by E. "You'll probably turn them all
up before I'll get it." Looks at groupings intently. "Color and different shapes theme."

9. Error demonstrated by E. "That ruined everything. I guess it
isn't anything constructive. It couldn't be. That wrecks it." Further
manipulation.

10. Demonstration. "I'll section it off into halves. Are you sure
there isn't one missing from this?" Sorts further, by height. "I'm

pretty sure that's how it goes, bigs and littles." Enumerates shapes again. "Did anybody ever get this?" Works a little longer. "It doesn't make any difference how many in each, does it?"

11. Demonstration. S. corrects last existing error. "I'll bet that's it. I knew it would be simple. There's two groups, height. And you separate that into two groups, small-little and big-little."

With a little help the subject now found it possible to formulate the classification scheme in terms of height and top area. He was able to repeat both the sorting and the verbal statement of the solution without hesitation. Since the performance described did not demonstrate undue rigidity, bizarre reasoning, or any essential lack of capacity for employing a conceptual approach, it was interpreted as essentially normal. He had, for example, employed shape, color, and height as possible alternative principles for classification. He had been able to comprehend why his attempts were inadequate after errors were demonstrated, and in the case of color, he recognized his error without aid. He resorted to complaints that the materials or instructions were faulty only when he could think of no other manipulative possibilities, and he grasped the essential principles of the task promptly at the end. These results suggested that the formal aspects of the patient's thinking were not pathologic and that his above-noted individualized responses primarily revealed the content of his interests.

5. Wechsler Memory Scale

a. Purpose. This test was devised in response to the need for a rapid and simple measure of memory capacity. Results can be stated in terms directly comparable to the I. Q. on a standardized test. Allowance is also made for memory variations with age.

b. Materials and Instructions. Direct questions evaluate personal and current information and orientation. "Mental control" is tested by the capacity to count backward, to repeat the alphabet, and to count by 3's. Finally the subject is tested for immediate recall of digits and of the content of meaningful paragraphs read to him, for visual designs which have been exposed for ten seconds each, and for paired word-associates presented orally. The material is, for the most part, offered in the form of simple questions to which the subject gives answers. The test requires, on the average, 15 minutes for administration.

c. Data and Scoring. Credits are given, according to specific criteria, for the accuracy of the subject's responses. A few items, namely, those measuring Mental Control, afford opportunity to acquire bonus credits for speed. The subject's raw scores on the separate subtests are totaled. To this sum is added a constant amount depending upon the age group within which the subject falls; age-corrections are supplied for ages 20–64. The new total is the subject's corrected memory score. The Memory Quotient (M. Q.) may then be read from a table provided in the manual for corrected scores at various chronological ages.

d. Interpretation. The M. Q. thus obtained is directly comparable to the subject's I. Q. on the Wechsler-Bellevue Intelligence Scale. It thus becomes possible to compare memory efficiency with other aspects of intellectual function. For example, one can distinguish between cases in which there is a specific memory defect, frequently found in conjunction with organic brain disease, and those in which memory impairment is merely one aspect of a generalized intellectual inefficiency, such as may occur during a functional psychosis.

Illustrative Protocol 1

The present case is that of the 44 year-old man suffering from an alcoholic psychosis whose performance on the Object-Sorting Test has already been described (see Illustrative Protocol 2, p. 60). It may be recalled that on the Wechsler-Bellevue Intelligence Scale he placed at bright normal level with an I. Q. of 113, and that his conceptual thinking ability, as studied by the Sorting Test, did not appear to be impaired. To investigate a further possible disability often found in alcoholic encephalopathy, the Wechsler Memory Scale was administered.

He was able to answer adequately all questions concerning personal identification and current information, and gave correctly the date and the name and location of the hospital. "Mental control" was not complete. He could accurately and rapidly repeat the alphabet and count backward from 20 to 1 but he became confused and made many errors in counting by 3's. His memory for the two stories read to him was faulty, with recall of only a few of the facts contained in them. Rote memory for digits was at least average; he could repeat 8 digits forward and 7 backward. He had difficulty in reproducing visual designs, showing a tendency to recall separate portions correctly but to organize them erroneously. Finally, he achieved only partial success in memorizing word-pairs presented to him orally.

His raw scores on the various items totaled 54. The age-correction value for the 40–44 year range is 40. Thus his total corrected memory score was 94, which, according to the table provided, corresponds to a Memory Quotient of 94.

These results indicated that the patient's memory capacity was only a little below the average level for his age. However, since he was classified in the bright normal range of general intellectual ability, the discrepancy between the two ratings (I. Q. 113, M. Q. 94) seemed to be significant. His ability to call into play already learned associations and, more particularly, his facility in establishing new connections appeared to be notably poorer than other capacities—a finding that might indicate a specific defect. Qualitative features of his performance, such as his poor perception of spatial relations in reproducing the designs, pointed in the same direction. After other confirmatory tests had been administered, it was concluded that some mild organic brain pathology probably did exist in consequence of his prolonged alcoholism.

Illustrative Protocol 2

A 58 year-old single woman was admitted to a mental hospital to be treated for her complaints of depression, worry, poor appetite, crying spells, and forgetfulness. Her formal education had taken her through the sixth grade. She had worked as a domestic most of her life.

Her present symptoms had displayed a gradual onset. After she had entered the hospital, psychologic examination was requested to ascertain whether mental impairment, perhaps associated with early senile or arteriosclerotic changes, might be contributing to her increasingly poor adjustment.

She was first given the Wechsler-Bellevue Intelligence Scale, which rated her at the low average level with an I. Q. of 92. This result was consistent with what was to be expected on the basis of her educational background and for her age. The Wechsler Memory Scale was then administered to determine whether the forgetfulness of which she complained was also within the range of normal expectation.

Her responses in the memory test will be described in some detail. She supplied current information readily and correctly (President, Governor, Mayor, date, month and year). She gave her age and birthdate and the city in which she now was, but she did not know the name of the hospital. Her results in the subtests for "mental control" were less successful. Although she could count backward from 20 to 1, she could not count forward by 3's and made four errors in repeating the alphabet. She was fully aware of her failures in this part of the examination and eager to blame them on her limited education. She did well in recalling the essential facts of the two paragraphs that were read to her. Her ability to repeat 6 digits forward and 4 reversed was consistent with her general intellectual level. She experienced some difficulty in reproducing visual designs, usually recalling only the basic form. When two designs were exposed at the same time, she confused parts of the one with those of the other. She was able to learn paired words with relative ease, and by the third trial earned a perfect score on this portion of the scale.

The patient's total raw score was 51½. The age-correction for the 55-59 year age group is 46. Her total corrected memory score was therefore 97—a figure equivalent to a Memory Quotient of 99 in her case. This rating closely corresponded to her general intellectual level (I. Q. 92), and the interpretation was accordingly made that her memory capacity was in keeping with her age and intelligence.

REFERENCES

General

Hunt, J. McV., and Cofer, C. N. Psychological deficit. Chap. 32, Vol. II, in *Personality and the Behavior Disorders,* ed. by J. McV. Hunt. New York: Ronald Press, 1944.

Babcock-Levy Measurement of Efficiency of Mental Functioning

Babcock, H. An experiment in the measurement of mental deterioration. *Arch. Psychol.,* 1930, 18, No. 117.

Babcock, H. Dementia Praecox: A Psychological Study. Lancaster: Science Press, 1933.

*Rapaport, D., et al. Diagnostic Psychological Testing. Vol. I. Chicago: Year Book Publishers, 1945.

Shipley-Hartford Retreat Scale

Shipley, W. C., and Burlingame, C. C. A convenient self-administering scale for measuring intellectual impairment in psychotics. *Am. J. Psychiat.,* 1941, 97, 1313–1324.

Shipley-Hartford Retreat Scale for Measuring Intellectual Impairment. Hartford: Neuro-Psychiatric Institute of the Hartford Retreat, 1940.

Object-Sorting Test

Bolles, M., Rosen, G., and Landis, C. Psychological performance tests as prognostic agents for the efficacy of insulin therapy in schizophrenia. *Psychiatric Quart.,* 1938, 12, 733–737.

Goldstein, K., and Scheerer, M. Abstract and Concrete Behavior: An Experimental Study with Special Tests. *Psychol. Monogr.,* 1941, 53, No. 2.

Lynn, J. G., Levine, K. N., and Hewson, L. K. Psychological tests for the clinical evaluation of late 'diffuse organic', 'neurotic', and 'normal' reactions after closed head injury. *Res. Publ. A. nerv. ment. Dis.,* 1945, 24, 296–378.

*Rapaport, D., et al. Diagnostic Psychological Testing. Vol. I. Chicago: Year Book Publishers, 1945.

Zubin, J., and Thompson, G. Sorting Tests in Relation to Drug Therapy in Schizophrenia. New York: New York State Psychiatric Institute, 1941.

Vigotsky Blocks

Hanfmann, E., and Kasanin, J. Conceptual Thinking in Schizophrenia. *Nerv. Ment. Dis. Monogr.,* 1942, No. 67.

Wechsler Memory Scale

Wechsler, D. A standardized memory scale for clinical use. *J. Psychol.,* 1945, 19, 87–95.

Chapter 5

Vocational Aptitude and Interest Tests

THE EXAMINATION of vocational skills and aptitudes is sometimes thought to lie outside the interest realm of the clinician dealing with personality problems. Experience has, however, shown that a
subject's adjustment or maladjustment is often determined in considerable measure by work placement and that personality patterns indicate or contraindicate fairly specific vocational choices. Sometimes an
individual's work interests may be symptomatic of underlying personality difficulties that require readjustment before more realistic
choices can be achieved. Special occupational abilities and disabilities
must also often be accurately appraised both in isolation and in relation to needs and motives. Vocational counseling is therefore closely
bound up with psychodynamics.

The technics selected for discussion in this chapter are, however,
a rather circumscribed sample. The selection has been influenced in
part by the relevance of the tests to the case study approach. The illustrative protocols should accordingly be read with the realization that
the vocational scale in question was usually a supplement to a personality study rather than part of a primarily vocational appraisal.

The technics described cover, on the one hand, the measurement of
skills and aptitudes required in various occupational fields and, on
the other, the appraisal of vocational interest patterns. It should be
observed that some effort to recognize special abilities or disabilities
is made in any careful analysis of the general intelligence test, and that
frequently this analysis is the starting point for vocational testing.
Occupational aptitude measures must similarly be interpreted in the
light of intelligence test results in order to disclose special talents. In

the same manner personality test findings may have important relationships to vocational interest patterns.

1. Detroit General Aptitudes Examination

a. Purpose. This is a paper-and-pencil test for measuring and comparing mechanical, clerical, and intellectual aptitudes. It is useful
both for general classification purposes and for individual counseling.

b. Materials and Instructions. There are 16 subtests, each of which
is printed on one page of the examination booklet. Problems concerned
with the three aptitudes occur in random order with the result that
verbal and nonverbal tasks alternate with each other and those involving speed of writing are placed far enough apart to permit some rest.
Included in the various scales are items measuring motor adeptness
(e.g., putting crosses inside rows of circles), visual imagery (e.g., mentally reorganizing disarranged sections of a picture to indicate what
the correct arrangement should be), and educational skills such as
arithmetic and handwriting. Each page includes a fore-exercise and
a timed test, the times ranging from three to five minutes. The entire
examination requires an hour and a half to administer and is ordinarily given at one sitting with a brief intermission. Administration
to either individuals or groups is possible.

c. Data and Scoring. The responses are checked against prepared
scoring keys. Certain subtests are included in more than one aptitude
scale, the intelligence scale embracing ten, the mechanical and clerical
scales, nine each. Total scores for the three aptitudes can be translated
into both age norms and letter ratings (A to E) according to tables
in the manual. While the tests are standardized on school groups
through 12th grade, the age norms extend through 21 years. The
scales can also be broken down into sections, and age norms assigned
separately for motor, visual imagery, general information, and educational aspects.

d. Interpretation. Ratings on the total aptitude scales are considered
the more reliable and valid measures. In individual cases it is possible

to select those ratings which are above the standards indicated by the general intellectual level and hence suggest specific talents. Areas of especially poor skill that should presumably be avoided in vocational training may be similarly identified.

Illustrative Protocol 1

A married man of 32 was admitted to a hospital for the second time with obsessive and compulsive symptoms of such severity that he was unable to carry on his daily work and other normal activities. He had always displayed a strong drive for intellectual attainment and was now attending college at night and receiving honor grades. He had been employed as a bank clerk and teller. His work had been considered to be satisfactory, but he had some feeling that its restricting and exacting nature created tension that contributed to his symptoms. Therefore when he was making plans to leave the hospital and to attempt community adjustment again, he requested information and advice about other occupational areas in which he might conceivably be successful.

In view of his superior intelligence (Wechsler-Bellevue I. Q. 124), it seemed that a number of fields might be open to him. It was noted further that on the intelligence scale he exhibited greater facility with performance items than with verbal tasks (Verbal I. Q. 116, Performance I. Q. 126). To delineate in a preliminary way the broad areas within which his selection might lie, he was given the Detroit General Aptitudes Examination and the Strong Vocational Interest Blank. His results on the latter will be discussed in Chapter 6.

His scores on the various scales and sections of the Detroit General Aptitudes Examination are represented in the accompanying summary chart (Figure 8). It will be observed at first glance that his intelligence rating bears out the superior classification on the individual intelligence scale, and that he is especially adept in those situations involving visual imagery. However, he apparently has some special native mechanical aptitude which places him in a higher group than

I. INTELLIGENCE

	Letter Rating	B
	General Mental Age	18-5
	Total Score, Intelligence	311

	Total Score	Age
A. Motor	53	16-2
B. Visual Imagery	89	22+
C. General, Verbal	92	17-6
D. Educational	77	17-2

Interpretation
Generally   SUPERIOR
Weakest in   MOTOR
Strongest in   VISUAL IMAGERY

II. MECHANICAL APTITUDE

	Letter Rating	A
	General Mech. Apt. Age	18-11
	Total Score, Mech. Apt.	287

	Total Score	Age
A. Motor	53	16-2
B. Visual Imagery	109	21-3
C. Mechanical Information	62	19-2
D. Educational	63	18-0

Interpretation
Generally   ABOVE MENTAL LEVEL
Weakest in   MOTOR
Strongest in   VISUAL IMAGERY

III. CLERICAL APTITUDE

	Letter Rating	B
	General Clerical Apt. Age	17-1
	Total Score, Clerical Apt.	248

	Total Score	Age
A. Motor	53	16-2
B. Visual Imagery	61	20-6
C. Educational	134	16-5

Interpretation
Generally   BELOW MENTAL LEVEL
Weakest in   MOTOR
Strongest in   VISUAL IMAGERY

Fig. 8.   Summary of Findings in the Detroit General Aptitudes Examination, *Protocol 1.*

he achieves on the basis of intelligence alone (Intelligence Scale, B rating; Mechanical Aptitude Scale, A rating). Moreover, his educational skills seem to be more closely related to mechanical than to other aptitudes. It is interesting to note that while his clerical aptitude is better than average, his occupational experience in this sphere has afforded him no special advantage and that his rating for this type of work is his lowest on the three scales.

These patterns were interpreted to indicate that the patient might experience success and satisfaction in some pursuit more mechanical than any in which he had been engaged previously. While his motor speed and skill were not exceptional, it was judged that his superior general intelligence and his particular ability in understanding drawings, sizes, and proportions could be applied to good advantage in such fields as mechanical drawing, drafting, or blueprint work.

The pattern of his test scores was discussed with the patient. He was pleased and enthusiastic over the possibility of success in draftsmanship, and felt that such an occupation might more nearly approach his unfulfilled early plans of becoming an engineer than anything he had yet done.

Illustrative Protocol 2

A male patient had previously been working as stock clerk in a warehouse and had had a fairly satisfactory employment record for several years. He then began to indulge in sporadic drinking bouts and during these intervals grew confused in his work and started to appropriate company property. He was finally accused of theft and discharged. His reaction to this event took the form of further drinking and the appearance of depressive symptoms that finally led to his hospitalization. The acute illness disappeared within a few weeks, but he remained in the hospital for more fundamental psychotherapy. During this period he was engaged in simple stenographic and clerical work which he performed quite satisfactorily. Before his discharge he asked for vocational guidance and reassurance that he could succeed in a secretarial position outside the hospital. The Detroit General Aptitudes Examination was included in the battery of psychologic tests administered in response to his request.

His ratings on all three scales were at the low average level, with letter grades of C—. He met a slightly higher age standard on the mechanical aptitude tasks (XIV-5) than on the measures of intelligence (XIII-7) or clerical aptitude (XIII-6). With the exception of four of the 16 subtests, his general level was consistently mediocre, ranging from the X-8 to the XIV-7 year levels. The notable exceptions were Test 2, General Verbal Information (XVIII-1), Test 3, Arithmetic (XX-11), and the two tests of mechanical information— Test 5, Tool Recognition (XXII-0), and Test 12, Tool Information (XIX-8).

These results were interpreted to mean that the patient had no very clear-cut aptitudes in the areas tapped by the examination. While his mechanical knowledge was superior, this fact seemed to reflect a strong interest based on factors other than genuine ability. His exceptionally high score on the arithmetic test was presumably due to specific occupational practice. On these grounds it was suggested that he would probably do better in work requiring no specialized technical skills. Further evaluation by means of other tests confirmed the hypothesis that his wish to acquire a "white-collar" status was more closely related to his sense of inadequacy and to his particular personality needs than to any outstanding talents he possessed.

2. MINNESOTA MECHANICAL ASSEMBLY TEST

a. Purpose. This instrument is intended to measure a person's ability in putting together the parts of mechanical devices.

b. Materials and Instructions. Thirty-three disassembled mechanical contrivances are used, e.g., a bicycle bell, an expansion nut, and a dieholder. A specific time is allowed for putting together each device.

c. Data and Scoring. Each item assembled within the time allotted yields the subject a score of 10, and partial credit is given in proportion to lesser amounts of work correctly done.

d. Interpretation. Facility in assembling these devices is related to mechanical ability—as demonstrated by the study of individuals engaged in mechanical occupations—and has been construed as an indication of aptitude for such trades as machinist, woodworker, iron-worker, toolmaker, sheet metal worker, and automobile mechanic. Assembly tests have proved useful in discovering mechanical talent and for estimating probable success in certain trade school courses or mechanical vocations. A person's verbal intelligence seems to have little relation to his performance in mechanical assembly tests. The subject's score cannot, however, be taken as a pure measure of mechanical ability but must be interpreted in the light of his previous background and experience.

Illustrative Protocol 1

A 27 year-old married man experienced a sudden onset of anxiety symptoms five months after his induction into military service. His illness led to his discharge from the army and he returned to live with his wife's family. He started to work in his father-in-law's restaurant and bar, but many interpersonal conflicts developed in this relationship. He had partial insight into the source of the difficulty but considered himself too unwell to face the demands of a full-time job that would not permit special consideration for his illness. His anxiety symptoms and some physical complaints persisted so that he finally applied for voluntary admission to a psychiatric hospital. During his hospitalization he became very much interested in the manual activities to which occupational therapy introduced him, and he raised the question of being trained in some mechanical trade under the law providing such education free for veterans. Vocational tests were requested shortly before he left the hospital to guide him in making his plans.

The patient was given the Minnesota Mechanical Assembly Test as part of the psychologic battery. He was less at ease here than in some of the other tests and was resentful of the time limits; when he could not assemble an object, he blamed the materials for being inadequate. His record is tabulated below in detail. It should be noted that perfect performance on an item is awarded 10 points credit, partial solution, proportionate credit according to the number of connections (separate pieces to be joined) required for completion.

Box A

Object	Number of connections to be made	Subject's score
1. Expansion nut	3	6
2. Hose pinch clamp	1	0
3. Hunt paper clip	2	0
4. Wooden clothespin	2	0
5. Linked chain	5	8
6. Bottle-stopper	3	6
7. Push-button door bell	3	0
8. Bicycle bell	4	5
9. Corbin rim lock	5	6

Total for Box A   31

Box B

Object	Number of connections to be made	Subject's score
1. Safety razor	3	6
2. Monkey wrench	2	10
3. Ringstand clamp	2	10
4. Test-tube holder	5	10
5. Spark plug	5	8
6. Inside caliper	5	2
7. Electric plug and wire	4	10
8. Handle for iron	5	6

Total for Box B   62

Box C

Object	Number of con- nections to be made	Subject's score
1. Hemostat	2	10
2. Die-holder	1	10
3. Pliers	3	10
4. Electric-light socket	2	10
5. Wing nut	2	10
6. Glass drawer-knob	2	10
7. Rope-coupler	3	10
8. Kettle-cover knob	4	5
9. Lock nut	2	10
10. Ford magneto-post	3	6
11. Petcock	3	10
12. Hose clamp	3	10
13. Radio switch	6	0
14. Pencil sharpener	2	10
15. Air-gauge valve	3	10
16. Metal pencil	3	3

Total for Box C 134

Total Raw Score for Three Boxes 227
(out of 330 points possible)

This score, according to the norms established for adult males, is approximately what may be expected of the lowest 7 per cent of the population and receives a letter rating of D— on a scale ranging from A + + to E— —. This result is obviously far below the averages for individuals employed as machinist, manual-training teacher, ornamental iron-worker, auto mechanic, skilled manual worker, or machine operator.

A person's score on a scale like the one under discussion is construed as being partially due to his inherent mechanical ingenuity and partly to his familiarity with other specific mechanical devices more or less similar in principle to those that comprise the test. His score is therefore not to be interpreted as a pure measure of mechanical intelligence but is to be appraised also in terms of his background. However, in the event of exceptionally low scores the subject is likely to have neither the natural ingenuity nor the particular experience and interest necessary to the development of the occupational skills in question—a conclusion that fits the present case. It seemed likely, after additional investigation, that the patient had developed certain emotional attitudes toward the protective occupational-therapy situation, and that he misinterpreted the security and relaxation he found there for satisfaction in manual work. Further definition of his vocational plans was therefore postponed until psychotherapy for his personality and emotional problems had been accomplished.

Illustrative Protocol 2

A man of 54 had been engaged in various aspects of personnel work for many years. Previous to his industrial connections he had been interested in group work and settlement house projects. His most recent occupation had been with a federal agency during the war. He had just been offered a position involving responsibility for the organization and administration of the maintenance department of a large institution. Though he was confident of his capacity to handle the personnel problems entailed, he was somewhat concerned as to whether he had sufficient mechanical ability for guiding the department in an understanding fashion and for assuring his prestige among his subordinates. His doubts assumed particular importance because he felt that his advancing age made it imperative for him to obtain a position with some guarantee of permanence. Psychologic tests were administered at his own request. He was given an examination battery that included a scale for general intelligence, a vocational interests inventory, a personality test, and the Minnesota Mechanical Assembly Test.

He handled the materials of the Assembly Test in an unhesitating and confident manner and seemed to be completely at ease as he worked. With the exception of four items, his solutions were entirely correct and were produced within the time limits. His failures, all of a partial nature, were on the bottle-stopper of Box A, the Ford magneto-post of Box C, and the radio switch and air-gauge valve of Box C. His total score was 309 points, with a letter rating of B+, and placed him at the 91st percentile of a population representative of the workers in an urban area. These results, considered in conjunction with his superior intelligence (I. Q. 138) and a confirmatory vocational interest pattern, offered no contraindications to his enjoying success in the position in which he was interested.

3. Seashore Measures of Musical Talents

a. Purpose. Many of the specific abilities involved in the hearing, appreciation, and performance of music can be measured. The Seashore Measures include six of the fundamental capacities for the hearing of sounds as these occur in music. Such tests are of obvious value for guidance in musical education but may also prove useful in various technical occupations that involve effective hearing.

b. Materials and Instructions. The six subtests comprising the examination are: *pitch, loudness, time, timbre, rhythm,* and *tonal memory.* The sounds presented to the subject have been produced by accurate laboratory instruments and are recorded on 12-inch double-faced phonograph records that may be played on any standard phonograph. Test blanks for recording responses are provided and may be used either with individuals or with groups. The directions are uniformly simple. The subject records by means of a letter mark the way in which the second of a pair of sounds differs from the first. For example, in testing for pitch, a series of tonal pairs differing in pitch are played. The subject is asked to write an *H* if the second tone is higher than the first; an *L* if the second tone is lower than the first.

c. Data and Scoring. Responses are scored on the basis of accuracy. The number of right answers given is converted into a "rank order" score. The highest rank is 1 and represents the highest 10 per cent in a normal unselected community. The next highest, 2, includes scores made by the next 10 per cent, and so on to rank 10 which includes scores made by the lowest 10 per cent of a normal population.

d. Interpretation. Most individuals are capable of some degree of musical appreciation. Musical education directed toward performance should be pursued in proportion to the amount of talent possessed. The ratings obtained on the Seashore Measures are significant for musical guidance, but many other factors must also be taken into account, e.g., general intelligence, imagination, emotional development, musical facilities and interests, family background in music, time to study, and willingness to work.

Illustrative Protocol 1

An 18 year-old boy was referred to an out-patient clinic for anxiety and panic states, nightmares, and a marked sense of inferiority that had lasted for several years. He had left high school in his third year, at the age of 16, because his extreme shyness interfered with his adjustment and progress. He was currently employed in his father's garage but his real ambition was a career in music. Although he played no instrument, he had done some composing. He maintained that a symphony he had written had been "seriously considered" in a contest sponsored by the National Federation of Music Clubs. Upon applying for a scholarship to further his formal training in music, he was told that he would have to complete high school before his application could be accepted. In requesting help and advice from the clinic as a basis for formulating his future plans, he explained that, though he believed he had some talent, he did not consider himself a genius. It was thought by the physician that psychologic tests would aid in evaluating the relationships between the young man's vocational interests, his abilities, and his personality problems.

The Seashore Measures of Musical Talents were administered as part of the psychologic examination. In the subtest for measuring recognition of *pitch,* where the subject is instructed to record whether the second of two tones is higher or lower than the first, the patient made 31 out of 50 possible correct judgments. In the second series of comparisons, where the relative *loudness* of the second tone must be judged, he made 37 correct, 13 incorrect decisions. On *rhythm,* where the subject decides between "same" and "different" for each pair of phrases, he rightly identified 26 out of 30 comparisons. Next, judgment of *time* is evaluated by having the examinee record whether a second tone is of shorter or longer duration than a first. Here the patient scored 41 out of 50. In the fifth section, concerned with *timbre,* where the subject decides whether two tones are the "same" or "different" in tone quality, he properly identified 30 of the 50 pairs. The final subtest investigates *tonal memory.* A short series of tones is played twice; in the second playing one note is changed and the subject is requested to record by number which note of the series is altered. The patient made no errors in this series.

When these scores were related to the norms for adults, the subject compared as follows:

Test Section	Rank
Pitch	8
Loudness	7
Rhythm	2
Time	1
Timbre	6
Tonal Memory	1

It is apparent that the patient ranked far above average with respect to rhythm, time and tonal memory, and that he actually failed in none of the specific capacities tested. Provided, therefore, that other necessary factors, e.g., intelligence, imagination, and emotional development, were favorable, a musical education might reasonably be recommended for him.

4. Strong Vocational Interest Blank

a. Purpose. Although knowledge of an individual's special abilities is important for occupational counseling, it is also essential in this context to have insight into his interests. The latter information may aid in predicting whether a subject would be motivated to complete any course of study required and, granting the necessary ability and training, whether he would be apt to enjoy a given type of work. Among the available tests is the Strong Vocational Interest Blank.

b. Materials and Instructions. A test blank of 400 verbal items is presented to the subject. He is asked to indicate his like, dislike, or indifference regarding each item, e.g., poets, mathematics, museums, cripples, working alone, etc. The questions cover the areas of occupations, amusements, general activities, school subjects, and personal characteristics. Two revised test forms are available—one for men and one for women. Administration either to individuals or to groups is possible.

c. Data and Scoring. After a person has checked the blank, appropriate weightings are assigned each response. The test has been validated by giving it to individuals successfully engaged in various occupations, e.g., dentists, artists, teachers, to determine their interests. The scoring keys provide the weights for various responses according to occupation.

d. Interpretation. By comparing the subject's responses with the norms, it is possible to determine how far his interests coincide with those of individuals actually engaged in the various occupations. It should be noted that these comparisons cover not only interests directly related to the occupation in question, but also attitudes and inclinations that are not in their immediate reference vocational.

Illustrative Protocol 1

The same young man (see p. 79) who, not wishing to return to his former clerical occupation, was given the Detroit General Aptitudes Examination was also administered the Strong Vocational Interest Blank for Men. His interest choices fell into the pattern represented in Figure 9.

The profile indicates that the subject's interests conform most closely to those identified with his past occupational experience (Group VIII).

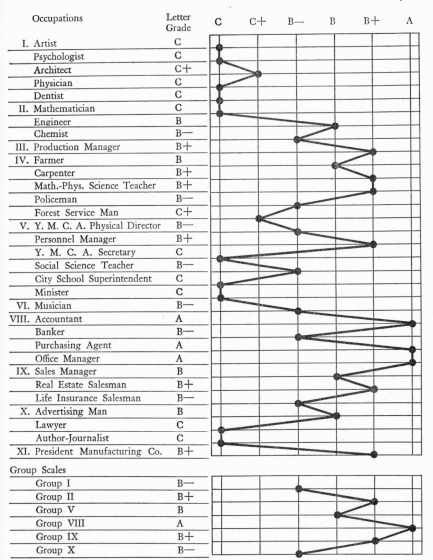

Occupations	Letter Grade
I. Artist	C
Psychologist	C
Architect	C+
Physician	C
Dentist	C
II. Mathematician	C
Engineer	B
Chemist	B—
III. Production Manager	B+
IV. Farmer	B
Carpenter	B+
Math.-Phys. Science Teacher	B+
Policeman	B—
Forest Service Man	C+
V. Y. M. C. A. Physical Director	B—
Personnel Manager	B+
Y. M. C. A. Secretary	C
Social Science Teacher	B—
City School Superintendent	C
Minister	C
VI. Musician	B—
VIII. Accountant	A
Banker	B—
Purchasing Agent	A
Office Manager	A
IX. Sales Manager	B
Real Estate Salesman	B+
Life Insurance Salesman	B—
X. Advertising Man	B
Lawyer	C
Author-Journalist	C
XI. President Manufacturing Co.	B+

Group Scales

	Letter Grade
Group I	B—
Group II	B+
Group V	B
Group VIII	A
Group IX	B+
Group X	B—

FIG. 9. Profile of Scores on the Strong Vocational Interest Blank, *Protocol 1.*

It should, however, be added that he rated especially high on the detailed aspects of the field in question. Supporting interests are concerned with pure science (Group II), especially engineering, and with related practical and sometimes manual activities (Carpenter, Mathematics and Physical Science Teacher). Finally, he scored high for selling (Group IX) and for other pursuits of the business world (Personnel Manager, Production Manager). The total pattern indicates an occupational area that is technical or scientific to a degree, but that is imbedded in a commercial setting. In view of these results and of his aptitude scores on other tests, the patient's inclination to train as a draftsman seemed to be well founded.

Illustrative Protocol 2

This case has also been discussed in the preceding section (see p. 86). The young man in question was ambitious for a musical career and was given the Strong Vocational Interest Blank to determine the details of his primary and supporting interests. His results are represented in Figure 10.

The record not only confirms his marked musical interests, but reveals related ones in other creative-expressive pursuits (Artist, Architect, Author-Journalist). On the other hand, it is apparent that he is averse to office routine, group leadership, personal contacts, and to work involving practical or manual services (Groups VIII, V, IV). He shares many of the attitudes and inclinations of the professions (Group I).

The total pattern was considered to be compatible with a program of training in music. It was pointed out, however, that he would probably have difficulty in adjusting to any training of a routine or repetitive nature and that his distinct preference for working by himself might signify an escape into situations of high prestige value where he would conceivably be sheltered from both criticism and direction.

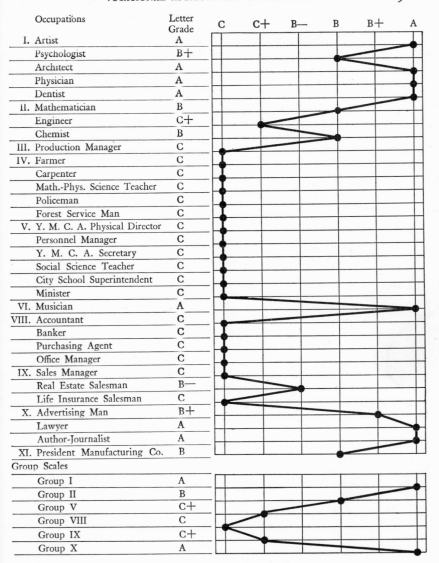

Occupations	Letter Grade
I. Artist	A
Psychologist	B+
Architect	A
Physician	A
Dentist	A
II. Mathematician	B
Engineer	C+
Chemist	B
III. Production Manager	C
IV. Farmer	C
Carpenter	C
Math.-Phys. Science Teacher	C
Policeman	C
Forest Service Man	C
V. Y. M. C. A. Physical Director	C
Personnel Manager	C
Y. M. C. A. Secretary	C
Social Science Teacher	C
City School Superintendent	C
Minister	C
VI. Musician	A
VIII. Accountant	C
Banker	C
Purchasing Agent	C
Office Manager	C
IX. Sales Manager	C
Real Estate Salesman	B—
Life Insurance Salesman	C
X. Advertising Man	B+
Lawyer	A
Author-Journalist	A
XI. President Manufacturing Co.	B
Group Scales	
Group I	A
Group II	B
Group V	C+
Group VIII	C
Group IX	C+
Group X	A

Fig. 10. Profile of Scores on the Strong Vocational Interest Blank, *Protocol* 2.

REFERENCES

General

Bingham, W. V. Aptitudes and Aptitude Testing. New York: Harpers, 1937.

Mursell, J. L. Psychological Testing. Chaps. 7 and 8. New York: Longmans, Green, 1947.

Detroit General Aptitudes Examination

Baker, H. J., Voelker, P. H., and Crockett, A. C. Detroit General Aptitudes Examination, Form A. Bloomington, Illinois: Public School Publishing Company, 1941.

Minnesota Mechanical Assembly Test

Paterson, D. G., Elliott, R. M., Anderson, L. D., Toops, H. A., and Heidbreder, E. Minnesota Mechanical Ability Tests. Minneapolis: University Minnesota Press, 1930.

Seashore Measures of Musical Talents

Seashore, C. E. The Psychology of Music. New York: McGraw-Hill, 1938.

Seashore, C. E., Lewis, D., and Saetveit, J. G. Manual of Instructions and Interpretations for the Seashore Measures of Musical Talents. Camden: RCA Manufacturing, 1939.

Stanton, H. M. The Measurement of Musical Talent: an Eastman Experiment. University of Iowa Studies in the Psychology of Music. Vol. 2. Iowa City: University Iowa Press, 1935.

Strong Vocational Interest Inventory

Darley, J. G. Clinical Aspects and Interpretation of the Strong Vocational Interest Blank. New York: Psychological Corporation, 1941.

Strong, E. K. Vocational Interests of Men and Women. Stanford University: Stanford University Press, 1943.

Chapter 6

Personality Inventories

THE MOST COMMONLY used tests of personality comprise two rather distinct groups each of which will be treated in a separate chapter. The first group typically employs the questionnaire or inventory in order to obtain from the subject his opinions about his own behavior or traits. In its most naive form this approach assumes—unjustifiably to a large extent—that the individual knows, understands and is willing to reveal his personality. The Bernreuter Inventory, the first test outlined in this chapter, may serve as an example. It should be added, however, that the assumption of complete self-knowledge with probity is not fundamental or explicit in these procedures since their validity is based in the course of standardization upon the patterns of answers obtained from groups with different, independently determined personality or psychiatric diagnoses. It would therefore be possible for an inventory to have a certain validity even if the subjects falsified their responses provided that such distortion happened in a typical and consistent fashion in each of the diagnostically different validating groups.

Nevertheless, to overcome the conscious falsification and negligence that notoriously enter into the completion of a personality questionnaire, several of the more recent tests, e.g., the Minnesota Multiphasic described below, have been constructed to include self-validating or trap devices that make it possible to evaluate the over-all reliability of a response record.

Some inventories approach rather closely to the projective methods—which will be discussed in the next chapter—since they depend upon eliciting the individual's opinions not about himself but about various issues or problems concerning which his judgment or taste serves as a reflection of his personality. The Allport-Vernon Study of Values, which is the third test outlined in this chapter, conforms to this description.

An obvious advantage of any questionnaire approach lies in its scope and ready availability for assessing the broadest possible field of personal behavior. Questions can be framed to cover every aspect of the individual's traits, values, needs, attitudes and experiences. Moreover, these tests can usually be self-administered, either by individuals or by groups, and their scoring can safely be performed by a clerical assistant or even by a machine.

As has already been indicated, however, the weakness of these methods derives from the erroneously implicit assumption that the individual knows and is willing to tell the facts about himself. As it has become more and more clearly recognized that personality is largely covert or unconscious, the limited value of the inventory approach has been disclosed.

These considerations make it easy to understand why most personality inventories have very high ratings for reliability but very low ones for validity. The high reliability results from the fact that whatever "opinion errors" the individual makes in responding to a questionnaire he presumably makes consistently throughout the test or on different occasions of testing. The low validity results from the further fact that there is apparently no significant discriminative difference from one diagnostic population to another either in terms of these "errors" or on other grounds. It is, however, possible that further research with the questionnaire, if based upon validating criteria that are behaviorally and psychodynamically oriented, may produce instruments of greater dependability.

In the meantime a popular current objective in the use of the personality inventory is to obtain a rapid survey of the person's opinions of himself. Such information is important since it must be taken into account in any complete evaluation of the individual. In addition to its other values a knowledge of the person's views of himself affords a basis for appraising his insight and integration when comparisons with more "objective" data are available.

At present the personality inventory is apt to be included in the work of the psychodiagnostician either as a screening device for grossly classifying the individual as more or less normal or abnormal, or as a preliminary survey that serves as a substitute for an interview and perhaps provides a basis for the selection of the more deeply probing projective methods.

1. BERNREUTER PERSONALITY INVENTORY

a. *Purpose.* This inventory is intended to assess various personality traits of the individual and to detect any important departures from normality.

b. *Materials and Instructions.* A series of 125 questions, all rather simply worded, with alternative answers are presented to the subject. He is instructed to respond by underlining "Yes," "No," or "?". The test is self-administering, with individuals or with groups, and the subject works at his own speed.

c. *Data and Scoring.* The traits measured are *neurotic tendency, self-sufficiency, introversion-extroversion, dominance-submission, self-confidence,* and *sociability.* Answers are weighted according to their significance for various personality patterns. This diagnostic scoring system yields six sets of weighted scores, one for each of the above-mentioned traits.

d. *Interpretation.* Scores obtained on the inventory are supposed to differentiate between emotional stability and instability. However, for the reasons given in the preceding general section the findings are seldom considered conclusive. The instrument is especially useful for discovering in a short time how the individual regards his own personality or how he wishes others to regard it.

Illustrative Protocol 1

A high-school boy of 16 was admitted to the hospital for study and treatment because during the past year he had exhibited various obsessive and compulsive symptoms. He had overwhelming ideas of uncleanliness and had to wash his hands many times an hour. He had a good school record and proved to be of superior intelligence when tested on the Wechsler-Bellevue Scale (I. Q. 120). To obtain a picture of his self-evaluation the Bernreuter Inventory was administered as part of the personality study.

The scores he achieved for the six traits assessed by the test will be cited and interpreted. By comparison with the norms for high-school boys he was in the 62d percentile for neuroticism—somewhat above the average but not as far above as would be expected from his clinical picture. For self-sufficiency he was in the 66th percentile, a result again indicating his tendency to over-value himself. For introversion he turned out to be somewhat above average—in the 58th percentile—but not as high as he would probably be judged by others. He appeared, on the other hand, to rate himself accurately as being rather submissive (37th percentile for dominance) and as relatively nonsocial (76th percentile for sociability). His score for self-confidence assigned him to the 52d percentile and by its closeness to the average reflected some lack of concern about his symptoms.

It was noted additionally that on only one of the 125 items did he resort to encircling the question mark instead of replying with a definite Yes or No. The exceptional behavior was in response to a question concerned with attitude toward the opposite sex. A complex of possible relationship to his symptoms may thus have been indicated.

Projective methods, including the Rorschach, the Picture-Frustration Study and the Thematic Apperception Test, administered later confirmed the leads afforded by the inventory and provided a basis for comprehending the patient's self-evaluation.

2. MINNESOTA MULTIPHASIC PERSONALITY INVENTORY

a. *Purpose*. This procedure is designed to provide a measure of personality deviation as determined from replies to a series of questionnaire items.

b. *Materials and Instructions*. The individual form of the test differs from the more usual leaflet in that each item or statement is printed on a small white card which the subject is required to sort in a filing box under "True," "False," or "Cannot Say," according to its applicability to him. There are 550 cards, covering a wide range of topics from physical condition to moral and social attitudes. The subject is, for example, asked whether he blushes characteristically, whether some members of his family have quick tempers, whether he hears strange things when alone, and whether he likes movie love scenes. The time required for administration varies with the individual from approximately 30 to 90 minutes. The device is self-administering and the subject works at his own speed. There is also a group form of the test in which the items, printed in a booklet, are marked by the examinee instead of being sorted by him.

c. *Data and Scoring.* The critical or unusual responses are separated from the subject's sortings and tabulated. Comparison is then made for typical patterns found among patients with various psychiatric disorders and the subject is thus assigned a raw score for the following scales: Hypochondriasis (Hs), Depression (D), Hysteria (Hy), Psychopathic Deviance (Pd), Masculinity or Femininity of Interests (Mf), Paranoia (Pa), Psychasthenia (Pt), Schizophrenia (Sc), and Hypomania (Ma). Self-validating scores are also provided for and cover the subject's carelessness or undue meticulousness (F) and his attempts to reply evasively (?), to place himself in the most socially acceptable light (L), or to minimize or exaggerate his symptoms (K). Tables are available for translating raw into "T" or standard scores in order to determine the subject's relationships to the standardization groups.

d. *Interpretation.* Scores that deviate beyond the normal range on any of the separate scales are noted. Most mentally sick individuals show deviance on more than one scale and it is therefore advisable to think in terms of patterns. Scores have, for example, been found to cluster in constellations suggestive of neurotic, as contrasted with psychotic disturbances, with the separate scales serving to identify the outstanding traits of the disorder. As has already been pointed out, conclusions based upon this type of test must be accepted with reservations. In this instance, however, the validating scores reduce the sources of error. Further value is derived from the procedure when, in addition to the quantitative diagnostic scores, the subjective content of the individual responses is examined for indications of specific problems, areas of conflict, or symptoms.

Illustrative Protocol 1

A 27 year-old woman was admitted to the hospital with a history of anxiety symptoms and physical complaints of a genito-urinary and digestive nature. Her capacity to work had thus been sporadically impaired over a period of ten years and she had experienced many medical examinations, treatments, and minor operations. About two months before admission her anxieties became sharply exaggerated; she began to fear that she had various incurable diseases and was about to die. Complete disinterest in social contacts or daily events developed and she spent most of her time in bed.

Routine psychologic examination was included in the early days of her hospitalization as one of the exploratory procedures. She was highly cooperative, willing to work for fairly long test sessions, and did not require external motivation to sustain her interest and effort. She was precise and businesslike, but she offered little spontaneous conversation during the examination.

Her scores on the Minnesota Multiphasic Personality Inventory are graphically represented in Figure 11. It will be noted, first, that all of the validating scales (?, L, K, F) were within the normal range, a result suggesting that the patient's other scores could with relative safety be interpreted at their face value. The next significant finding was that she deviated from the range of normal adjustment only on the first three diagnostic scales—Hypochondriasis, Depression and Hysteria. Elevated scores on these three measures have been found to be closely related in many patients and are referred to by various investigators as the "neurotic triad"; in contrast, the factors charted on the right-hand side of the psychogram are more related to psychotic adjustment. The present patient could thus be tentatively classified as neurotic, with hypochondriasis and depression being especially prominent.

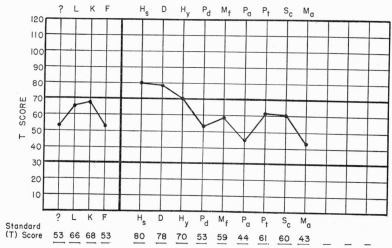

Fig. 11. Profile of Scores on the Minnesota Multiphasic Personality Inventory, *Protocol 1.*

Scrutiny was then turned to the particular items that had contributed to her scores. Her characteristic responses seemed to cluster around several sustained themes. One of these centered upon physical complaints such as fatigue and insomnia. Another expressed her ideas of futility and discouragement; e.g., she sorted under "Cannot Say" the items concerned with whether she was getting all the sympathy she should, whether anyone cared much what happened to her, and whether she could do anything well. A specific source of maladjustment was disclosed in her family relationships. She questioned the statements referring to whether her relatives were in sympathy with her, and whether she occasionally felt hatred toward members of her family whom she usually loved; she similarly classified as false the item concerned with having been free from family rule and as true the one expressing the occasional wish to leave home. A last group of significant responses indicated some difficulty in accepting an adult sexual role. She agreed, for instance, that sexual things disgusted her, denied that she was attracted by members of the opposite sex, and questioned whether she liked mannish women.

These results as a whole contributed to the general clinical evaluation that the patient was neurotically disturbed. They indicated further some specific areas of maladjustment toward which psychotherapy might be oriented.

Illustrative Protocol 2

A young married woman was administered a battery of psychologic tests, including the Minnesota Multiphasic Personality Inventory, at the request of her physician who had been treating her for mental symptoms over the past three or four years. During this period she had displayed increasing disinterest in her home and family, had been preoccupied with the belief that her husband was unfaithful to her, and had periodically drunk to excess. She was also concerned that people were talking about her. Her history revealed that a year after completing high school she had married because she had become pregnant. She now had two children and said that she had also had an operation for abortion.

The patient's pattern of scores is represented in Figure 12. It will be noted that here, again, the validating scores were essentially negligible; the various diagnostic scales could therefore be regarded as comparatively dependable. The psychogram showed a much more general deviance than that found in the preceding case. Especially prominent were the elevated scores for Schizophrenia, Psychasthenia and Psychopathic Personality, but the components of the "neurotic triad" were also at or near the limits of normality. Such a combination of results is not uncommon among psychotic patients; the more severe mental illness is then construed to rest upon a scaffolding of neurotic attitudes and symptoms. It is also noteworthy that this patient who was later officially diagnosed as having Schizophrenia, Paranoid Type, did not have an elevated score on the Paranoia scale.

The psychopathic attitudes disclosed by the Inventory were interpreted as representing her characteristic hostility toward her environment.

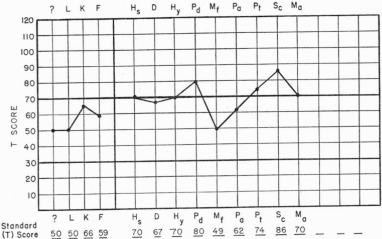

Fig. 12. Profile of Scores on the Minnesota Multiphasic Personality Inventory, *Protocol 2.*

The subjective content of the patient's responses exhibited several consistent trends. She pictured herself as being shy and uncomfortable with other individuals, as disliking parties and crowds, and as preferring to be by herself. She expressed the beliefs that most persons would lie to gain an advantage and that it was acceptable to break the law if one could be certain to "get away with it." These views were, however, in apparent conflict with her religious ideas and standards. Another source of unrest was sex. In a succession of items she disclosed that she considered her sex life to be unsatisfactory, that she disliked to talk about the subject, that she was worried about it, and wished that she were not bothered by sexual thoughts. To the question about whether she had ever indulged in any unusual sex practices she was non-committal.

In this psychotic case the Inventory thus contributed some valid, though incomplete, information for purposes of psychiatric diagnosis and offered several leads of a psychodynamic nature.

Illustrative Protocol 3

A 16 year-old boy, who was a high-school senior with a very superior record, developed withdrawal symptoms and made a suicidal attempt of doubtful validity. He had stammered since the age of four and seemed to be making compensatory efforts for his speech handicap in his school work. On being hospitalized for psychiatric study and treatment he was given a series of psychologic tests which demonstrated, among other things, that he was of very superior intelligence (W-B. I. Q. 138), with more verbal than performance ability. Along with other tests of personality, the Minnesota Multiphasic Inventory was included to elicit a picture of his self-evaluation and to aid in the psychiatric diagnosis.

The profile of the patient's scores on this Inventory is shown in Figure 13. As will be at once noted, he presented a constellation of very broad pathology. The scales for Depression, Psychasthenia and Schizophrenia were above 100 and those for Hysteria, Hypochondriasis, Psychopathic Deviance and Paranoia were also significantly elevated. A record with so much deviance indicates either a very sick patient or one who is highly exaggerating his symptoms. It was therefore necessary to examine carefully the validating scores he had obtained. It will be seen that his F score was 78 (significantly high), his K score, 42 (significantly low). Elevation of F occurs when a subject through carelessness inappropriately credits himself with unusual behavior or through undue meticulousness exaggerates his symptoms. When the score for K is significantly low, the interpretation favors the second alternative since, as will be recalled, low K provides another indication of symptom-exaggeration.

It was therefore concluded that this adolescent boy was morbidly introspective and was concentrating upon his maladjustment in a severely neurotic fashion. While the Inventory was at face value inconsistent with the clinical impression (and with the eventual psychiatric diagnosis of Psychasthenia), the test turned out upon interpretation in terms of the self-validating scales to contribute reliably to the picture of the patient's orientation. This case thus illustrates not only how the Inventory can afford important information about the subject's self-evaluation but how in some instances this self-evaluation may in itself have clinically diagnostic significance. It should be added that the more qualitative data provided by the content of individual responses was less specifically useful in this record because so many items were answered in an unusual fashion.

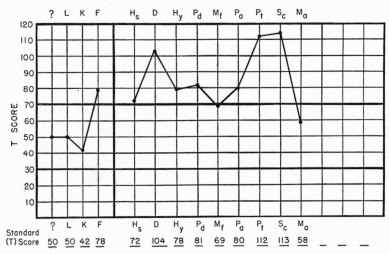

Fig. 13. Profile of Scores on the Minnesota Multiphasic Personality Inventory, *Protocol 3.*

3. Allport-Vernon Study of Values

a. *Purpose.* This instrument is designed to measure an individual's relative standing with respect to six main types of values or general interests. These dominant directions of personality were suggested by Spranger's classification of "ideal types": theoretical, economic, aesthetic, social, political, and religious.

b. *Materials and Instructions.* There are 45 printed items, arranged in a booklet, which call for a total of 120 responses—20 for each value. The test is self-administered, either by individuals or by groups, and may be completed in about 20 minutes. The subject is required to put stated alternative answers to questions in the rank order of his preference. For example, one item presents to the examinee the possibility of influencing the educational policies of a public school system with the instructions that he indicate in the order of his intent whether he would undertake (1) to further the study and performance of dramatics, (2) to enlarge the laboratory facilities, (3) to encourage cooperativeness and the spirit of service, or (4) to promote savings banks in the schools as an educational measure in thrift.

c. *Data and Scoring*. If the subject gives (2) in the preceding example as his top-ranking preference, he receives 3 points for theoretical values. If he indicates (1) as the lowest in his order of preference, he receives zero for aesthetic interests. The other two alternatives similarly are credited against social and economic values. By summing the points for the responses to all items a range of scores from 0 to 60 is possible for each type of value. With the aid of tables provided in the manual raw scores may be converted into percentile scores based on norms derived from college undergraduates and older adults.

d. *Interpretation*. There is considerable agreement between the scores obtained on this test and the real life interests of individuals. The interests found to be predominant by the test are likely to be the same as those displayed in choices of vocation or avocation. Women consistently rate higher than men in aesthetic, social, and religious values; lower in theoretical, economic, and political values. Business, theological, science, and art students give expected results. This inventory is accordingly useful both for personality study and for vocational guidance.

Illustrative Protocol 1

A 26 year-old graduate student at a university had specialized in economics, sociology, and personnel administration before entering military service. During his service he came in contact with units engaged in psychologic and psychiatric work and developed an interest in the clinical field. Upon returning to the university for the completion of his training, he decided to transfer to clinical psychology. In response to his request for some guidance, the Study of Values was included in the battery of tests he was given.

The raw scores he obtained and the corresponding percentile scores are shown in Figure 14. The results showed clearly that social values were the most important to him (92d percentile) although the economic (65th) and political (66th) were still prominent in his pattern of interests. For example, he indicated strong disagreement with the view that it was justifiable for great artists, such as Wagner and Byron, to be selfish and inconsiderate of others; similarly, he believed that contemporary charitable activities should not be curtailed merely because they might undermine individual initiative. As compared to his marked social values, his interests in theoretical (34th percentile) and religious (35th) matters were weak.

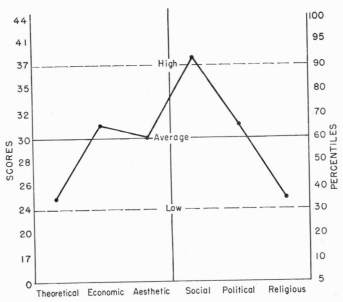

Fig. 14. Profile of Scores on the Allport-Vernon Study of Values, *Protocol 1*

The results of the test were therefore interpreted as consistent with his avowed interest in the social adjustment of individuals. It was concluded that his choice of clinical psychology was not contradicted by the Study.

Illustrative Protocol 2

A printer of 44, who was a college graduate and an advanced degree holder as well, became preoccupied with purely intellectual pursuits to an extent that began seriously to interfere with his job. He had always taken an interest in literature, philosophy and religion but now he added to these a number of obsessive and compulsive ideas, e.g., the belief that he had to perform certain religious rituals regularly. His preoccupations were not organized or sustained and he frequently discarded one interest in favor of another. When he found himself left with little, if any, impetus for his regular job, he came to the hospital for psychiatric help.

He was admitted for a period of observation during which he was given a battery of psychologic tests. These indicated that he was of superior intelligence and was able to apply his abilities accurately and efficiently. He seemed at ease, however, only in situations that allowed him to employ his theoretical knowledge; he received little satisfaction from interpersonal relationships. To aid in understanding the part that his various intellectual interests played in his personality disorder the Study of Values was administered.

From the profile of his scores it was evident that he approached nearly every situation with a theoretical frame of reference (100th percentile). He was also high in social interests (94th) but, presumably, gave these an intellectualized and impersonal emphasis. Religious values were also prominent (74th). In contrast, political (9th) and economic (12th) contexts were avoided by him, perhaps because they too directly implied practical intercourse with the environment.

This constellation of interests, in conjunction with the findings from other tests, was interpreted to mean that the patient was making an intellectualized retreat from his everyday world. He was defending himself against contacts that represented a threat to his sense of personal inadequacy or that in other ways exceeded his frustration tolerance.

REFERENCES

General
Maller, J. B. Personality tests. Chap. 5, Vol. I, in *Personality and the Behavior Disorders,* ed. by J. McV. Hunt. New York: Ronald Press, 1944.
Rosenzweig, S. Investigating and appraising personality. Chap. 18 in *Methods of Psychology,* ed. by T. G. Andrews. New York: Wiley, 1948.

Bernreuter Personality Inventory
Bernreuter, R. G. The theory and construction of the personality inventory. *J. soc. Psychol.,* 1933, 4, 387–405.
Bernreuter, R. G. Validity of the personality inventory. *Personnel J.,* 1933, 11, 383–386.

Minnesota Multiphasic Personality Inventory
Hathaway, S. R., and McKinley, J. C. The Minnesota Multiphasic Personality Inventory. Minneapolis: University Minnesota Press, 1943.
Hathaway, S. R., and McKinley, J. C. A multiphasic personality schedule (Minnesota). I. Construction of the schedule. *J. Psychol.,* 1940, 10, 249–254.
Supplementary Manual for the Minnesota Multiphasic Personality Inventory. New York: Psychological Corporation, 1946.

Allport-Vernon Study of Values
Vernon, P. E., and Allport, G. W. A test for personality values. *J. abnorm. soc. Psychol.,* 1931, 26, 231–248.

Chapter 7
Projective Methods

THE SECOND group of personality tests—the projective methods—has a much broader psychodiagnostic scope than the inventories. These apperceptive devices are not *tests* in the strictly psychometric sense since they have a different relationship to traditional statistical norms and depend in large measure upon the interpretation of intra-individual psychodynamic content. The field of these technics is still in a state of active research much of which will need to concern itself with basic problems of definition and methodology as well as with the more usual problems of test construction.

The projective methods attempt to probe the inner content and organization of the individual personality by eliciting spontaneous reactions to stimulus materials that are themselves ambiguous, equivocal, or in some other sense only partially structured. Ink-blots, incomplete pictures or other similar media are presented to the examinee as a foil for his "projections." Scoring and interpretation depend upon the apperceptive selection made by the subject and consider the patterns of these selective responses in their contextual relationships and in their sequence.

Each of the formal projective technics employs some standard set of stimulus materials as a basis for comparing subjects with each other in their reactions. Complementary to such a comparison by group norms is the comparison of the subject's own responses with one another. The latter relationships frequently reveal the implicit or unconscious levels of the personality; psychoanalytic principles are of value in such interpretation.

The history of the projective methods is a fairly recent one, the term itself having been introduced, or at least given wide currency, by the usage of L. K. Frank in 1939. The first of the deliberately constructed projective technics was the word association method, published by Francis Galton in 1879. As a modification of this technic Freud devised free association, initially employed for interpreting dreams and later as a general tool of psychoanalysis. Notable also is the contribution of Jung who enlisted the word association procedure for revealing complexes and for otherwise validating the psychoanalytic theory of personality. The Word Association Test as we know it today is based largely upon Jung's important studies. Rorschach published his ink-blot method of psychodiagnosis in 1921, and play technic, for use mainly with children, was devised early in the century by a group of child therapists. The Thematic Apperception Test was described by Morgan and Murray in 1935, and since that date a number of other technics have been introduced. Among the latter is the picture-association method.

As instruments of clinical examination the projective technics have several advantages over other tests of personality. The subject is usually unaware of the meaning or value of different types of response and hence can not deliberately create an impression of himself that is falsely favorable or unfavorable. Since the examining situation imposes a minimum of restrictions or demands, feelings of failure or inability are in the usual case much reduced. For the same reason even the erratic and seemingly irrelevant responses of the severely disturbed patient, who cannot adhere to the limitations of more formal procedures, afford material for analysis according to projective dynamics. Since, moreover, the aim is largely to understand the individual in his own terms—his productions being considered from within as much as from without—interpretation does not rest heavily upon the statistical determination of "cut-off scores" that arbitrarily differentiate the normal from the pathologic. Finally, because these methods encourage the expression of the total personality, they provide evidence for appraising intellectual as well as personality factors and for evaluating the interaction of the two. The elicited picture of the individual in the process of his selective behavior and in his inner organization thus often serves as a basis for applying interpretively the known psychodynamic principles of growth, frustration and adjustment.

These technics have greatly extended the psychodiagnostic scope of clinical psychology. In them, however, are also inherent pitfalls which make for easy abuse by the untrained. More adequate professional training and further relevant research will both be necessary to provide the stable foundation upon which these methods will have to depend for their sound development.

For presentation in the present chapter a selection has been made of five representative projective procedures. These run the historical gamut briefly reviewed above, exemplify the application of these technics to both adults and children, introduce a typical variety of stimulus media, and illustrate the manner in which the more usual psychometric or group norms are combined with intra-individual analysis in psychodynamic interpretation.

1. Word Association Test

a. *Purpose.* This projective method is intended to reveal the associative connections between stimulus words and free verbal responses. Since the subject is at liberty to choose from a multiplicity of logically possible reactions, the ones he spontaneously produces are expected to have a more or less personal significance for him. Complexes (unconscious constellations of ideas and attitudes) may be disclosed by unusual response content; thinking disturbances, by the formal characteristics of the associative process.

b. *Materials and Instructions.* The test material consists of a standardized list of words, usually numbering between 50 and 100 items; several such lists have been widely used.* (Sometimes special

* In the two following illustrative cases a list of 55 words was used and was adapted from the 60 word list taken over by Rapaport from Orbison. The words included will be found in the second protocol; the five excluded words verge on the "shocking" and were ordinarily omitted in the routine testing of our Laboratory. The norms for popular responses, referred to below, are those given by Rapaport.

lists are drawn up to meet the requirements of a particular case or selected words may be interpolated in one of the standard lists.) The subject is instructed to respond as quickly as possible with the first word that comes to his mind after the examiner gives the stimulus item. A stop-watch is used to measure the reaction time. Some examiners repeat the procedure immediately after the first administration, requesting the examinee to reply as far as possible with the responses given originally. The subject is also sometimes asked to explain any obscure connections between stimulus and response words.

c. *Data and Scoring.* The verbatim response to each word is recorded, together with any comments, sounds, or gestures made by the subject. Reaction times are systematically noted. For scoring purposes each response is compared with norms from a large group of previously tested subjects to determine whether it is one more or less ordinarily given or is unique for this particular individual. Unusual associations are analyzed according to content, special attention being paid to groupings of reactions that might reveal complexes. Besides unusualness of content, other complex indicators are lengthened reaction time, repetition of a previously given stimulus or response word, multi-word reactions, and laughter or other signs of embarrassment. From the standpoint of formal thought disturbances the unusual responses are also scrutinized to see whether they represent "close" reactions, indicative of rigid inhibition, or "distant" ones, signifying weak boundaries between ideational systems.

d. *Interpretation.* The extent to which the responses agree with those commonly given by normal individuals yields a measure of the conformity between the subject's thinking and that of the average person. Poorly adjusted individuals have a larger number of unique responses. More qualitative disturbances of association also have diagnostic significance, e.g., the occurrence of many "distant" reactions in schizophrenic patients. Responses of unusual content, especially when grouped in observable systems, are analyzed as a source of information about special problems in the personality. Such complexes may, for instance, be found in relation to sexual, vocational or social adjustment.

Illustrative Protocol 1

A 26 year-old man was admitted to the hospital with complaints of depression, with suicidal preoccupations, sensations of blurred vision, tightness about his head, and a feeling that his mind had stopped working. He had been married for five years to a woman seven years his senior who refused to bear the children he desired. He found himself further burdened with the support and domination of his brother-in-law and mother-in-law. Because the patient did not express his feelings readily in interviews, psychologic tests were used as an aid in revealing the particular aspects of his life situation that might have been repressed in the formation of his illness. Included in the battery was the word association technic.

His reactions to the stimulus words were made rapidly, most of them being given in three seconds or less. The content of 21, or 38 per cent, of them agreed with that commonly given—a result indicating adequate participation in popular modes of thinking. His more unusual reactions, however, were readily related to his personal problems. Lengthened reaction times occurring on the items *breast-child, nipple-pipe,* and *suck-to taste,* suggested that the infant-mother relationship was one that preoccupied and perhaps disturbed him. To the word *screen* he responded with *protection* after a delay of 15 seconds; later in the session he again gave the word *protection* when *house* was the stimulus. There thus seemed to be further evidence of his interest in a role of protective dependence. A striking result that fell into the same general pattern was his responding with the term *companionship* to the four stimuli *wife, mother, woman* and *girl friend.* In their entirety the findings seemed to warrant the view that his conception of the heterosexual relationship was not a mature one and that, moreover, his immature orientation was a source of conflict to him.

Taken in conjunction with the patient's social and clinical history, this conclusion led to further tests directed toward the exploration of his early parental ties and their possible role in his selection of a wife older than himself. In this case, therefore, the word association technic disclosed a complex; the associative process revealed no formal thinking disturbance.

Illustrative Protocol 2

A 26 year-old woman, a paranoid schizophrenic, who was actively hallucinated and believed she was the Virgin Mary, served as the subject of a word association test which will be used to exemplify the value of the procedure in the study of thinking disturbances. As contrasted with the preceding case, this one emphasizes not the content of the patient's responses but the formal characteristics of the associative process.

In the testing situation the patient was friendly and cooperative but her replies to questions were confused and were interspersed with many irrelevant comments. It was clear from the dull normal level she attained on the intelligence scale (W-B. I. Q. 82) that her present intellectual efficiency was below what it must have been when she satisfactorily completed high school some years before her illness. The patient's responses and reaction times to the stimulus words are listed below, an asterisk indicating agreement with commonly given or popular content.

Stimulus Word	Response	Reaction Time (in seconds)
1. Hat	Bonnet	1
2. Lamp	Light*	2
3. Love	Soul	3
4. Book	Novel	11
5. Father	Parent*	2.5
6. Paper	Sheet	10
7. Breast	Nipples	2
8. Curtains	Sash	1
9. Trunk	Case	1
10. Drink	Water*	2

Stimulus Word	Response	Reaction Time (in seconds)
11. Party	Crowd	3.5
12. Spring	Pump	1
13. Rug	Carpet*	1.5
14. Boy friend	Friendship	2.5
15. Chair	Seat*	3
16. Screen	Linen	10
17. Radiator	Thermometer	5
18. Frame	Square	3
19. Suicide	Death*	2.5
20. Mountain	Peak	1.5
21. Snake	Mammal	3.5
22. House	Shelter*	9
23. Tobacco	Plant	1.5
24. Mouth	Wind	8
25. Horse	Animal*	1.5
26. Wife	Partner	3
27. Table	Toy	18
28. Fight	Quarrel	4
29. Beef	Cow*	2
30. Stomach	Abdomen	1
31. Farm	Ranch	2
32. Man	A partner	1.3
33. Taxes	Levy	4
34. Nipple	Mouthpiece	4.5
35. Doctor	Assistant	7
36. Dirt	Dust	1
37. Cut	Bruise	2
38. Movies	Show*	1
39. Cockroach	Insect	2
40. Bite	Mark	2.5
41. Dog	Animal	1.5
42. Dance	Exercise	4
43. Gun	Field artillery	4
44. Water	Fountain	5
45. Husband	Mate	5
46. Mud	Clay	3.5
47. Woman	Mother	2

Stimulus Word	Response	Reaction Time (in seconds)
48. Fire	Flint	5
49. Suck	Draw*	2
50. Money	Coin*	2
51. Mother	A virgin	7
52. Hospital	Building	11
53. Girl friend	Schoolmate	14
54. Taxi	Emergency car	4
55. Hunger	Waste	27

Analysis of these results disclosed, first, that only 13 of her 55 responses, or 24 per cent, agreed with those commonly or popularly given. Moreover, when she was asked to recall and repeat her original responses as the list was administered a second time, she failed to do so in 31 instances. These two features of her performance suggested that her associative reactions were transient, loosely organized and highly personalized. It was further observed that disturbances of association were as likely to occur with impersonal and innocuous stimuli as with those expected to have emotional connotations. For example, she displayed lengthened reaction time to the words *book, paper, screen, house, mouth, table,* and *hunger.* This unpredictability of approach was coupled with occasional lapses into multi-word responses and with distant or poorly related associations such as *mouth-wind* and *table-toy.*

The findings as a whole were typical of those often encountered among schizophrenic patients. It was evident that while she was now and again capable of reacting in a logical or conventional manner, there were erratic fluctuations between such adjustive behavior and a kind of thinking determined by transient, egocentric factors.

2. RORSCHACH METHOD OF PERSONALITY DIAGNOSIS

a. *Purpose.* This general psychodiagnostic technic attempts a picture of the total personality, including such aspects as emotional lability and stability, temperament, intelligence and the thinking processes, interests, imagination and creative ability. It is applicable to both normal individuals and to mental patients.

b. *Materials and Instructions.* A series of ten ink-blots, some in black and white and some in color, are presented to the subject one at a time with the instruction that he mention anything the blots remind him of or that they could represent. After all the associations have been given, a nonleading inquiry is conducted to obtain from the subject elaborations of his responses that are needed for scoring purposes. Additional associations may also be produced at this stage. Sometimes a final step of the administration consists in "testing the limits" of under-productive individuals by suggesting to them possible responses in graduated degrees of explicitness.

c. *Data and Scoring.** The responses, as well as the data obtained during the inquiry, serve as material for scoring and interpretation. Observations of first-response reaction time, time spent on each card, card turning, etc., are also made. The associations are scored under three chief headings: (1) formal characteristics of *location,* i.e., whether the whole or some part of the blot was used by the subject in his responses; (2) *determinants* of the reactions, i.e., whether and in what combination form (shape), color, shading, etc., were employed; (3) *content,* i.e., whether plant, animal, human figure, etc., were seen.

d. *Interpretation.* The various scoring factors, such as color and seen movement, are interpreted as signifying different functions of the personality—e.g., outgoing emotion, intellectual creativity, practical-

---

* The method of Rorschach analysis developed at the Psychology Laboratory of the Western State Psychiatric Institute selectively combined that of Beck and of Klopfer. Since, however, the presentation of this approach would exceed the limits of discussion appropriate here, it has been decided to adopt for the purposes of the exposition in Parts II and III the Klopfer system described in his published manual. In the following illustrative protocols the usual Rorschach scoring symbols have been replaced with the unabbreviated equivalents as an aid to the uninitiated reader.

mindedness. Considerable emphasis is placed upon the way in which the different factors are related to each other as an expression of the total personality. According to norms derived from subjects belonging in various well-characterized groups—normal personality, neuroses and psychoses—the subject may be found to exemplify one or another diagnostic pattern. Results are psychodynamically interpreted as disclosing different kinds and degrees of intelligence, various temperaments, and the presence of neurotic or psychotic trends.

Illustrative Protocol 1

A 29 year-old woman suffered from an obsession about cleanliness and a hand-washing compulsion which began about three months before the birth of her first child. When the baby was nine months old the mother had to be hospitalized because of the still continuing symptoms. Preliminary interviews had revealed that she was rather closely tied to her parents and had relied on their guidance and support even after her marriage. It seemed likely that the impending birth of a child had aroused intolerable insecurity concerning the responsibilities which she would soon have to face for the first time. To explore the psychodynamic situation further the Rorschach method was employed several weeks after she was admitted to the hospital.

The patient was friendly and in good spirits throughout the test. She recognized the general purpose of the examination and spontaneously began to speak of her difficulties. She sometimes tended to underestimate the quality of her performance, possibly in an effort to obtain the praise she needed to bolster her self-confidence.

Reproduced below is the verbatim record of her associations to the ten ink-blots together with the reaction times for the first response to each card, the total times spent on each blot, the elaborations of the responses during the inquiry, and, finally, the scoring. Initial reaction time is given in seconds before each first response; total time, after each final one.

Response	*Inquiry*	*Score*
I 1.(15″) Looks like two bunnies pulling at something to eat. I don't know what this thing might be; a bone, maybe.	Bunnies with two ears and two legs together here.	Whole; Animal movement; Animal.
2. That makes me think of donkeys too, long ears and little tail. Couple of donkeys arguing about something.	Tails like donkeys and long ears the same way. Might be arguing about their load in between them here.	Large usual detail, Animal movement; Animal.
3. The center thing doesn't resolve into any particular thing except some kind of animal. (157″).	That's a little dog that started off after the bunnies and they got him by the ears. I see the tail, too.	Large usual detail; Form; Animal.
II 4.(25″) Two puppies to me. Just the upper portions of them, starting with their front legs right there. I don't know how you account for things like this (center detail). If that wasn't there it would look as though they were posing for pictures.	Got their feet up. A bull dog with ears pulled back and snout and eyes here.	Whole, cut-off; Animal movement; Animal detail; Popular.

Response	*Inquiry*	*Score*
5. The red doesn't add up to anything much as far as I can see. Unless they might be a Christmas card, and a little red to give it some color.		Large usual detail; Color symbolism; Art.
6. Could be they had one of those little clown things and were tearing it apart.	Dunce cap and face, and they've pulled the lower part apart. Like a baby plays with.	Small usual detail; Form; Object.
7. The upper part makes me think of a Christmas stocking hanging there on each side. (130″).	A Christmas stocking on each side and they're tearing up something the baby got for Christmas.	Large usual detail; Form predominant over color; Object.
III 8. (15″) That makes me think about Macbeth, that quotation about the brewing where they stir and stir and the trouble comes out. The figures are pretty near out of this world.	There's the kettle and witches stirring from both sides. Weird looking, and don't seem to be human, and being black.	Whole, cut-off; Human movement, achromatic color; Human; Popular.
Or it looks a little like two gentlemen in tails coming home from a drunk and bringing something		(Not scored.)

Response	*Inquiry*	*Score*
with them, a basket.		
9. This bow tie is symbolic of the way they started out.	It's a red one.	Large usual detail; Form predominant over color; Object; Popular.
10. Also makes me think of two grass-hoppers cooking up some trouble for somebody. (115″).	Faces with eyes there. In youngsters' books pictures of grasshoppers look like that. And dressed in long tails. The bow and the other red doesn't enter in.	Whole, cut-off; Human movement; Animal.
IV 11. (70″) That takes a lot of im-agination. It makes me think of that hang-dog expression they mention. If you look very hard it's like a dog with the head hanging down between his legs, looking at you as though he'd had a very hard day.	Eyes. Wire-haired ter-rier with stringy things hanging on his mouth and ears here. They have shaggy paws, and he has a scruffy-looking body.	Whole; Animal movement, shading used as texture; Animal.
12. Or a clown doing one of those things, do-ing "behind-the-crab." Stomach up on top and feet and head down underneath. Big feet there.	They always have built-up shoes with the sole looking large in a photo-graph. Some of his crazy clothing on the sides. Head up under legs, facing you.	Whole; Human movement; Human.

Response	Inquiry	Score
13. Makes me think a little of a bearskin rug, if I think this is the head of it here (bottom). (165").	Head and paws out in front, and back part which usually doesn't have as much form to it.	Whole; Form, shading used as texture; Animal object.
V 14. (3") That looks like a bat to me.	It looks better reversed. Wings out here and they always have scallops, and things out in front and feet hanging down. Wing-spread they have in flight.	Whole; Animal movement; Animal; Popular.
15. Could be a bunny doing the split but I still think a bat is more like it. (85").	Back view of bunny. Ears and back of head. Legs as though it had had too much and legs were sliding. Fuzzy as a bunny is in back.	Whole; Animal movement, shading used as texture; Animal.
VI 16. (55") Makes me think of a cross-section of a very unusual flower where they show you the stamen, pistil, etc.	This part where they show you the stamens with pollen and the pistil through the center and petals, one half of them.	Whole; Form; Plant.
17. Or it could be a fancy fountain. (105").	This is where the water goes up through and you're looking from the side so this would be the cup part it goes into. This is water spraying. Some sort of dark metal shaped into a flower shape.	Whole; Form with inanimate movement, achromatic color; Object.
VII 18. (35") Looks to me like two very	Nose, chin, eye, forehead, floppy ears. Body,	Whole; Animal movement; Animal.

Response	Inquiry	Score
sassy-looking pups with floppy ears perched on top of two chunks of ice.	and tail out behind. Here is the ice. I thought of a Christmas card for one thing and you usually find ice in that connection. The shape is irregular.	
19. It does look, too, like little boy's b r e e c h e s t h a t they'd torn in two and looking at each other to see w h o d i d i t. (110″).	Break in each side like crotch. Seam split so it's spread out.	Large usual detail; Form; Object.

VIII

20. & 21. (25″) Looks like two tigers climbing a tree, but rather up the branches than the trunk.	Face with nose, eyes, ear. Shape of tiger with back leg stretched way down, stealthy way of walking. Thought of pine tree. Being green made me think of it.	Large usual detail; Animal movement; Animal; Popular. Large usual detail; Form predominant over color; Plant.
22. & 23. Or like two insects crawling along a piece of foliage.	Side view of them. Head and feet and back and body. Beetles, but aren't right color.	Large usual detail; Animal movement; Animal. Large usual detail; Color predominant over form; Plant.
24. In that case this is a butterfly d o w n b e l o w. (85″).	Spread out with body there. Shape of the wings and the coloring, too.	Large usual detail; Form predominant over color; Animal.

IX

| 25. (40″) Could be a forest fire with green trees and tongues of flame licking high into the air. | Upper 2/3. Just blotches — green to indicate trees. This represents smoke; kind of a hazy color. | Whole, cut-off; Color predominant over form, inanimate movement, shading as diffusion; Fire. |

Response	Inquiry	Score
26. Also a very fancy Christmas candle, with candle in the center and green and red trimmings on each side. (100″).	Candle setting in a holder with holly ringed around it. Possibly pieces of ribbon or something red up here.	Whole; Form predominant over color; Object.
X (40″) To me that's a collection of various crabs and beetles and worms.		(Not scored.)
27. These two beetles are crawling up a stalk in the center.	Got antennae extended along stalk.	Large usual detail; Animal movement; Animal.
28. And two green worms arguing over a piece of food.		Large usual detail; Form predominant over color, animal movement; Animal; Popular.
29. & 30. These crabs look to be pinching a piece of flesh there.	Pink is flesh. Makes me think of a piece of raw meat.	Large usual detail; Animal movement; Animal; Popular. Large usual detail; Color predominant over form; Anatomy.
31. There are two beetles up there diving off the feelers of the crab.	Have heads and feet extended as though diving.	Large usual detail; Animal movement; Animal.
32. Makes me think, in general, of some invertebrates that have probably gathered at somebody's picnic. (235″).		Whole; Form; Abstraction.

The essential features of this record as analyzed by scoring categories may be tabulated as follows:

Total number of responses:		32
Location:	Whole	15
	Large usual detail	16
	Small usual detail	1
Determinants:	Human movement	3
	Animal movement	12+1*
	Inanimate movement	1+1
	Diffusion (Shading)	+1
	Form	5 (16%)
	Shading representing texture	1+3
	Achromatic color	+2
	Form with color secondary	6
	Color with form secondary	3
	Pure color	1
Content:	Whole human figure	2
	Part of human figure	0
	Whole animal figure	15 } (50%)
	Part of animal figure	1 }
	Art	1
	Architecture	1
	Anatomy	1
	Object	5
	Animal object	1
	Plant	3
	Fire	1
	Abstraction	1
Popular Responses:		7

* In the summary tabulation, here exemplified, a plus sign signifies either additional responses, elicited for the first time during the inquiry, or additional determinants of the main responses. New responses in the inquiry are entered in the *Score* column of the protocol in parentheses; additional determinants of any main response follow, after a comma, the score for the main determinant.

Ratio of human move- ment to color: (Experience balance)	(M:ΣC)	3:7.5
Ratio of other movement to surface shading:	(FM+m:Fc+c+C′)	13:1
Proportion of total re- sponses found on last three cards:		41%
Aver. first reaction time to gray cards:		36″
Aver. first reaction time to colored cards		29″
Ratio of whole to part human and animal figures:	(H+A:Hd+Ad)	17:1

Preliminary structuring of a personality description which is to be based upon the verbatim responses and tabulated data from a Rorschach examination proceeds in a more or less orderly fashion to consider the various aspects of the material. One may begin, for example, with analysis of the intellectual aspects of personality as exhibited in the subject's approach to the blots (location), his capacity to be creative (human movement responses), the accuracy of his descriptions, the extent to which he conforms with popular modes of reaction or introduces original ideas, the variety of the associative content, and the succession in which his reactions occur. While the intellectual aspects of personality are influenced to a large extent by emotional factors, the latter receive separate attention in the preliminary survey. Here one considers the nature of the individual's promptings from within (movement responses), their role in his mental life (ratio of whole to movement reactions), his contacts with outer reality (use of color), his control over his emotions (form), the ease with which he expresses anxiety (shading and color), and his maturity. These lists are by no means exhaustive but are intended to suggest the nature of the information for which the clinician is searching as he reviews a specific set of Rorschach data. No one record provides equally clear evidence on all items, nor are the same items of equal interpretive value or importance in all records. In actual practice the preliminary survey serves to highlight the points at which the given record deviates most strikingly from expected norms for frequency, proportion, and pattern. These points contribute to the record its individuality and usually constitute the framework of interpretation, with the other factors playing a supportive role to explain, elaborate, and delimit the unique features. One continues to balance, compare, and contrast until the characterization has used or accounted for all of the available data. This process is illustrated in the analysis of the present protocol.

1. The outstanding feature of the patient's intellectual approach was the frequency with which she responded to the blot as a whole. While the expectation for this sort of reaction is 20 per cent to 30 per cent of all responses, there were 47 per cent in her record—an indication of intellectualization commonly found among obsessional neurotics. However, she did not stress this abstract sort of thinking to the exclusion of usual details and her concepts were, in general, clearly described and elaborated. She was, within the limits of these indications, of better than average intelligence. The absence of the small and rare detail responses which are so often encountered in the Rorschach records of psychasthenic patients should be noted.

2. Since her organized thinking thus gave evidence of capacity for good intellectual performance, her human movement responses were next examined as a representation of free productiveness and mature creativity. There being only three, they were considered to be disproportionately few since one normally anticipates a human movement score equal to approximately half the size of the whole response score (15 in this case). It thus began to appear that the patient was lacking in intellectual maturity.

3. Not only human movement but human content (figures) in general was notably low in the record. She produced only two such

responses as compared to 16 (50 per cent) with animal content. While the latter score is not high enough to warrant interpretation of stereotypy or poverty of associations, a human content score as low as the present one often signifies immaturity in accepting adult social roles and relationships. The patient's lack in this direction is exemplified in her response to Card III where she first described "Two gentlemen in tails" and then added, "In youngsters' books grasshoppers look like that—often dressed in long tails." Apparently the latter interpretation was more acceptable and satisfying to her.

4. A further observation concerns the frequency of animal movement responses which one expects to equal, approximately, the human movement score. In this instance, as will be noted, the patient produced 12 such reactions and an additional one during the inquiry—four times the expected number. Since animal movement responses in such frequency are characteristic of pre-adolescent fantasy, the result constituted another indication of immaturity.

5. Confirmatory evidences were readily noted from the general content of her associations. These were simple, childish and pleasure-seeking; e.g., she reacted to the bright colors of the blots by repeated references to Christmas although the test was given in midsummer.

6. It is noteworthy in this connection, as well as in relation to the earlier mentioned lack of human content, that she selected the one area of the blots (in Card VI) which is most frequently given a human sexual interpretation by the average subject for the response "Makes me think of a cross-section of a very unusual flower where they show you the stamen, pistil, etc." Both avoidance of direct reference to human sexuality and an adolescent stage of sexual curiosity and instruction may be reflected here.

7. From the standpoint of emotional control the preponderance of animal movement responses has significance in another direction. The more usual result is for reactions based on form alone to be the most numerous. Since the form category represents control, the more other determinants outweigh it, the more likely is the person to be at the mercy of his inner drives, without benefit of

inhibitory or discriminative guidance. In the patient's record, as will have been observed, only five of the responses were attributable to form alone while 13 fell under the heading of animal movement.

8. Though there were few shading responses, indicative of anxiety and depression, in the record, close scrutiny of the reactions to Cards IV and VI—the ones most apt to yield such evidence—revealed blocking and other traces of inner conflict. The most marked evidence was found in the very long reaction times for these two cards—70 seconds and 55 seconds, respectively; the average reaction time for all other cards was 25 seconds. Marked blocking was thus indicated. The masked sexual reference in Card VI has already been noted. In addition, the occurrence here of her only description of inanimate movement (responses construed to represent awareness of inner conflict) should be observed.

9. The features mentioned thus far have referred chiefly to the patient's intellectual life, self-concepts and fantasy outlets as distinguished from her overt behavior, emotional expression and social adjustment. These latter aspects are more apt to be represented by the reactions to the brightly colored blots. Though in this area of the record, she demonstrated adequate capacity to control her emotional responsiveness (predominance of form over color in associations involving both) and, further, exhibited some sensitivity to the feelings and needs of others (shading employed as texture), there was evidence of a more primitive and egocentric sort of emotional expression (one pure color response). Moreover, since color-determined reactions as a group were so numerous (about one-third of the record)—next in frequency to the animal movement category— there was additional indication that the inhibitory control signified by the pure form responses was notably outweighed. The interpretation was made that the patient exerted little conscious effort to limit her indulgence in pleasurable fantasy or emotional expression.

10. The sequence of her reactions to color was also of some interest. At the first impact (Card II) she gave a symbolic explanation of the red; only two responses later was she able to combine form and

color meaningfully. However, when she was immediately again subjected to the presence of the red in Card III, she reverted to a symbolic use of the color. In Cards VIII and IX she was unable to maintain form-controlled responses but kept reverting to color-dominant interpretations; this vacillation between intellectual control and infantile affective discharge yielded a sequence of color responses (20 through 26) as follows: FC, CF, FC, CF, FC.

11. A final point concerns the adequate presence of seven popular responses—those that are construed to imply conformity with usual modes of social thinking and behavior. This positive indication, together with the previously noted intellectual potentialities and the general richness of associative content, pointed to the patient's capacity for adjustment in a superficially normal way. Since there were no signs of thinking disturbance or personality disintegration, there was little question of any psychotic process.

A summary of the foregoing considerations may now be attempted. It would appear that the patient was above average in intelligence. However, she had a strong need for intellectualization—a feature commonly found in the behavior of obsessional neurotics—and her immaturity was so great that her actual achievement was likely to be empty and uncreative. Her affective outlets were child-like, unrealistic and egocentric. She readily conformed to social standards but such social situations had little genuine meaning for her personality. Her heterosexual adjustment had evidently also been expressed on an infantile-fantasy level. The underlying dynamics were not, therefore, typical of the fully developed obsessive-compulsive personality pattern. Instead it would appear that her environment had continually so fostered and protected her in a dependent, childish role that she was able habitually to express her drives directly and without conflict. Her recent and sudden responsibilities, which represented the first major challenge to her immature patterns of adjustment, had apparently precipitated the obsessional symptoms by reactivating some till then latent pregenital fixation or even some constitutional sensitivity.

It may be noted, in conclusion, that the Rorschach protocol of the present psychasthenic patient was by no means typical of what would have been expected according to the existing literature on Rorschach diagnostic patterns in the various mental disorders. The fact of this difference is, however, illustrative of the essentially psychodynamic, as contrasted with the psychiatrically diagnostic, aim of this projective method. Other patients with the same observed symptoms would undoubtedly have conformed more closely to the just mentioned expectations but, with our lack of any reliable knowledge about the systematic relationships between psychiatric diagnosis and underlying dynamics, the unstable affinity between the two which is exemplified in the present case and in its projective study is more instructive than surprising.

Illustrative Protocol 2

A 31 year-old Negro man was admitted to the hospital with a diagnosis of Psychosis with Syphilitic Meningo-encephalitis. He had delusions of grandeur, particularly about possessing great wealth, and he was suspicious that the institutional personnel might be plotting to obtain his money. His speech was relevant and coherent but exhibited mild slurring. Fever therapy was begun soon after his admission to the hospital and produced evident improvement in his condition. He no longer expressed the grandiose ideas that had been prominent before and made a distinct effort to adapt on most occasions. He became irritable for brief periods but there was no evidence of generalized hostility or suspicion. The problem remained, however, to determine whether and to what extent residual effects of his acute illness were still influencing his adjustment. To this end, and along with other tests, the Rorschach method was administered since it has been found to evoke a more or less unique pattern of reaction from patients with cerebral pathology. The patient's Rorschach record is reproduced below.

Response	*Inquiry*	*Score*
I 1. (10″) Looks something like a bat to me. That's about all it looks like to me. (51″).	The spread of the wings, and a bat has a little thing up on its head. Just the shape of it. I've seen pictures of them like this.	Whole; Form; Animal; Popular.
II 2. (5″) This looks like two Scotties, dogs. (25″).	Here looks like an eye and there's their ears. They're rough and black like a Scotty. Down to here, half of him. Both of them look like they're standing.	Large usual detail; Animal movement, achromatic° color, shading as texture; Animal detail; Popular.
III 3. (7″) These look like ostriches, their heads. (25″).	The way the thing is, they look like they're apart. Their legs don't connect or nothing. You can see some of their body. But that's all you could see.	Large usual detail; Form; Animal.
	This looks like a butterfly. The spread of the wings and the way they come in on an angle.	(Large usual detail; Form; Animal; Popular.)
IV 4. (12″) To me this one looks like a bear-rug. That's about all I could see on it. (30″).	Here's his head and to me he looks like a bear. The fur looks sort of silky. But where's his other legs? He's been skinned.	Whole; Form with shading used as texture; Animal object.
V 5. (25″) Could this be a skinned goat? It's got horns. (42″).	Horns (top), and legs (side projections) and this is his back. The ink wouldn't give the right color of it, but he'd be skin side up.	Whole; Form (poor quality); Animal object.

Response	*Inquiry*	*Score*
VI Are these pictures enlarged? 6. (40″) The way the top of the head looks, it looks like it would be a fly. I can't imagine anything else in it. A funny little head and such a big body. It couldn't be a monkey! (95″).	Head, and there's his feelers and his wings. Looks like just part of it, but it goes all the way down. I've never seen a lion or a tiger, so I don't know what it is.	Whole; Form; Animal.
VII 7. (15″) These look like two old ladies with their hair done up in an awful style. (55″).	Just part of them down from the neck to the end of the breast. That's on their dress (usual hands). There's their mouth and nose and eyes.	Large usual detail; Form; Human detail.
VIII 8. (12″) Are these beavers building a dam? They look like it. Yeah, that's what it is, beavers building a dam. (34″).	That looks like the dam what they got their feet on (Blue). That's a mountain there, isn't it supposed to be? (Gray). And this is water all around, the white.	Large usual detail, white space added; Animal movement; Scene; Popular.
IX 9. (27″) This looks like a man's hands down here on the bottom.	He's holding onto something.	Unusual detail; Human movement; Human detail.
10. These are buffalos, aren't they, or bison? I think they are.	(Green sections)	Large usual detail; Form; Animal.
11. And this looks like a mule's head.	(Unusual inner section of green)	Unusual detail; Form (poor quality); Animal detail.

Response	Inquiry	Score
9. And then there's the pair of hands at the bottom. (125″).		
X 12. (22″) This looks like a parrot on the left. And then they look like men and they got helmets over their heads to signify birds because of their nose and mouth. Birds don't have that kind of a mouth.	(Top gray)	Large usual detail; Form; Animal and human.
13. These look like scorpions.	(Blue)	Large usual detail; Form; Animal; Popular.
14. And it looks like two dogs down here in the yellow.	They have nose and eye and mouth. They look like they got a tail.	Large usual detail; Form; Animal.
15. And there's crabs.	(Outer gray)	Large usual detail; Form; Animal.
16. And these red things look like lobsters. (120″).	The long redness of it, but lobsters have claws.	Large usual detail; Color predominant over form of poor quality; Animal.
	Now it looks like two figures blowing something — two imaginary figures.	(Large usual detail; Human movement; Human.)

The essential features of this record as analyzed by scoring category may be tabulated as follows:

Total number of responses:		16+2 additional
Location:	Whole	4
	Large usual detail	10+2
	Unusual detail	2
	White space	+1
Determinants:	Human movement	1+1
	Animal movement	2
	Form	11+1 (69%)
	Form with texture secondary	1+1
	Form with achromatic color	+1
	Form with color secondary	0
	Color with form secondary	1
	Pure color	0
Content:	Whole human figure	+2
	Part of human figure	1
	Whole animal figure	9 ⎱ (69%)
	Part of animal figure	2 ⎰
	Animal object	2
	Scene	1
Popular Responses:		4+1

Ratio of human movement to color: $(M:\Sigma C)$ 1:2
    (Experience balance)

*Ratio of other movement
to surface shading:* $(FM+m:Fc+c+C')$ 2:1

*Proportion of total responses found on last
three cards:*   56%

*Aver. first reaction time
to gray cards:*   20″

*Aver. first reaction time
to colored cards:*   15″

*Ratio of whole to part
human and animal
figures:* $(H+A:Hd+Ad)$ 9:3

While the qualitative features of the patient's record are perhaps more revealing than the quantitative ones, the latter contribute significantly to the interpretation and will be briefly discussed first. All of the following features, especially when considered in their interrelationships, point to a reduction of mental productivity and efficiency: the small total number of responses (about half of what would be normally expected); the elevated proportion of reactions determined by form alone (69 per cent); the limited range of content highlighted by the high frequency of animal associations (69 per cent); and the paucity of popular responses. A concrete, literal-minded and stereotyped approach, lacking in spontaneity or richness, is thus demonstrated.

On the qualitative side several main indications may be mentioned. There is, for one thing, the *perplexity* that the patient exhibits about the adequacy of his reactions and his need for reassurance from the examiner. Examples are found in the phrasing of responses 5, 6 and 8—all in question form. Sometimes patients with an organic defect assume that the ink-blots represent a definite object that they are expected to recognize; hence their perplexity.

Closely related to such an attitude is that which has been described as *impotence*—another feature of the present record. The patient recognizes that his association does not fit the blot well but, in despair, completes the reaction somehow. Illustrative instances are found in inquiry comments for responses 3 ("They look like they're apart; their legs don't connect or nothing.") and 6 ("I've never seen a lion or a tiger, so I don't know what it is.").

A similar poverty of ideas is revealed, further, in the patient's tendency toward *repetition* of the same response from one ink-blot to another with decreasing accuracy. The first of such responses is apt to involve an appropriate form while the following ones fit the blots in question less well. The sequence of responses to Cards IV, V and VI exemplify this approach.

These qualitative features of the present record, as well as the quantitative ones previously noted, are typical of the Rorschach pattern encountered among individuals with some organic brain impairment. It was therefore concluded that the test had disclosed definite residual effects of the patient's former acute illness.

Illustrative Protocol 3

An 11 year-old boy, one of nine siblings in a coal miner's family, had for three years been a student in a class for retarded children. He was repeating work of third-grade level for the second time when he was referred to a local out-patient clinic because of his persistent misconduct. His behavior was described as stubborn, forgetful, untidy and thoughtless. Incidents of firesetting, stealing and attempts to undress younger children, especially little girls, were reported. It had long been recognized that he was probably of defective intelligence but community authorities felt that he might now require institutional supervision. At this point the question arose as to whether his difficulty could be attributed solely to mental defect or whether some additional personality or emotional disorder requiring specialized psychiatric attention and treatment existed.

To aid in this decision the Rorschach test was administered since it permits evaluation of both intellectual and emotional factors as well as their interaction with each other. No attempt has, however, been made to tabulate the scoring of the bizarre record obtained in this case since the boy's ability to define his responses during the inquiry was so limited. The protocol is chiefly remarkable for the extent to which it is revealing despite the lack of full formal scoring. The verbatim Rorschach record follows.

Response	Inquiry
I 1. (5″) A butterfly, or it could be one of those things that turns into a butterfly on the tree. (67″).	This could be the back end, and these could be holes in the wings and its head up here. It hangs on a tree and gets brown and when it's real hot it turns into a butterfly.

Response	*Inquiry*
II 2. (20″) Is that supposed to be fire on there?	This red part.
3. It could be a part of black clouds or something. Could be like when the sky is red. (63″).	
III 4. (60″) It could be the black of the night, and it's going away; coming toward morning.	These here parts breaking apart and this in here is brighter.
5. And that could either be red paint or something. I guess that's all. (97″).	
IV 6. (25″) It could be something with horns on it. It could be some kind of animal that has lots of legs on it. (70″).	Horns and the back of the hide. Furry.
V 7. (20″) That could be an animal that has four legs and two legs and could fly.	Could be some kind of bird flying.
8. Looks a little bit like lightning. (55″).	That's the way lightning goes, crooked.
VI 9. (20″) Could be some kind of a map.	A map that will tell you where the place is, like where the streets and houses are.
10. Could be something that had little horns on it. Could be something that could bite somebody. (75″).	(Refers to isolated edge projections.) Whiskers, claws, etc. The rest is the map.
VII 11. (18″) Could be something that could be falling apart. Could be something that could be white and black.	Could be the sky.
12. Could be some kind of an insect or something. (40″).	(Center section)

Response	*Inquiry*
VIII 13. (15") Could be something that could be all different kind of colors. Could be cracking, split in the middle.	
14. Maybe it could have different kinds of animals on, maybe tigers on both sides of it. (60").	Looks like they're going to walk.
IX 15. (10") It looks like it could be some kind of sun that changes all different colors. It has all kind of pointy edges on it.	
16. Like a waterfall in there. (57").	Water running down.
X 17. (10") This here looks like a rabbit-face.	
18. This looks like them things on top of a butterfly.	("Wishbone")
19. These could be different kinds of insects, black and red and blue.	I don't know what kind it could be; got these colors.
20. This looks like a deer's horns. (65").	(Side gray) Whole deer, jumping or running. These are his horns.

Analysis of this protocol disclosed that the boy's thinking was inaccurate and vague (concepts poorly related to the form of the blot), stereotyped (many simple animal forms), perseverative (repetition of previous responses on succeeding cards); and far removed from conventional modes of thought (few popular or common responses). However, the sporadic occurrence of occasional clear percepts (responses 14, 16, 17, and 20) suggested that the prevailing low level of function was not the best of which he was natively capable. There were, furthermore, features associated with emotional disturbance that could not be attributed solely to intellectual limitation. He was overly stimulated by the emotional Rorschach determinants (frequent reactions to both bright and achromatic color) and completely unselective in his responses as if unable to inhibit or control his behavior. He seemed at the mercy of threatening and anxiety-provoking stimuli and much concerned with aggressive concepts of biting, hurting or disintegrating (content). The phrasing of some of his responses, their helpless, repetitive quality, and the long time required for each of them raised the question of possible neurological impairment to which both the intellectual deficit and his uncontrolled emotionality might be related. Other aspects of his confusion, however, suggested a schizophrenic type of thinking disturbance (responses 1, 4, 11, and 15).

On the basis of these considerations, it was reported to the physician that while the exact nature of this boy's difficulty could not be clearly determined, there was evidence that he could not be classified simply as mental defective. There were definite signs of a mental illness since his thinking, as well as his emotional reactions, showed disturbance. Some features of his performance raised the question of a neurologic basis for his maladjustment; others were more schizoid in nature. In general, the results clearly indicated the need for a period of closer observation and study from a medical and psychiatric point of view.

3. THEMATIC APPERCEPTION TEST (T A T)

a. *Purpose.* This projective method is intended to reveal the needs, conflicts and traits that underlie the behavior of the individual. Some of these trends may not even be known to the person himself since they are implicit, i.e., "unconscious," rather than explicit in his living. The subject supposedly projects these underlying tendencies in his fantasy productions.

b. *Materials and Instructions.* A series of from ten to twenty pictures, available in separate sets for men, women and children, are presented one at a time with the instruction that the subject regard them as illustrations for stories. Toward the end of the test a blank card is introduced and the subject is requested to imagine a picture as well as a narrative. He must tell each story by identifying the characters and explaining their relationships in the depicted situation, by describing what led up to that situation, and by supplying an outcome.

c. *Data and Scoring.* The responses are taken down verbatim. The examiner includes also any questions or comments that he himself makes in the course of the test. The stories or picture-descriptions, together with any attendant conversation and behavior, comprise the data subjected to interpretive analysis. Such analysis is conducted in different ways by various psychodiagnosticians. A comprehensive and fairly typical procedure is the Composite Portrait Method of T A T Analysis.* The underlying premise of this method is that the subject's productions in the T A T must be superimposed and condensed, like a series of photographs are in composite photography (Galton), to yield one composite projective picture of the inner personality. The steps of the procedure are: (1) Assimilation of the stories by several careful and complete re-readings. (2) Descriptive analysis of the productions, one by one, under the six headings as follows: (a) Identification—determining the central character of each narrative, the one with whom the subject is presumably identified and from whose standpoint he tells the story; (b) Figures—ascertaining the chief other figures of the production and the manner in which they are characteristically depicted; (c) Trends—the needs and goals (aggression, anxiety, etc.) around which the stories revolve; (d) Dynamic clues, including sequence—outstanding distortions in the description of the pictures, blocking as indicated by long initial reaction times, displacement and other dynamic clues evident in the relationships between successive stories; (e) Endings—in terms of happiness, realism, etc.; (f) Formal features—narrative level (enu-

---

* This method of analysis, here described in abbreviated form, was developed by the senior author during the past five years in seminars on the Thematic Apperception Test and in the supervision of trainees in clinical psychology. A detailed presentation is planned for a future publication.

meration, description or interpretation), breadth of vocabulary and other indications of creative capacity. (3) Statistical evaluation of the responses by reference to available norms in order to determine the degree to which the subject's picture-descriptions and narratives deviate toward uniqueness from those usually given. (4) Topical generalizations (horizontal) in which the common elements of the stories under each of the six analytic headings are abstracted. (5) Composite generalizations (vertical) in which the relationships among the topical generalizations are developed. (6) Integration of the composite generalizations with anamnestic and other-test data to educe significant psychodynamic hypotheses.

d. *Interpretation.* The foregoing outline has included, in addition to scoring, the method of interpretation. It is assumed that the subject projects himself into the stories, usually through the vehicle of each central character, and that the figures and themes with which the stories are populated represent the population of his psychologic world. The idiosyncratic ways in which he describes a picture or relates the characters to each other thus become significant of him as an individual person. The recurrence of such unique features from story to story provides the other main basis for interpretation. Since detailed norms for this test even at the descriptive level are still lacking, adequate interpretation depends upon broad clinical experience and upon consistent use of this projective technic with various subjects.

Illustrative Protocol 1

A 23 year-old unmarried man came to an out-patient clinic shortly after his twin brother had begun to receive psychiatric treatment there. The patient was a high-school graduate who had been employed in a variety of mill and factory jobs. He now complained of nervousness and tension, headaches and inability to concentrate. He was especially ill-at-ease in social groups and found that if he attempted to go out with girls, he had acute physical symptoms, including nausea. His condition had recently compelled him to give up work.

There was a history of similar "nervous" symptoms for a period during his grade-school years. His mother was recognized as being extremely neurotic and while she sporadically contributed to pampering and overprotecting the boys, she was frequently too preoccupied with her own complaints to give them much attention. She ordinarily dated her difficulties from the birth of the twins. The father was a somewhat austere figure who was plainly disappointed in his sons. Although he sometimes lent a helping hand, it appeared that he did so in order to placate his own pride rather than to offer any genuine understanding.

Since the patient was not readily communicative in his psychiatric interviews, the Thematic Apperception Test was enlisted as an aid in discovering his feelings and attitudes toward himself and the other persons with whom he was enmeshed in interpersonal relationships. He made an effort to be friendly and cooperative in the test situation but was obviously tense and uncomfortable; he blushed continually during the examination.

In the following verbatim record of the subject's test protocol, Arabic numbers are used to indicate the stimulus pictures selected from the series published by Murray in 1943; Roman numerals refer to the order in which the pictures were presented.* Initial reaction time is given in parentheses at the start of each story; total time spent, at the end. A dash has been used to indicate momentary hesitations of speech; longer pauses have been designated by the word *pause* in parentheses. Incidental remarks or behavior of the subject are recorded in parentheses; questions or comments of the examiner are given in brackets.

1. (A boy is looking at a violin which rests in front of him on a table.)

I. (13″) This is a boy that's taking violin lessons. He seems depressed. His parents have hopes that he'll be a great violin player some day and probably play with big orchestras but—(too fast?)—he himself doesn't

---

* In all subsequent TAT records throughout the book the pictures are from this same standard set unless otherwise indicated, and the system of notation is the same as that here employed.

seem to have any hope to amount to anything in this line. He continues to take violin lessons for awhile but sees no improvement in his playing so he becomes discouraged and drops it altogether. He finally ends up as a machinist in a mill. He figures he'd rather work in that kind of work than play a fiddle. (2'10").

2. (A country scene showing a young woman, with books in her hand and, in the background, a man working in the fields; an older woman is leaning against a tree.)

II. (5") That's a farmer and his wife and daughter and (pause) she seems—his wife seems to be praying that they'll have a fine crop. Her husband seems to be working vigorously, hoping that he'll be rewarded for his hard work. His daughter seems—she's on her way to school. She's bidding them the time of day and telling her father not to work too hard. I don't know how to end it. [Why not tell me first what led up to this situation?] Well, a beautiful spring day, probably a fine day for plowing, and his wife came out to get a little sunshine and air. And in the end they are rewarded for their hard work and good spirits. They have a fine harvest. (2'5").

3 BM. (A human figure is huddled on the floor against a couch. Beside him is an object often described as a weapon.)

III. (10") That looks like a girl that's melancholy. She seems depressed about a love affair and is undecided whether to commit suicide. She ponders over the idea and decides that she'll (pause) try to patch up the romance. (pause) Her feelings are hurt but she considers it and says she'll give it another try. [How will it turn out?] In the end both of them see each other's problem and try to adjust themselves and they get married and—lead a happy life. (2'10").

4. (A woman is grasping the shoulders of a man who is turned away from her and apparently trying to pull away.)

IV. (25") This is a man and wife and he's come home from a hard day's work at the mill. Seems depressed and has a problem that he's concealing inside of him. His wife—she's trying to raise his spirits. She's asking him whether there seems to be an interest on the outside somewhere. She seems to feel that he—that he's not being truthful with her, that he's associating with other women. He doesn't want to look at her because he feels guilty (pause) and in the end they—she finds out that he has been cheating on her and they separate. (This story was told with unusual hesitation.) (2'55").

6 BM. (An elderly woman is standing with her back turned to a young man who appears perplexed.)

V. (20″) That's a picture of a mother and her son. She's called him home because there's been a disaster. She tells him that his father's been killed. He's trying to comfort her through all this. She's grief-stricken from shock and (pause) he says she can come and live with him. (pause) So in the end, after the burial, when she gets her bearings and decides it's too lonely in the house—all his memories are still there—so she goes to live with her son and his wife. [How does the son feel?] He is broken-hearted but he's trying to conceal it from his mother. He had many fond memories of his father (pause) but he has a wife to comfort him and he soon gets over it. (3′).

8 BM. (A young boy is shown on one side of the picture while on the other is dimly depicted a scene of what might be a surgical operation.)

VI. (37″) That's a father and his son. There's a doctor and a helper. This boy has shot his father (pause) because his father has reprimanded him (pause) and the boy seems to have a guilty look on his face and his father seems to be in agony. The accident seems to have taken place at night. They seem to be using emergency lighting. (pause) In the end the boy comes to grief for his wrong-doing because his father doesn't recover and he dies. [How does the boy in the picture feel?] Well, after he shot his father he was sorry that he had done it (pause) because he done it—in a fit of impulse. He's hoping that his father recovers but the damage is already done; it's too late. (3′30″).

7 BM. (An older man is gazing at a younger one who is staring into space.)

VII. (18″) (Sighs) That's a picture between father and son. The son has come home to tell his troubles to his father. The father tries to comfort him. The boy seems to be discouraged about the future—he's had domestic troubles at home. His wife is—he believes—is untrue to him. Since he found this out he hasn't been able to work, probably, and finds he is losing out in his position—means of making a living. (pause) And his father tells him if this trouble continues with his wife to break away from her and come home and live with him. Things go from bad to worse. And in the end he finally can't live with his wife any longer and sees no alternative than to live with his father; so he goes home and lives with him. (2′45″).

13 MF. (In the foreground is a young man who stands with his head buried in his arms; in the background is the figure of a woman lying in bed.)

VIII. (30″) Let's see, that's a picture of a father and his daughter. She's come home from a spree of drinking—seems to be—intoxicated, and he's shielding his face. He's ashamed to see the condition she's in. (pause) Finally when she sobers up enough that he can reason with her, he asks her to—to try to refrain from drinking. It's ruining her health, it's causing a bad reputation in the family, and it's upsetting her mother. (pause) He scolds her because he feels that the good home she had—she didn't appreciate it. She was brought up to know better. And he tells her that if she continues to act the way she has in the past, she'll have to find a new home. [How does the girl feel?] (pause) The girl feels that she—she's doing wrong, but she's trying to escape from some of her troubles. She doesn't wish to tell her parents what's troubling her. So every time she becomes melancholy she goes out and becomes intoxicated. And in the end her father (pause) he calls the preacher. They reason with her and tell her there's other ways to solve her problems beside drinking. So she finally sees their point of view and uses all her will power to quit drinking. And she reforms in other matters and settles down and marries a respectable man and her life is much happier from there on. (6′30″).

16. (Blank card.)

IX. (15″) I see a young boy and his father standing in the back yard of their home. This boy's swinging a ball bat. He looks like a natural ball player. His father's proud of him and tries to encourage him and hopes that some day he'll be a famous ball player. The boy continues to play ball. (pause) As he grows older he seems to become better at his playing. When he's in high school he makes the varsity team—the first squad. He's a left-hander. He's a powerful hitter. He's respected by all his fellow players for his sportsmanship and his fine playing. While he's still in high school, word has gotten around what a good player he is and scouts from professional teams come and look him over and they decide he's a natural ball player and think he'll make a good player. So they sign him to a contract. After he finishes high school he is sent to a minor league club for a season. He seems a little green for—to be up in the major brackets. After one year of minor league playing he's considered so good that they decide to send him to the top, where he becomes—reaches the major league top bracket—he becomes a star. Although he becomes a star, he is not proud and he still associates with his former friends. And he thanks his dad for his encouragement that he has given him. He sees that his dad is financially fixed and builds him a nice home. As yet he's not married but after he reaches the top, he begins to look for a mate and he—finally he gets married. He—gives his wife all that *money* can buy, treats her swell. I don't know how to end it. In the end he's satisfied with his profession. He feels that he's done everything to make his family happy and thankful for his ability to attain stardom. (pause) And all through life he continues to keep an interest in baseball. When he finally dies, he's still wearing a baseball uniform—he's dedicated his whole life to that sport. (Don't you get tired writing?) (9′45″).

18 BM. (A man is being clutched by three hands that belong to invisible antagonists.)

X. (30″) This is a young fellow that's been drinking and (pause) he's been disorderly in the community. (pause) He's so—drunk that he needs assistance to find his way home. (pause) His reason for drinking seems to be family affairs—a run-in with his parents. He's not been able to find a job so he's downhearted (pause) and tries to forget it by drinking. He doesn't want to go home because (pause) his parents are respectable people and he knows they'll not care to see him in such a condition. So this friend of his gives him assistance—takes him to his place for the night. Next day he goes home; his father asks him where he had been. He said he's spent a night with his buddy because he hadn't gotten a job and didn't like to come home without having gotten a job. His parents tell him never to do this again because they worried about him and if they scold him it's only for his own good. (pause) His father sees the trouble that's bothering him. He goes with him and helps him locate a job. After he gets this job he leads a respectable life. (5′30″).

9 GF. (From behind a tree a young woman with some objects in her hand is looking at another girl who is running along a beach.)

XI. (45″) Can't seem to figure out what she's carrying. Seems to be two neighbor ladies. They've had a quarrel. (pause) This one lady tells the other that her boy has been—let's see (pause)—telling the neighbor lady that her boy has been a bad influence on her own son. He's leading him astray, she's heard bad reports about him—he's associating with the wrong friends, with the wrong people, he stays out late at night. She tells him if he continues to do so—(pause)—if he continues to tempt the boy out in bad company, she'll have to see that they separate. (pause) This other lady—she had no idea that her boy was causing all this trouble. She's startled by the remarks made by her neighbor concerning her boy's character. She tells her neighbor that she's sorry for what has happened and that she'll see that it doesn't happen again. So when her boy comes home she gives him a cross-examination and asks if the reports she's heard are true. He denies it at first but later he confesses. She tells him what her neighbor lady told her about him so he becomes angry and does not associate with the neighbor boy any longer. So the two boys separate but the two ladies remain friends. (5'50").

18 GF. (A woman has her hand around the throat of another whom she seems to be pushing over a stairway banister.)

XII. (25") This is a picture of two old ladies. (pause) The one leaning against the bannister seems to have had a stroke. The other one seems shocked and is trying to assist her. She finally leads her in to the couch and lays her down. She calls her doctor and the doctor comes and says that she's had a stroke; she'll be paralyzed for the rest of her life. The other woman begins to cry because she knows that she'll be a burden on her. She doesn't know what to do because she's not well herself and she needs help. Finally she calls her daughter and asks her if she'll come home. She explains the case and asks her if she'll come home and help take care of her sick aunt. She comes home—the daughter comes home—but her mother nags her too much (pause) so she doesn't feel she can stand it any longer so she leaves again. So she's left by herself to take care of the invalid. (pause) So the invalid doesn't receive the proper treatment now that her niece is gone. Soon she has another stroke and this one proves fatal. So after her burial, her sister doesn't know where to turn. She's living by herself. So in the end she sells her home and goes to live in an old people's home. (6'5").

Lack of space makes it necessary to condense the various steps of the analysis outlined in the preceding section. Emphasis will accordingly be placed on the topical and composite generalizations which constitute the heart of the thematic method. The reader can for himself accomplish the *assimilation* of the subject's personality idiom by re-reading the preceding stories with care several times. The *descriptive analysis,* which comprises the second step, must be omitted but may be readily reconstructed from the topical generalizations to be presented shortly. The *statistical evaluation* of the responses may be illustrated by noting that the subject's story VIII for Card 13 MF, in which he described a father and an errant daughter, deviates markedly from the usual variety of responses in which some sexual relationship between the male and female figures constitutes the essence. The avoidance of the sexual theme as well as the unique designation of the figures as being in a parental relationship must be considered further.

The *topical generalizations,* which constitute the fourth step in the method of analysis, are reproduced below in detail. The supporting evidence for each generalization will be found in the stories for the cards cited in parentheses.

(a) *Identification:*

Central character is depressed over failure (1), love affair (3BM, 7BM), guilt for aggression (4, 8BM), father's death (6BM). Twice he is disgustingly drunk (13MF, 18BM). Once he is a baseball idol (16)—the only identification with a happy, fortunate person. Once a mother worried about her son's character and once an old woman deserted by her daughter (9GF, 18GF). Not only depressed in response to problems, but also inadequate, dependent and neurotic (3BM, 4, 7BM, 13MF, 9GF).

(b) *Figures:*

Father-figure is generally unsympathetic; twice dead or dying (6BM, 8BM), once as result of being shot by central figure. Three times said to scold, reprimand, etc. (8BM, 13MF, 18BM); but also three times provides help, support, encouragement (7BM, 16, 18BM). Could represent ambivalent attitude; good father possibly autistic, unsympathetic father, real.

Mother-figure also seen with some ambivalence, but does not figure as prominently in the stories. Twice seen as scolding, nagging person (9GF, 18GF); hint (18GF) that this attitude may be related to sibling-rivalry situations. Once is helped by son after father's death (6BM), but without much expression of feeling; does not give central character much strength or security.

Wife (or sweetheart) is frequently untrue, hurts feelings of central figure, etc. (3BM, 7BM). Once is originally sympathetic, but leaves husband because he is untrue (4); once comforts him on his father's death (6BM). Once married her because it was the thing to do but treats her well (16). General lack of strong, positive feelings concerning wife and marriage.

(c) *Trends:*

Themes are generally unhappy, falling mainly into two groups:

Sex, either in or out of marriage, leads to trouble, disharmony, possibly suicide (3BM, 4, 7BM). Though two of the three marriages in which the central figure is involved are unhappy (4, 7BM), subject makes frequent use of "got married and lived happily ever after" endings.

Aggression against strictly moral parents, usually father, with concomitant guilt for this reaction and for original misdeed (1, 6BM, 8BM, 13MF, 18BM, 9GF, 18GF). Lack of real trust in parents (13MF, 18BM) but turns to them when has trouble with wife (7BM).

Blank card story presents an obvious wish-fulfillment in which the hero is acclaimed and respected for masculine prowess. All themes portray extremely immature orientation, with main concern over whether central character can remain dependent, chiefly on father; not ready to solve problems by himself.

(d) *Dynamic clues, including sequence:*

Blocking marked in several types of situations:
  1. Where death of or aggression toward father is described (6BM, 8BM, 18BM).
  2. Where identification is with critical, "moral" mother (9GF, 18GF).
  3. Where sex is a problem (7BM); or where sex is avoided (13MF). The latter is an especially unusual production on account of its complete avoidance of any sexual implication and the substitution of the theme of the punishing-father vs. the wrongdoing-child so prominent in the other stories. The identification of the subject with the "daughter" instead of with the sexually aggressive male usually seen should be noted.

Autistic qualities: Wishful nature of ambitious story told for blank card, together with passive "it will turn out all right" character of many endings.

Ambivalence and superficial acceptance of parents' moral standards, indicated by the expression of guilt and the reform of unworthy children (13MF, 18BM).

(e) *Endings:*

In general, fairly happy in a passive, unrealistic way. Outright revolt against parents or unfaithful wife leads to unhappiness (8BM, 7BM, 18GF).

(f) *Formal features:*

Interpretive level well maintained, with successful attempts at plots. Vocabulary and syntax good. Stories usually short.

The *composite generalizations* which could be made from the preceding topical ones produced the picture of an individual who was depressed and anxious in outlook, who felt inferior, and was still essentially dependent upon his elders. Conflict with the parents was evident. Toward the mother the patient appeared almost completely negative. It was possible that she alienated him to some extent by favoring his brother. The relationship to the father was more ambivalent, with manifest hostility, on the one hand, respect and dependence, on the other. The dependence grew more out of the patient's apparent insecurity than out of the father's sympathetic understanding. Autistically the young man pictured this parent as essentially helpful and encouraging but the reality appeared more in the rebellion that the son expressed and for which he then seemed to suffer remorse and guilt. To these evidences of insecurity and immaturity was added an indication of naive indulgence in adolescent fantasy centering around concern about masculine prowess. Closely related to this trend was his conflict regarding sex. While he pictured marriage as a necessary and more or less natural step, there was little in it which was genuinely attractive to him. Sex in all its aspects appeared dangerous and unhappy in its consequences. In one way or another his sexual maladjustment seemed linked with his parental dependence and, more especially, with his ambivalent relationship to the father.

In completing the final step of the T A T analysis it is possible to be brief since data from other tests are not in this instance to be incorporated, and the facts of the history as known are in obviously good agreement with the findings of the projective method. It was not surprising, in view of the already mentioned characterizations of the mother and father, to obtain the foregoing portrayal of their personalities through the psychologic eyes of the son. Less was learned about the relationship between the twins than might have been hoped for. Leads became available for psychotherapy in relation to his sexual maladjustment—one of his chief complaints. In view of his immature and anxious approach to everything sexual, his experience of such physical symptoms as nausea during dates with girls could be readily appreciated. The Thematic Apperception Test, therefore, jibed well with the patient's social and clinical histories and, moreover, provided psychodynamic hypotheses in terms of which it became easier to establish a diagnosis and proceed with treatment.

Illustrative Protocol 2

A 16 year-old boy was admitted to a psychiatric hospital after threatening and slapping his mother during a trivial quarrel. Eight months earlier he had been seen in the out-patient clinic because of truancy, temper outbursts and extreme ennui. It had been apparent at that time that his problem was mainly one of family adjustment in which his mother, especially, played a prominent role. The family history will therefore be reported in some detail.

The father, aged 44, had come from a broken home, and was the fifth of ten children. He had been expelled from a teachers' college because of drinking. He then worked as an accountant. After marrying at 28, he continued to drink. About three years following the outbreak of World War II, he was hospitalized for one month because of acute alcoholism. In the next year he was drafted into the army but after only a few months of service was given a medical discharge on account of chronic nephritis. He did not return to his family.

The mother, aged 42, was an only child who was sent to a Catholic convent during adolescence to "learn discipline." Attendance at junior high school completed her education. At the age of 26 she married. A year later she was discovered to have tuberculosis and was sent to a sanitarium. Though, according to her statement, the doctor there said she had only six months to live, she left in nine days, spent two months in bed at home, and recovered. Her father, vice-president of a small bank, frequently gave her financial assistance. He was clearly the parent she preferred. He died the year her husband entered the army. Soon thereafter she took in a divorced man and, a year later, his married daughter with her two small children as boarders. She became attached to the male boarder, who shared a decided interest in music with her. At the time of the patient's hospitalization she was considering a divorce from her husband although she was not sure she wanted to marry her new friend.

The patient's parents had married secretly and were never happy together. There had been several separations. The mother regarded her husband's drinking as the chief source of conflict. They had one child in addition to the patient, another boy two years older. The brother, physically larger, was also a behavior problem, and had been dismissed from high school in his senior year for striking a fellow student.

The patient had been a healthy, normal infant. At 18 months he and his older brother were taken to live with the maternal grandmother because of the mother's illness. This arrangement continued off and on for years because of parental discord. During childhood he had severe attacks of vomiting and diarrhea that sometimes woke him in the middle of the night. He would "scream all night and sleep all day." He was temperamental and did not always get along with his brother, the favorite of the grandparents. His school work was good until the seventh grade, approximately the time of the father's final separation from the home. He regularly attended Sunday School and was active at the YMCA. Classical music strongly appealed to him and he knew many symphonies by name. He had had dates with girls, but there had apparently been no sexual intercourse. While in the eighth grade the patient was charged with truancy and was not promoted. A year and a half later, after being thrown from a wagon onto a fence, he developed a small inguinal hernia. He completely lost interest in school work, often refused to get up in the morning, and attributed his need for rest to his injury.

In the following month he was brought to the out-patient clinic. During the first interview he bit his nails, said he felt rejected by his mother, and had had suicidal thoughts after quarrelling with her. He had once even wet his lips with a bichloride of mercury tablet. He expressed fear over the possibility of a hernia operation. The psychiatrist had him taken out of school and arranged for several industrial placements none of which was successful because the patient left one after the other on the least pretext. In the next few months he was given to repeated outbursts of temper and other unruly behavior. Once he broke the boarder's ribs in a friendly wrestling match which ended in the mother's rescuing the boarder from the boy's grip by beating the latter on the head with her fists. The mother suspected the boy of stealing small sums of money from her purse and said he had slapped her and threatened to kill her when she refused him a new pair of shoes. She told of sexual advances he had made toward her on one occasion by putting his arm around her and reaching inside her dress. She described similar sexual behavior on his part toward the daughter of the boarder.

The precipitating situation for the patient's hospitalization was an argument which he had with his mother and the boarder's daughter over a program of radio music. The patient had commented that the performance was poor. The girl replied sarcastically that she supposed he was the only one in the country who knew anything about music. In the ensuing argument the mother interceded, where-upon he slapped her. The mother sent for the police who took the boy to the county jail. He remained there for nine days awaiting disposition.

The patient construed his commitment to the hospital by the judge, whom he called a "crooked politician," as a form of punishment. In other respects the boy was friendly and had no obvious mental symptoms. While in the beginning he refused to see his mother and spoke of her as "that old woman," later he became anxious if she did not visit.

In order to explore the dynamics of the patient's family relationships, the Thematic Apperception Test was administered * in two sessions about a month after his admission. He cooperated fully in the procedure. The stories he told were too long and too numerous for verbatim reproduction but a tabulation of the main themes is here presented. Examples of actual responses will then be given.

SESSION I

I (1) A boy is disillusioned, disgusted and has keen sense of failure; a victim of poor education and unsatisfactory home life.

II (2) Longing for secure home on farm with son taking over after father's death. Critical of mother not helping very much.

III (6BM) A son who is first pampered and then let down by his mother turns to antisocial conduct and meets with a bad end.

IV (3BM) A boy spoiled by his parents and then let down becomes a social problem and ends up in prison.

V (9GF) A young man is a victim of the selfish love and rivalry of two women both of whom finally let him down.

VI (13B) A boy is lonely and without opportunities for education or other advantages because of parental poverty; will in the end be led through bitterness to antisocial behavior.

VII (18GF) A girl, who is victim of miserable relations between parents, is eventually killed accidentally by drunken father. Mother has father thrown into prison where he does away with himself. She herself dies of sorrow.

* Both the mother and the son were studied by this means to discover the complementary relationships between their projective worlds (see *Am. J. Orthopsychiat.*, 1947, 17, 129–142), but the mother's record is here omitted because of space limitations.

Session I—(Continued)

VIII (10) A boy is dreaming about the kind of home and loving parents he would have desired.

IX (16— Blank Card) A boy is enjoying the solitary pleasure of fishing while he dreams about a happy home life and the happy home he himself will one day create in the pattern of what his own father taught.

X (7BM) A boy is receiving good advice, though reluctantly, from a father who, finally, will be obeyed since he is so right.

XI (13MF) A man who has not treated his wife considerately repents of the fate he has unwittingly brought upon her and tries to make restitution.

XII (5) A boy is being persecuted by a self-centered and strict stepmother who is attempting to get rid of him; the father fails to realize the terrible situation of the child.

Session II

XIII (13G) A woman who has lost her family is on the verge of suicide and might have to go to a mental hospital.

XIV (6GF) A man is happily married and is enjoying a wonderful family life.

XV (8GF) A girl who has failed to learn the importance of responsibility at last recognizes its necessity and becomes frugal.

XVI (20) A wayward youth who has been keeping bad company —drinking heavily—repents and returns to the bosom of his family.

XVII (4) A man who is too successful for his own good, who drinks and philanders, is quarreling with his wife; she eventually reforms him.

XVIII (11) A family group—cavemen—have lost their home and possessions as the result of a landslide and of a prowling monster loosed by the catastrophe; but they rebuild a happy group life.

XIX (7GF) A little girl is being consulted by her mother, a widow, who is planning to remarry. The child is observed as first questioning the step, as not showing anger, and finally welcoming the proposal as an advantage.

XX (8BM) A boy who has not taken advantage of favorable family circumstances to get his education, etc., finally comes

SESSION II—(Continued)

face to face with reality, realizes his errors, and begins
to reform.

XXI   (3GF)   A girl who has frittered away her early opportunities
by drinking, smoking, and loose living realizes that her
parents knew better—though it is up to her to reform
herself.

XXII   (14)   A boy who at first resists his parents' advice to delay
marriage recognizes in the end the wisdom of waiting
and does what is right.

XXIII   (12F)   A girl who has neglected her self-sacrificing parents
realizes too late what she has done; tries to atone by
helping orphans, etc., but never succeeds in becoming
really happy.

XXIV   (12BG)   A boy is living with a brother and sister in an idyllic
environment—blissfully enjoying the country—and eventually all three grow up to be happy and successful
parents like their forebears.

A few verbatim examples of his productions may serve to clarify
this material. The first two stories indicate the nature of his unstable
family relationships, the former referring specifically to the mother,
the latter, more generally to the life of the group.

For Card 6 BM, showing an elderly woman and a young man,
the patient reported:

Once upon a time there was a young boy—had a nice home—nice
family. They were well-to-do.—He didn't like to go out on dates or sports
or anything, but he thought it was kind of smart to drink and gamble.
Then his father died. His mother took over. She told him what he was
doing was wrong. Finally one night he was gambling—and he came to
his mother and asked for money to pay his gambling debt. She told him
she couldn't do it and they had quite an argument.—[What is he thinking
about?] Well, probably how wrong she is. She's done him a great injustice by not giving him the money.—He calls her a few choice words, then
leaves and does something drastic maybe. [What will the outcome be?]
He'll probably get into trouble for not paying his gambling debt. Maybe
he'll drink himself to death or get put in jail—maybe rob somebody to
pay the debt or maybe kill somebody—maybe get electrocuted.

Card 11—a representation of a deep chasm between high cliffs from among which the head and neck of a dragon vaguely protrude—elicited the following story:

This looks like it might have happened back in the caveman days. Something about cavemen. I think there was a small group of them. They lived together; men, women, and children. They all lived together. They were as happy as they could be. They made their existence, that's about all. Things were very hard; tools were very crude. They seemed to make a lot of progress, especially in building things. One day they were out making a bridge, out trying to construct a bridge over a big ravine and there was a kind of landslide which pushed away part of a big hill and a monster, a huge lizard I guess this is, pushed his way through, exposed himself to them. They looked up terrified and ran across what's left of the bridge and tried to escape to safety. Their village was destroyed in the landslide. Everything that they had built and constructed was just all gone. They couldn't get back to it because of the monster. They lost everything they had. They had to start all over again in another part of the country.

The final example sheds light on his attitude toward his mother's possible remarriage. In his response to Card 7 GF, showing an adult woman and a young girl, he describes a widow who is talking to her little daughter, then continues: "Her mother met a man that she liked very much and the man and the girl's mother decided they would get married so they decided that they wouldn't get married right away so they would talk to the daughter first to see what she would think about it. Here the mother is talking about the possibility of a new father. The girl doesn't seem to be very happy, doesn't look like she's angry, doesn't look excited, not angry just looks not very happy. She never realized what a father is like because she never had one. She's not quite sure that she would like the idea or not. She finally tells the mother that it is all right with her. What her mother does is for her good because she sacrificed everything for her during the years when she was a baby, brought her up. She decided if her mother wanted to get married it was all right because her mother knew best about things like that . . ."

The part which the boy's intense Œdipus strivings may well have contributed to his present problem with the mother and which is discernible in the history of the home situation—absent father, interloping boarder as rival for the son—is strikingly confirmed by this unusual story for the picture in question. In the light of the anamnesis the over-insistence by the patient upon the daughter's lack of anger takes on an obvious significance. The attempt at the end to gloss over the problem is clearly specious, being couched, parrotlike, in the words with which a moralizing mother would exhort a resistive son.

The main trends may be summarized in the following schema:

Main theme: Family as unstable for son who is either neglected or spoiled; son as wayward.

Social orientation: Affiliative striving: family orientation even in matters of individual concern.

Mother-son relationship: Hostility to mother (ambivalent).

Attitude toward father: Condonement of father and identification with him.

Attitude toward possible new father or husband: Attachment to mother and hostility to prospective new father.

Wishful future outlook: Need for family as stable unit, with strong guilt in son and emphasis upon restitutive behavior.

The patient thus consistently pictured himself as the victim of an unwholesome home in which the mother appeared as the villainess. The father knew not what he did and was therefore guiltless. The boy seemed, in fact, to be identified with the father—in gambling, drinking and other misbehavior. He believed that the mother had got rid of the father and was now trying to get rid of him. There was, therefore, an understandable trend toward antisocial conduct. Also present was a tendency toward wishful penitence and restitution.

The Thematic Apperception Test had made it clear, especially as its results were collated with the social history and with other tests, that the boy's orientation toward his home was basically negative. It was concluded that he would probably be most readily and successfully treated outside the family environment. Such re-education would require that a model for healthy growth be provided him over a long period—a father figure with whom he could identify as a support against antisocial inclinations. The interpretation of the mother's record on the Thematic Apperception Test, which was fortunately available in this case, lent support to these recommendations.

4. THE WORLD TEST

a. *Purpose.* This projective procedure was designed for use in the investigation of children's emotional problems and is based on the well-known value of play as a medium in which the child naturally and readily expresses himself. The test is best adapted to children between the ages of 4 and 11 but is occasionally useful up to the age of 15 with either neurotic or retarded subjects.

b. *Materials and Instructions.* The materials consist of a box containing 150 miniature objects from which a town, village, farm, or zoo can be constructed, or with which a fictional game can be played. The child is shown the toys and permitted to play with them as he wishes. He is ordinarily stopped after twenty minutes but may be allowed a longer time if conditions warrant.

c. *Data and Scoring.* While the child is playing, notes are made of his construction, procedure, fictional play, verbal comments and physical movements. The play productions and activities are the data subjected to scoring and interpretation. Occasionally (as in one illustrative case cited below) successive productions are compared. The formal aspects of the world construction itself are scored according to the appearance of certain "signs"—features which have been observed to occur more frequently in the play of children with recognizable emotional problems than in the play of those who are well adjusted. Among the signs noted are *aggressive content* (soldiers fighting, biting animals or wild animals, accidents involving crashing or killing); *formal emptiness* (less than 50 elements used, less than 5 types of elements, absence of persons, i.e., either none present or children only); and *formal distortion or disorganization* (many enclosures or barriers, many small closed units, rigid or schematic arrangements of toys in rows, absence of any organized or related placements).

d. *Interpretation.* According to norms derived from normal and maladjusted groups of children, the appearance of two or more symptoms is regarded as indicative of personality disturbance. Particular combinations of symptoms point to different kinds of maladjustment. The content of the world structure and plot aspects of the play carried on during its production are, further, interpreted qualitatively to throw light upon the child's emotional problems. The test is not intended as a final or exclusive source of information but as an aid in obtaining insight into the child's fantasies, attitudes, family relationships and degree of emotional adjustment.

Illustrative Protocol 1

An 11 year-old boy had failed to adjust in one foster home after another. His mother, a patient in a state hospital, was believed to be both mentally deficient and psychotic. There was no available information about the boy's father. The child was said to be high-strung, quick-tempered, stubborn and cruel to other children. A series of four intelligence tests, at intervals over a seven-year period, gave evidence of progressive decline from I. Q. 98 to I. Q. 70. This pattern suggested that continued emotional disturbance had been interfering with his capacity to assimilate and profit by his daily-life experience throughout this period. The World Test was employed in order to obtain a picture of his personality and behavior. The record of his activity and a verbatim account of his comments are given below.

(The patient puts in the sand a bowl filled with water to represent a lake. He places the boats in the lake.) Is about all I'm going to do is put the water in? [He is told that the toys are his to play with as he wishes while he is in the room.] Who has been down in your office before? (Runs the airplane and makes humming noises. Then he smooths the sand into a hill.) Here's a real steep slope. The airplanes are over here. Here is a police car. (He moves the police car, making a noise like a siren.) Here's a fire truck. (Moves the truck along, making a noise like a siren.) Look at that car. (Points to the tank.) Here's another fire truck. Here's a taxi. (He puts all the cars in a row.) They're all stopping until the airplane stops. What's this? An ambulance or police car? It's an ambulance because here's where they take the men out in back. Which one do you like the best? (He holds up two red cars.) [The examiner indicates her choice.] (The patient indicates his choice of the other car.) Because the roof comes up higher. Here's the nurse. Can you make these soldiers the Nazis? The nurse is with the Americans. Here's a police, a Nazi police. Here's a child diving into the water. (He holds the child under the water and looks at the examiner. Then he puts the child back into the box. He places another child in the boat.) Here is a lion. (He imitates a roar.) Lions are the toughest animals in the world. The snake is the second. Can you unwrap this? (Referring to the snake coils.) This is the jungle. The trees are too small for the lions. When are you going to bring me down again? [The patient is reassured that he can come down again.] Here's a stop sign, goes right here. Here's where they go. Where shall I put the houses? Oh, yes, I have to put the men in the boats. And the alligator, he goes under the water. Oh, here are two little children. This little children lives here and is running to his mamma. Here's another running into the school. This house is way back here. The Red Cross house is way down here. Can you have trees around it? Here's two black stallions. A brown stallion and a white stallion. You have to have the girl and boy riding. Girl jumps in the water and jumps out. He gets on the horse. Oh, this man joins the army. Here's a barn. This stallion is running away. He jumps over the car. Here he jumps right on the cop. All these horses are in the lead. Have to have a fence around the pigs. I have to have a little water fountain for them. If I had some I could put it in the pen. Look at the two little bunnies. These bunnies make holes. Here's the two lions, sister and brother. Because the brother lion has more hair. That's two ladies having a fight. (He pushes them together.) These two ladies go walking down the road. (He walks back and closes the door of the bathroom. Then he asks the examiner to close the window. The examiner, who has dropped her pencil, thanks the patient for picking it up.) You don't have to thank me. Where should I put the church? Oh, yes, we have to have the mother at the house. These three ladies were walking down the street. (He picks the alligator up out of the water.) This little nurse runs and runs and jumps. [The patient is told that he has only five more minutes.] (He inquires whether the other little boy is coming down to play. He puts certain toys to one side on the shelf.) Don't want Billy to muss them up. (He goes to the bathroom, taking airplanes with him. He stays there for some time, making a humming noise as if he is playing with them. When he returns he is very concerned about the toys he laid aside and wants to be reassured that Billy will not play with them.)

The important formal features of this performance may now be summarized. For one thing, the boy included 83 elements of 16 different types in his play. He made use of both human and animal figures, both wild and tame animals, and inanimate objects. The two aspects of his production which indicated emotional disturbance were the occurrence of fighting and accidents and the lack of formal organization in the construction.

Qualitative features of the boy's play in the order of their occurrence were also informative. He was initially quite uncertain of the limits or restrictions inherent in the situation. He began by playing with inanimate objects, rather than human figures, and selected chiefly those of an aggressive nature (police cars, airplanes, fire engines). When he first introduced human figures, permissive reassurance was required before he could further express his aggressiveness. ("Can you make these soldiers the Nazis?") It then became possible for him to advance to more personally meaningful hostility; he held the child under water. As his anxiety mounted, however, he returned the doll to the box. At this point recourse to a slightly more masked representation of his hostility appeared in his identifying with the lion. ("Lions are the toughest animals in the world.") After some parallel aggressive play he tentatively approached his more personal preoccupations again in the comparison between brother and sister lions. A need for dependent security was then evidenced in his request that the examiner close the window for him and advise him on the placement of the church. At the end of the session he took steps to insure his security by singling out certain toys as his own and requesting that other children not use them.

From the content of his play as well as from the more formal features of his production it was concluded that the boy was disturbed and confused about his security and "belongingness" in a world which had offered him little to which he could cling. Conflict in expressing hostility toward the responsible adult figures, on the one hand, and in grasping whatever acceptance he could achieve from them, on the other, could be discerned. Aggression against sibling figures was undoubtedly one aspect of his needs; he wanted as much affection as he could get. In this setting, the formal disorganization of his "world" was understandable and appropriate. The interpretation was also tentatively made that the apparent intellectual decline could probably be attributed to rather severe anxiety. Further investigation of this hypothesis was indicated.

Illustrative Protocol 2

This second case is similar to the first in the nature of the problem presented but for illustrative purposes it adds a comparison of two "world" constructions and shows them diagrammatically. With such emphasis in mind the verbatim protocols are not given.

A six year-old girl had been placed in a foster home because, it was charged, her parents had been neglecting her. The foster mother, who brought the child to an out-patient clinic, complained that the girl rolled incessantly in bed and frequently wet it. When the patient was given the Stanford-Binet Intelligence Scale she appeared very timid and restless. An I. Q. of 93 was obtained. To study her emotional problems the World Test was administered twice (A and B)— once before therapy and again after two treatment sessions. Diagrammatic representations of the constructions are shown in Figure 15. Comparison of the protocols will illustrate how this test may be employed for studying the progress of a case in therapy.

World Test A

In her excitement upon being shown the test materials the patient rubbed her hands together, fingered her dress, and laughed. The first thing she picked up was the snake. She looked at this object carefully, then replaced it in the box. Her interest in the snake continued throughout the test but she did not put it on the table with the other objects until after she was told that she would have to leave. She often talked about putting people into her "world" but never actually did so. Once she did place two little girls on the table only to put them back in the box at once with the comment "they'll get hurt" (referring to the wild animals). Animals were very interesting to her. She was careful, however, to fence them all in, both those that "hurt" and the domestic ones. Other elements (cars, houses, trees, boats) were arranged in rigid row patterns.

Construction A

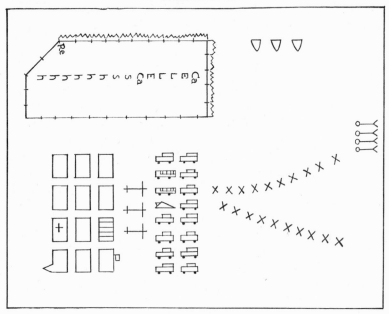

SYMBOLS

⊢—⊣	FENCE		CAR	Ca	CAMEL
	HEDGE		TRUCK	E	ELEPHANT
	HOUSE		FIRE ENGINE	L	LION
	CHURCH		BOAT	S	SHEEP
	HOSPITAL		AIRPLANE	h	HORSE
	PRISON		TANK	Re	REPTILE
	SCHOOL		SIGNPOST	Co	COW
×	TREE		SOLDIER	d	DOG
	MAN			r	RABBIT
	WOMAN				

Fig. 15. Two Successive Constructions, A and B, in the World Test, *Protocol 2.*

The emotional maladjustment detectable in the child's social behavior was plainly indicated by the appearance of two clear signs in the World protocol (distortion and aggression). Although she had average intelligence, her construction was unusually rigid and schematic in form.

Construction B

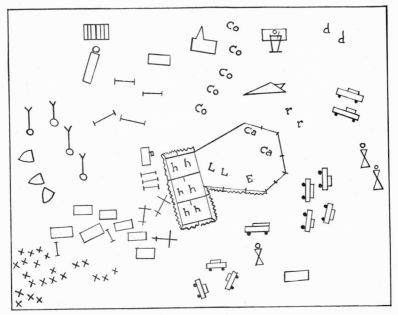

This sign reflects serious emotional inhibition. The disturbance is reflected further in symbolized outbursts of anxiety (animals that bite, careful attention to placement of fences) which alternated with restraining actions (orderly rows, replacements in the box). Overt aggression was inhibited until the end of the test, at which point she was able to express it tentatively and in veiled form (placement of the snake in the corner of the world structure). That relationships to people are poor was shown by the avoidance of human figures.

This first World construction thus exhibited asocial, rigid and defensive characteristics. It was the production of a child whose chief preoccupation is that she must protect herself from impending danger and that she must, in particular, avoid human beings. The toys were arranged in a somewhat primitive and, at the same time, rigid pattern, significant of emotional constriction and anxiety.

World Test B

The patient, in general, was more at ease on the second occasion. She immediately began using human figures aggressively (a soldier fell off the church, a car ran into the fence, a woman was knocked off the church, a man was kicked into jail). Then with fences she built an enclosure for all the wild animals. During this phase of her play she asked to be reassured that her Mummy was still waiting for her. After the request, her aggressive activity ceased and quieter behavior began. She made a sidewalk for all the ladies and men, compared the domestic animals to those on her grandfather's farm, commented on the little boys and girls, and drew the examiner's attention to her new dress. However, as soon as she was informed of the time limit, aggressive activity reappeared. She very willingly left the room, saying, "The boys and girls can stay here and play."

This construction was more free and spontaneous than the previous one. That emotional maladjustment was still present was indicated by the same two signs found before (distortion and aggression). The distortion was, however, of a less severe nature. After a symbolized outburst of aggression, anxiety appeared and was dealt with by protective measures (building fences). The anxiety seemed, moreover, to bring associations involving the mother figure. Upon reassurance that her mother was still waiting for her, her play became more constructive. In contrast to the previous rigid pattern, the present production was haphazard and disorganized. This change from rigidity to disorder may indicate that she had been enabled by therapy to give up some of her inhibitions; a clearer picture of her emotional confusion could then be revealed. As a whole, this second World protocol showed characteristics of aggression, disorganization and anxiety. A suggestion emerged that her fears concerned security in relation to the mother figure. The patient's ability to resume better adjusted activity after the symbolized outburst of aggression had been allayed by reassurance was interpreted as an indication that play therapy would probably be successful.

A comparison of the two protocols discloses that after two sessions of therapy this girl was able to express aggression more openly, especially toward adult figures that she feared. Anxiety remained but she was freer to deal with it. Emotional inhibition and rigidity, while still in evidence, were beginning to be narrowed to a specific area (the mother). The changes that were reflected in the second test were regarded as propitious for psychotherapy in this case.

5. ROSENZWEIG PICTURE-FRUSTRATION STUDY

a. *Purpose.* The Picture-Frustration (P-F) Study, or—by its full name—the Picture-Association Study for Assessing Reactions to Frustration, is a limited projective procedure for disclosing patterns of response to everyday stress that are of widely recognized importance in both normal and abnormal adjustment.

b. *Materials and Instructions.* The material of the test is a series of 24 cartoon-like pictures each representing two persons who are involved in a mildly frustrating situation of common occurrence. The figure at the left of each picture is shown saying certain words which either frustrate the other individual or help describe what is frustrating him. The subject is instructed to examine the situations one at a time and write in the blank space the first reply that enters his mind as likely to be given by the anonymous figure. There are two forms of the Study—one for adults (14 years and older) and one for children (4 to 13 years)—which may be administered either to individuals or to groups in 15 to 20 minutes. A nonleading inquiry is conducted after the more careful, individual administration. With small children or with illiterate or mentally ill adults who can not write for themselves, the Study may be administered orally, in which event the examiner writes the responses for the subject. The inquiry is then best conducted at the completion of each item.

c. *Data and Scoring.* Scores are assigned each response as to *direction of aggression* and *type of reaction.* Under *direction* are included extrapunitiveness—in which aggression is *turned out* upon the environment; intropunitiveness—in which it is *turned in* upon the subject himself; and impunitiveness—in which aggression is *turned off,* i.e., evaded in an attempt to gloss over the situation. Under *type of reaction* fall obstacle-dominance—in which the presence or the nature of the barrier occasioning the frustration is emphasized in the response; ego-defense—in which the protection of the ego predominates; and need-persistence—in which the solution of the frustrating problem stands out. From the combination of these six categories there result for each item nine possible scoring factors (and two variants, E and I). Brief definitions of the factors together with the symbols conventionally employed in scoring are given in the accompanying chart. Either a single or a combined factor score is given each response and the frequencies with which these factors appear in the record are calculated.

d. *Interpretation.* It is assumed as a basis for interpreting the P–F Study that the subject unconsciously or consciously identifies himself with the frustrated individual in each pictured situation and projects his own bias in the replies given. Percentages of total extrapunitiveness, intropunitiveness and impunitiveness and of obstacle-dominance, ego-defense and need-persistence thus indicate the degree to which he tends to employ these modes of reaction, explicitly or implicitly, in his everyday behavior. The subject's responses are also compared as to score with criteria from a large normative group. The extent to which the subject's results agree with expectations is expressed as a *Group Conformity Rating* (GCR). This rating affords one basis for judging social adjustment. Any consistent trends in the sequence of the individual responses are also noted for their significance in revealing the subject's reactions to his own previous behavior. Since the capacity to adjust in circumstances of stress and the characteristic

SCORING COMPONENTS OF THE PICTURE-FRUSTRATION STUDY

	DIRECTION OF AGGRESSION		
TYPE OF REACTION	*Extrapunitive*	*Intropunitive*	*Impunitive*
Obstacle-Dominant	E': The presence of the frustrating obstacle is insistently pointed out.	I': The frustrating obstacle is construed as not being frustrating or even as in some way beneficial; or, in some instances, the subject emphasizes the extent of his embarrassment at being involved in instigating another's frustration.	M': The obstacle in the frustrating situation is minimized almost to the point of denying its existence.
Ego-Defensive	E: Blame, hostility, etc., are turned against some person or thing in the environment. E̲: In this variant of E the subject aggressively denies that he is responsible for some offense with which he is charged.	I: Blame, censure, etc., are directed by the subject upon himself. I̲: A variant of I in which the subject admits his guilt but denies any essential fault by referring to unavoidable circumstances.	M: Blame for the frustration is evaded altogether, the situation being regarded as unavoidable; in particular, the "frustrating" individual is absolved.
Need-Persistive	e: A solution for the frustrating situation is emphatically expected of someone else.	i: Amends are offered by the subject, usually from a sense of guilt, to solve the problem.	m: Expression is given to the hope that time or normally expected circumstances will bring about a solution of the problem; patience and conformity are characteristic.

patterns of reaction in such situations are important indices of personality, this technic is apt to provide useful data in a wide variety of personality and personnel problems.

Illustrative Protocol 1

The first illustrative protocol is that of a 26 year-old male factory worker who participated in a routine psychologic examination for research purposes. His verbatim responses in the 24 P–F items are listed below. Preceding each response there is given in parentheses a brief description of the pictured situation.

1. (The driver of an automobile is apologizing to a pedestrian for having splashed the latter's clothing.) I shouldn't be standing near it in the first place.
2. (A hostess is expressing consternation at a guest's having broken a favorite vase.) I'm awfly sorry. I'll repay it or buy one just like it.
3. (A girl is remarking that her companion, seated in a theatre behind a woman with a large hat, cannot see a thing.) I wish people would be more considerate.
4. (A man who has driven his friend to the railroad station is apologizing because the breakdown of his car led to missing the train.) Thanks for the lift anyway. Fate favors no one always.
5. (A customer is complaining to a clerk that she has brought back a new watch three times now because it refuses to go.) We'll take another look at it and see what's wrong.
6. (A library attendant is explaining to a girl carrying four books that the rules permit only two books to be taken at a time.) Yes, but couldn't you make an exception since it's urgent?
7. (A waiter is accusing a customer of being too fussy.) I'm not very particular, sir, but this food is deplorable.
8. (A young man is explaining to a companion that the latter's girl friend has invited him to a dance.) Well, have a good time. Sorry I can't come along.
9. (While it is raining a clerk in a pawn shop is refusing a customer his umbrella until the manager arrives in the afternoon.) I'll take it now, please. Here's the money.
10. (A man is accusing another of being a liar.) I beg your pardon! I am as truthful as you think you are.

11. (A party in a telephone booth at 2:00 A. M. is apologizing for a wrong number to a person who has apparently just been awakened by the call.) Enunciate more clearly next time, please. This is no fun at this hour.

12. (A man is pointing out to another that the latter's hat has been taken by someone else who has left his own instead.) I'll see him tonight and give him his for mine.

13. (A man at his desk is stating that he cannot keep a previously arranged appointment with a caller just arriving.) Well, when can I see you then?

14. (A woman standing on a windy street is remarking to a companion that someone for whom they are waiting should have been there ten minutes ago.) Well, maybe she was delayed for something.

15. (A woman is apologizing to her partner in a card game for having made a stupid play.) I understand. Better luck next time.

16. (At the scene of an automobile accident one man is accusing another of having had no right to try passing.) You're right and I'm very sorry. I will make amends.

17. (A woman standing with a man beside an automobile is reprimanding him for having lost the keys.) Accidents do happen.

18. (A clerk in a store is apologizing to a customer for having just sold the last of some item.) I'll wait a few more days.

19. (A motorcycle policeman is accosting an automobilist for passing a school-house at 60 miles an hour.) I'm sorry, officer. This is a very urgent trip.

20. (A girl is musing aloud to her friend as to why they were not invited to a party in an adjoining room.) Maybe we're not wanted.

21. (A woman upbraids two others for saying mean things about someone who was in an accident the day before and is now in the hospital.) I'm sorry to hear that. She really isn't such a bad egg.

22. (A man who has fallen down is being asked whether he is hurt.) Just a little. I'll be all right.

23. (A woman dressed for travel has interrupted a telephone conversation to explain to a man surrounded by luggage that a relative wants them to wait till she arrives and bestows her blessing again.) Where was she all this time?

24. (A man returning a torn newspaper explains apologetically that the baby caused the damage.) That's perfectly all right. I can get another.

The completed record blank for this protocol is shown in Figure 16. The scoring symbol for each item has been entered in the appropriate box on the left-hand side of the sheet. Marginal (+ or —) notation has been made of the subject's agreement with the modal response for those items on which such criteria are available. His scores agreed fully in 8 instances, partially in 2 others. The Group Conformity Rating (GCR) was therefore 75 per cent—a result well within the range for normal subjects. Adequate capacity for conformity with conventional behavior under stress was thus indicated.

Total scores for the various directions of aggression and types of reaction were computed and expressed in percentage under "Profiles." According to the norms, this young man's percentage of extrapunitive responses (29 per cent) was lower than the average result of three-quarters of the population. He was accordingly considered to be less outwardly aggressive than most comparable subjects. His score for intropunitiveness (35 per cent) was reciprocally and significantly elevated, that for impunitiveness only slightly higher than average. Analysis of the reaction type results revealed a significantly low obstacle-dominance score (6 per cent) and an elevated tendency toward need-persistence (35 per cent). Not only did he assume blame too readily but he emphasized somewhat excessively the solution of problems in a favorable direction. The Patterns of predominant modes of response added nothing important to these conclusions but the analysis of Trends brought out several interesting points. By comparing the first with the second half of the record it was clear that he not only had a low E percentage, indicated above, but that he became progressively less extrapunitive (trend away from E) and more intropunitive and impunitive (toward I and m). He was apparently made insecure by the expression of aggression and tended to react from it with some guilt, substituting instead a reliance upon apology or hopeful conformity.

In summary, then, it appeared from the P–F Study that this young man was superficially well adjusted to his social environment but that he achieved this end by accepting restrictions and blame. He was apt not to express his hostility, preferring instead to suppress his aggression and, as frustration accumulated, escape into apology or hopefulness, at his own expense if necessary.

RECORD BLANK FOR THE ROSENZWEIG P-F STUDY

Name of Subject *Illustrative Protocol* Date of Test
Sex Duration of Test *22'*
Age Name of Examiner

Item Scores

		O-D	E-D	N-P
—	1.		*I* M	
+	2.		I	*i* i
	3.		*E*	
	4.		*M*	
+	5.			*i* i
	6.			*e*
+	7.		*E* E	
	8.		*M*	
+	9.		E	*e* e
+	10.		*E; E* E	
—	11.		*E* M	
	12.			*m*
	13.			*m*
	14.		*M*	
	15.		*M*	*m*
	16.		*I*	*i*
	17.		*I*	
	18.			*m*
+	19.		*I* I	
	20.		*I*	
.5	21.	*I'* I'	*I*	
+	22.	*M'* M'		
+	23.		*E* E	
.5	24.	M'	*M* M	*i*

G C R

75 %

Profiles

	O-D	E-D	N-P	Total	%
E	0	5	2	7	29
I	.5	5.	3	8.5	35
M	1	4	3.5	8.5	35
Total	1.5	14	8.5		
%	6	58	35		

Patterns

1. *E = I > M*
2. *(E = I) > m > M'*
3. *E = I > M*

E = *1.5* = *6* %
I = *2* = *8* %
E + I = *3.5* = *15* %

Trends

1. *None*
2. *E ←.60 ; −.60→ I*
3. *−.43→ m*
4. *E ←.71*
5. *None*

Comments

Copyright, 1948, by Saul Rosenzweig

FIG. 16. Record Blank for the Picture-Frustration Study, *Protocol 1*.

Illustrative Protocol 2

A 42 year-old man was admitted to the hospital with a diagnosis of Dementia Praecox, Paranoid Type. He had attended parochial schools where he had apparently been rigidly disciplined, and had always been a shy and withdrawn person. Between the ages of 19 and 23 he had served in the merchant marine. Then he found employment as a house-painter. He had never married nor had he apparently ever had any very strong heterosexual interests. A few months previous to his hospitalization he began to believe that he was being accused and threatened both by his family and by outsiders; people were attempting to "dope" and poison him. At the time of the psychologic examination he was fully cooperative although his responses were sometimes circumstantial and suggested a deliberate and guarded evasiveness.

The patient's responses in the Picture-Frustration Study were of particular interest because they seemed to reflect his underlying attitudes of guilt and inferiority rather than his more hostile symptomatic behavior. An intropunitive score was assigned to 54 per cent of his responses—20 per cent higher than the median for a normal group. For example, to the picture that shows a waiter accusing a diner of being a little too fussy, the patient's reaction was, "Maybe I am—I'm sorry"; a directly hostile response is given here by most subjects. The majority of these intropunitive replies were, moreover, need-persistive in character (i) and showed an over-readiness to assume responsibility for personally solving problems. The patient's score for extrapunitiveness was, reciprocally, only 19 per cent and he exhibited a directly defensive reaction to personal criticism but once. He was similarly submissive to the restrictions imposed by the environment (high m). As a result of this rather markedly deviant record, his Group Conformity Rating was—not surprisingly—42 per cent. Such a low figure is hardly ever encountered among either normal or neurotic adults, but is frequently found among psychotics who distort social situations autistically. The P–F Study in this case penetrated to some of the deeper personality patterns which in the paranoid projections of the patient appeared as delusions of reference and of persecution.

Illustrative Protocols 3 and 4

These protocols represent a comparison between six year-old twins, a boy and a girl, who were referred by their foster mother to an out-patient clinic for problematic behavior including sexual play between them. The mother of the children had died when they were two and they had since then been living in foster homes. The father appeared to be an inadequate individual with little interest in the twins. The boy was described as the more seriously disturbed. Not only did he have a heart murmur but he was given to crying spells at night and frequently wet his bed. The speech of both children was indistinct and apparently retarded in development. On an intelligence test administered to them at the age of three, the girl had achieved an average level, the boy, a dull normal one. The most disturbing aspect of the present problem, according to the foster mother, was the sexual play and in this behavior the girl seemed to take the lead.

The psychologic examination conducted as part of the out-patient study included both intelligence and personality tests. Both children were cooperative, the boy being somewhat noisy and obstreperous in contrast to his sister's quiet and passive manner. Despite his boisterousness the boy was critical of his own performance and attempted to correct such errors as he recognized. He showed some rivalry with his twin, asking, for instance, to see her test productions and requesting that the examiner compare them with his. The girl was obviously attempting to win approval by being on her best behavior. She, too, gave evidence of competing with her twin; she inquired several times whether he was to take the same tests.

Both children tested at the dull normal level of intelligence (Stanford-Binet I. Q.'s 86 and 87). Ratings on the Goodenough Draw-A-Man Test confirmed these findings but gave indications of a somewhat higher optimal level. The drawings of the girl substantiated the history by revealing her obvious interest in sexual matters; e.g., she drew the picture of a man with an elaboration that resembled a penis (which she refused to identify for the examiner) and related the male drawing to that of the woman as boy friend and girl friend. The Rorschach method, employed with both children, showed the girl to be, in general, a better adjusted person for her age than her brother. In contrast to him she was capable of greater freedom of emotional expression and of rapport with other individuals. He, on the other hand, appeared to resort far more frequently than she to autistic passivity as a defense against anxiety.

The Children's Form of the Picture-Frustration Study was used to disclose any characteristic patterns of reaction in situations of stress— the kind of situation that must have played so great a part in the insecure lives of these children. Since they were obviously too young to write for themselves, the examiner recorded the responses they gave orally. The verbatim protocols of both subjects are reproduced below. To make comparison easier, the boy's record is given on the left side of the page, the girl's, on the right. After each item number a brief description of the situation is given in parentheses. Brackets have been employed for comments or behavior elicited during the inquiry. The score of each response follows the response itself.

1. (A girl who is reaching into a cupboard for something is being told by a woman that she gave "the last one" to the girl's brother.)

BOY	GIRL
O.K. [Feels bad—because her brother got something] E'/M/	I want the last one. [Doesn't feel bad.] / /e

2. (A girl is forbidding a boy to play with her scooter which he is riding.)

| No.   /E/ | You can't have it—I want to ride on it.   /E/ |

3. (While seated at their desks alone in a school room, a boy is explaining to a girl that he did not mean to tell on her.)

| But you did so.   /E/ | You did [mean to].   /E/ |

| BOY | GIRL |

4. (A woman is telling a boy that she does not know how to fix his truck.)

O.K. I guess I'll fix it
[with his pliers].   / /i   I might break it all up [on
                                    purpose].   /E/

5. (A man is explaining to a girl as they stand in front of a store window that if he were rich he could buy for her the doll at which they are looking.)

O.K. I guess you will
[tomorrow].   / /m   I want it now.   / /e

6. (One of two bigger boys is saying to a smaller boy that the latter is too little to play with them.)

But you-uns too big for
me to play with.   /E/   I am not—I can play.   /E/

7. (A woman is reprimanding a girl for picking her flowers.)

                                Don't you want some flowers
Oh, I am not.   /E/   in the house?   I'/ /

8. (One girl is reproaching another for having broken the former's nicest doll.)

                                It ain't yours—it's mine and
You're bad.   /E/   yours.   /E/

9. (One of two boys playing on the floor is explaining that he has won the game and that the objects on the floor are his.)

Oh yeah!   /E/   I did too.   /E/

10. (A woman is expressing regret to a girl for having to punish her.)
O.K.   /M/   I want to get up.   / /e

11. (A man is telling a boy to be quiet since Mother wants to sleep.)

                                I don't want Mother to sleep
O.K.   / /m   —I want some breakfast.   /E/e

12. (One boy is calling another a sissy.)
No, I ain't. [You are.] /E/   You're a sissy, too.   /E/

13. (A man has one of three boys by the arm and is exclaiming that this time he has caught the boy—presumably in the act of stealing fruit from the man's orchard.)

BOY   GIRL

Don't get the hammer. [Be-
cause he don't want to hit
O.K. I'll go away.   / /i   him on the head.]   /I/

14. (A man demands of a boy sitting on a chair in another room that the
boy explain what he is doing.)

I'm sitting down.
[Because he's bad.]   M'/I/   I'm sitting down.   M'/ /

15. (A woman standing at the head of some stairs is asking a boy who lies
at the bottom whether he has hurt himself.)

Yes.   E'/ /   Yes.   E'/ /

16. (A woman standing beside a young child is telling an older girl that
the baby should not have taken her ball.)

Can't say.   Unscorable   She can't play with it.   /E/

17. (Two parental figures standing beside the bed of a child explain that
they are going out and that the child will have to go to sleep.)

O.K.   / /m   No, I want to go out, too.   / /e

18. (A girl is saying to a boy that she is not going to invite him to her
birthday party.)

When he has a birthday he
O.K. [Doesn't care.] M'/ /   will ask her.   / /e;i

19. (A woman with a small boy beside her is reprimanding an older boy
for having wet his bed and accuses the latter of being more of a baby
than his little brother.)

O.K.   [i.e., he is a
baby.]   /I/   He [other brother] is a baby.   /E/

20. (A boy is apologizing to another boy for having pushed the latter's
marble by mistake.)

O.K.   /M/   I won the game.   /E/

21. (A girl on a swing is telling another girl that she is planning to keep
the swing all afternoon.)

O.K. I never give you
a turn or let her on
again.   /E/   I won't never push you.   /E/

BOY		GIRL	

22. (As a child enters a classroom the teacher states that he is late.)

It's over now [school		My mommy gave me no	
is].	I'/ /	breakfast.	/I/

23. (A woman serving a boy at a table expresses her regret that the soup is cold.)

O.K. I don't like it			
cold—I like it warm			
and it's cold.	E'/ /	I don't care.	M'/ /

24. (A librarian is telling a boy that his hands are not clean and that he must wash them before he can take a book.)

O.K.	/ /m	I won't take a book or he	
		won't wash his hands.	/E/

Even without formal scoring or interpretation the differences in the personalities of these twins are unmistakably evident from the protocols. As is apparent from the recorded scores, the responses of the boy were significantly less extrapunitive than were those of the girl. While her extrapunitive percentage was 77, his was only 43. As compared to the norms for children of six, her score was markedly elevated, his was slightly low. While both the intropunitive and impunitive scores of the girl were low (15 per cent and 8 per cent, respectively), the brother had a normal intropunitive percentage (22 per cent) but a significantly elevated impunitive score (35 per cent). Even from these incomplete findings it would appear that the twins contrasted sharply in their aggressive reactions to frustration, the boy being characteristically submissive and conforming, the girl more overtly aggressive and hostile. The scores of both subjects for the various types of reaction (O–D, E–D and N–P) conformed closely to the expected levels for six year-olds.

There was little of interest in the sequence of the several responses in the girl's record except for one trend toward obstacle-dominance which was not highly significant. The boy's record, on the other hand, showed several mutually interdependent trends in keeping with the rest of the protocol. He moved significantly away from extra-punitiveness (giving evidence of E in 8 of his first 12 responses but in only 3 of his second 12 responses) and toward intropunitiveness. The Group Conformity Ratings provided further evidence of the children's maladjustment. The boy's GCR percentage was 50, the girl's, 54; both lower than the expected mean of 60 per cent for the age range in question, with the brother's deviation from the norm being more marked. In general, it appeared that the girl was more capable of conventional responses in stressful social situations and would therefore probably be, at least superficially, better adjusted.

The findings of the Picture-Frustration Study were obviously in good agreement with the social history and with the results of the other personality tests, especially the Rorschach. The overtly aggressive girl would more naturally be the instigator in the sexual play with her brother. The boy's maladjustment was, again as reported, presumably the more serious because he was withdrawing from the hostility of his world as he saw it. His sister was more capable of aggressively defending herself. The source of their over-developed sexual interest is perhaps to be found in the loneliness and insecurity which they felt and which therefore heightened their interest in and need for each other. While this conjecture is not specifically derived from the test results, and certainly not from the P–F Study, what can be reliably inferred is the difference between the twins in patterns of self-protection and in the roles they assumed in the sexual play which distressed their foster mother.

REFERENCES

General

Bell, J. E. Projective Techniques. New York: Longmans, Green, 1948.
*Frank, L. K. Projective Methods. Springfield: Charles C Thomas, 1947.
Rosenzweig, S. Projective methods in psychodiagnosis. Encyclopaedia Britannica, in press.

Word Association Method

Galton, F. Psychometric experiments. *Brain,* 1879–1880, 2, 149–162.

Jung, C. G. Studies in Word-Association. London: Heinemann, 1918.

Kent, G. H., and Rosanoff, A. J. A study of association in insanity. *Amer. J. Insanity,* 1910, 67, 37–96; 317–390.

O'Connor, J. Born That Way. Baltimore: Williams and Wilkins, 1928.

Rapaport, D., et al. Diagnostic Psychological Testing. Vol. II. Chicago: Year Book Publishers, 1946.

Rorschach Method of Personality Diagnosis

Beck, S. J. Rorschach's Test. Vols. I and II. New York: Grune and Stratton, 1944 and 1946.

*Klopfer, B., and Kelley, D. The Rorschach Technique. Yonkers-On-Hudson: World Book, 1946.

Rorschach, H. Psychodiagnostics. Berne: Huber, 1932. English translation by P. Lemkau and B. Kronenberg. New York: Grune and Stratton (distr.), 1942.

Thematic Apperception Test

Morgan, C. D., and Murray, H. A. A method for investigating fantasies: the Thematic Apperception Test. *Arch. Neurol. Psychiat.,* 1935, 34, 289–306.

Murray, H. A., et al. Explorations in Personality. Chap. 6, Section 18, 530–545. New York: Oxford University Press, 1938.

Murray, H. A. Thematic Apperception Test. Cambridge: Harvard University Press, 1943.

Stein, M. The Thematic Apperception Test. Cambridge: Addison-Wesley, 1948.

*Tomkins, S. S. The Thematic Apperception Test. New York: Grune and Stratton, 1947.

The World Test

Buehler, C., and Kelly, G. Manual for the World Test. New York: Psychological Corporation, 1941.

Lowenfeld, M. The world pictures of children: a method of recording and studying them. *Brit. J. med. Psychol.,* 1939, 18, 65–101

Rosenzweig Picture-Frustration Study

Rosenzweig, S. The picture-association method and its application in a study of reactions to frustration. *J. Personality,* 1945, 14, 3–23.

Rosenzweig, S., Fleming, E. E., and Clarke, H. J. Revised scoring manual for the Rosenzweig Picture-Frustration Study. *J. Psychol.,* 1947, 24, 165–208.

Rosenzweig, S., Fleming, E. E., and Rosenzweig, L. The Children's Form of the Rosenzweig Picture-Frustration Study. *J. Psychol.,* 1948, 26, 141–191.

Part Three
THE PROCESS OF
PSYCHODIAGNOSTIC INTEGRATION

Chapter 8

The Picture of the Individual

THE PERSON under psychologic examination is practically never studied by the psychodiagnostician through the use of one test alone. Ordinarily, two, three or more instruments are employed and, in any event, data from social history, psychiatric study and other avenues of observation and understanding are included. It thus becomes a matter of obvious importance to consider the manner in which findings from various sources are integrated in psychodiagnosis. Since such integration is accomplished hand in hand with the writing of the report of the psychologic examination, the two problems will be jointly discussed in this chapter and illustrated in those that follow.

As has been indicated earlier, the effort will be made to present several cases in which various tests were employed with the same subject. The actual responses elicited by each test will be exhibited, scoring and interpretation described, and the basis for the selection of succeeding tests stated. The cumulative impact of the evidence will be sketched so that the reader can obtain a more intimate understanding of how the picture of the personality emerges—in particular, how the various instruments contribute from one direction or another to yield the final picture. Three cases representatively different in type will be treated in this fashion. They have been selected chiefly to illustrate the variety of available tests, secondarily, the variety of subjects on whom examinations are made.

In the consideration of the psychologic report, it is necessary to note at the outset that there is no one binding method universally employed. The purpose of the report will naturally determine to a large extent its nature. In every instance, however, the writer attempts to bear in mind who his reader will be—whether other psychologists, physicians, social workers, teachers, or laymen. In the reports that are to be presented here, the readers in question were ordinarily expected to be workers in the field of mental health. In essence, however, the audience does not make a crucial difference if the psychologist bears in mind—as he must—that few individuals without specific training in clinical psychology are capable of deriving much benefit from a report couched in scientific jargon.

The reporting of psychologic findings by the psychologist to his colleagues allows for many degrees of aptness. Whether these reports are made orally or in writing, technical language should, wherever possible, be avoided. Occasionally the insecure psychologist hides behind the technical expressions afforded by a particular test as a way of escaping translations and interpretations which would put him on his mettle. In adequate practice the examiner has mastered the instruments he uses so that he can clothe the raw findings of an individual test in the context of the patient's total examination behavior and of the social and psychiatric studies wherever these are available.

In the body of the report, *behavior* in the examining situation is discussed first. Generally a paragraph will cover some or all of the following points: (1) *General cooperation.* Was the subject capable of test cooperation; was he preoccupied and withdrawn, confused, only partially aware of his surroundings and of the questions put to him? (2) *Attitude toward tests and examiner.* Was he hostile, or eager to please? Did he think the tests were childish and silly, a necessary duty, or an enjoyable activity? (3) *Comprehension of the demands of the situation.* How well did he grasp instructions? Was he suggestible?

(4) *Productivity while working.* Was he highly productive, and, if so, were his productions relevant to the tests or concerned with his own problems and ideas? Was his direction of attention good; was he easily distracted; was his effort well sustained for fairly long periods? Was there any abnormality of tempo which might have affected his performance on timed tests? (5) *Emotional expression.* What was his general emotional tone, degree of anxiety and tension? Under what conditions were these manifest? Was emotional expression suitable to the situation or inappropriate? (6) *Special handicaps.* Were there any special defects, e.g., visual or hearing disturbance, speech disorder, or motor disturbance? (7) *Appreciation of own performance.* What was his reaction to difficulty and failure? How self-critical was he? Did he recognize inferior performance as such? What was his response to encouragement?

The answers to the foregoing questions will help in the important decisions that the clinical psychologist is required to make regarding the *representativeness* of the results he obtains in the examination. There is a considerable range of difference among patients in this regard. The results may, on the one hand, represent the best of which the subject is capable at the period of the examination. On the other hand, there may be interferences associated with the mental illness itself which, while they definitely lower the intellectual findings, do not invalidate the representativeness of the examination. Interferences of an extrinsic and transient nature, however, make the results unrepresentative and indicate retesting under better conditions. A cold or a headache may serve as examples. In terms of the history of the individual the *optimity* * of the test results needs also to be taken into account. Optimal performance is that which represents the best of which the patient has ever been capable. If, however, there has been permanent mental impairment, such as might follow cerebral injury, the test results in respect to the capacity displayed are not optimal

* The term is from the usage of the Psychology Laboratory of the Worcester State Hospital and was introduced by David Shakow.

even though the likelihood is that the patient will never again reach any higher level. This latter criterion applies, obviously, more to intellectual than to personality factors.

In presenting the *results* of the formal examination, it is advisable to avoid a discussion of the separate tests seriatim. The report should be written from the point of view of the *individual patient,* not of the *individual tests.* Since the aim is to disclose him as a unique and integrated personality, the natural divisions of the report correspond to the different spheres of the subject's abilities and traits, material being derived from any and all tests as indicated.

Intellectual factors are profitably considered first. This section ordinarily includes a statement of the patient's position with reference to the general population, especially in the broad areas in which he rates notably high or low. Specific abilities and disabilities are noted, reference being made to everyday tasks that might involve the ability under consideration. An effort is also made to depict the pattern of abilities and disabilities occurring within the individual, regardless of his relative rank in the population, and this pattern is related to the clinical picture if a basis offers itself.

Material included in this section will be drawn largely from tests of general intelligence and from any special tests for intellectual efficiency. Sometimes vocational aptitude tests may be included. However, certain of the tests designed primarily to evaluate personality, e.g., the Rorschach, also provide direct evidence of intelligence; and in any event, the effects of motivation and emotion upon intellectual functions must be taken into account.

Personality factors may be similarly considered in the next division of the report. The data here will derive primarily from "personality tests," of both the inventory and projective types. Qualitative observation of the subject's behavior in the examining situation offers an important source of supplementary data.

The *integration of findings* from the various examination procedures and from other observation represents the distinctive task of the psychodiagnostician. While the psychometrician may be able to administer, score and statistically interpret data from one test device and thus place the subject in relation to other members of a population, the highest degree of clinical skill is required for marshalling the evidence from all available sources into an integrated picture of the functioning individual. Such interpretation requires not only a knowledge of the several test instruments but an understanding of personality dynamics—the principles in terms of which the person expresses his capacities, needs and traits at various levels of organization—and the ability to comprehend in terms of such principles the syntax and semantics of the individual as these emerge from the subject's every psychologic expression. In such a framework every act or statement of the person can be construed to yield an understanding of him; and the incidental examination behavior as well as the more formal test findings fall into place according to the psychodynamics of personality through which all individual expression is mediated.

Under the circumstances described, it is obviously impossible to expound any set of rules or even principles which will assure the accomplishment of an integrated understanding of the individual subject. It may, however, be briefly indicated how the psychologist, operating with the assumed special aptitudes, knowledge and experience, ordinarily attempts, explicitly or implicitly, to fit together his observations in a psychologic report. Taking it for granted that all expressions of the personality are, if properly understood, meaningfully related to each other, the interpreter attempts to single out the cardinal strengths and weaknesses, drives and interests, attitudes and symptoms in terms of which the various manifestations of the person seem to be most significantly oriented. To arrive at such basic axes of the personality considerable cogitative experimentation is required in every case analysis. One hypothesis as to these cardinal forces or facets may be adopted, tried, found wanting or corroborated up to a certain point; then dropped, perhaps, in favor of some other hypothesis which must in turn be subjected to similar experimental manipulation. The process demands time and persistence as well as skill. Without the weighing and balancing of one finding against another and of both against some third or fourth aspect of the behavior, repeatedly and patiently, the process of insightful comprehension demanded of the clinician cannot be achieved. In this context it may be decided to employ some previously unconsidered test or other mode of observation as a basis for checking an hypothesis that has emerged. Thus every individual subject becomes a research project in his own right.

The method of interpretation outlined may with certain advantages be designated that of the *minimum hypothesis*. The picture of the subject that will in the end be embodied in the psychologic report must account for the largest number of possible observations and facts in terms of the smallest number of underlying or explanatory variables. When two alternative interpretations are in competition, the foregoing statement provides the only currently accepted basis for deciding between them. Such an approach, while not explicit in the textbooks, is implicit in the actual work of every psychodynamic clinician.

From the present standpoint it is easy to recognize the importance to the psychologist of all sources of knowledge concerning the patient. While examination procedures offer many advantages in terms of standardized test situations, population norms and diagnostic syndromes, an adequate interpretation of the person will equally be served by the incidental observations in the test situation, by data from the psychiatric interviews, the social history, and nurses' notes—to say nothing of the principles represented in the current theoretical knowledge of behavior and personality. "Blind psychodiagnosis," although useful for some experimental purposes, becomes from this frame of reference irrelevant to the clinician's function. Instead he seeks every advantage that available data afford. He expends his energy not in blind fortune-telling but in achieving insight which, on the clinical-experimental basis of interpretation, will explain the maximum number of facts with the minimum number of assumptions and yet not sacrifice the individuality of the person to over-simplification.

When the necessary integration has been accomplished, it becomes possible not only to write more adequately the portions of the report already outlined but to prepare a brief section of *Summary and Con-*

clusions. In this final part the salient points of the preceding discussion are recapitulated and perhaps further digested. Recommendations are, wherever reasonably possible, also included, with particular reference to the problems posed by the patient for the psychiatrist, social worker, nurse, teacher or parent. The omission of such suggestions by the examiner is more often a reflection of incompetence than of humility since humility belongs at the starting point rather than at the terminal point of the psychologist's activities.

Chapter 9

A Young Woman with Anxieties Concerning Adult Status

A TWENTY year-old girl sought the help of an out-patient mental health clinic because she was concerned and confused about her personal adjustment. She was preoccupied with her relationship to her fiance, especially in its sexual aspects. She was depressed and constantly fearful and felt "all mixed up." Little things unduly upset her and her condition was reducing the efficiency of her work.

The patient was the youngest of three children. Her brother, seven years older, and her sister, five years older, were both married. She had never felt especially close to either of them, even in childhood. When she was only two her father left the home. The patient did not realize until adolescence that the separation had been preceded by infidelity on his part. When she made this discovery the patient felt very sorry for her mother, who apparently had had a "nervous breakdown" at the time of the separation and was characteristically a tense and excitable person. There was a close attachment between the girl and her mother.

The patient met her fiance when she was 17 and a junior at high school. He then went into military service and was away for almost two years. During this interval she completed high school and one year of college. She had a good scholastic record but was dissatisfied with her college life and decided that she would rather work. Accordingly she obtained a clerical position in a large manufacturing company and was still maintaining an acceptable adjustment there despite her concern about being less efficient in her work.

Since her fiance's return from overseas, she had been having an intimate sexual relationship with him. The experience had not been especially satisfying to her physically but it gave her marked emotional satisfaction to know that he wanted and depended on her. She expressed this feeling in the statement, "I want to possess a man." At the same time she was beset with guilt over the relationship since she was, in general, quite rigid in her moral standards. She was, for instance, likely to be disturbed by any vulgarity or jokes with sexual reference that might be told in her presence. She was now beginning to be uncertain that she really wanted to be married, and it was in this state of hesitancy, anxiety and confusion that she came for help.

Her early psychiatric interviews were devoted to repetitive statements of her feelings about the present situation; she seemed resistive to discussing the underlying experiences and relationships that might have prepared the ground for her present reactions and disturbance. A psychologic examination was therefore included as a possible means of tapping these sources without having to interrupt the cathartic relief afforded by the therapeutic sessions.

The girl's reaction to the examination was marked by a cooperative recognition of its purpose and a tense determination to do well in any procedure related to her treatment. She worked with undiminished effort and interest for several hours, preferring to complete the test battery in one session.

1. Shipley-Hartford Retreat Scale

The patient's academic record indicated that she had superior intellectual endowment. Furthermore, her employment history revealed no essential reduction in her efficiency even though she was subjectively aware of some difficulty in keeping up with her work. It was therefore decided to check her mental level and efficiency by use of the brief Shipley-Hartford Retreat Scale and to reserve for later any more intensive intellectual examination that might prove necessary.

a. Protocol. The patient wrote her responses promptly, manifesting easy comprehension of the instructions. She gave 31 correct answers to the Vocabulary items and thus earned a vocabulary age-equivalent of 17.4 years. Her errors involved only one item in addition to the eight at the end—a group which was apparently beyond her capacity range. She was unfamiliar with the following words: *mollify, plagiarize, orifice, querulous, pariah, abet, temerity,* and *pristine.* She left two items of the Abstraction test unanswered and made one incorrect response. On all other items she earned credit and obtained an abstraction age-equivalent of 18.1 years. Her Conceptual Quotient—the ratio between these two scores—was thus 103. Her total mental age rating was 17.9 years.

b. *Significant Results and Leads.* These results confirmed the earlier assumption that this girl had superior intellectual capacity which was not notably impaired. The majority of normal subjects have Conceptual Quotients over 90; her performance was therefore not atypical. However, the authors of the test issue the caution that scores above 90 do not necessarily signify mental normality and that high quotients may co-exist with emotional maladjustments. It was, therefore, considered advisable to devote the remainder of the examination battery primarily to the evaluation of personality since intellectual difficulties were clearly of secondary importance in this case.

2. *Rorschach Method*

This technic was used first in the exploration of the patient's reaction patterns because its breadth and flexibility permit it to highlight a wide variety of facets for further study. It is therefore especially valuable for isolating areas of possible difficulty or conflict in the personality.

a. *Protocol*

Response	Inquiry	Score
I 1. (10″) These look like hands in gloves.	They look like mittens.	d F Hd*

* The Rorschach scoring categories for which these letter-symbols stand have been indicated in Chapter 7. Further brief identification is provided in the summary tabulation at the end of this verbatim record.

Response	*Inquiry*	*Score*
2. This looks like legs, calves, and hips of a nude woman here.		D F Hd
3. Looks like she's standing behind the figure of a large buxom woman who has two heads. Can't see her head (referring to #2), just to waist.	Perspective, really behind, maybe it's the coloring.	D M,FK H
4. Looks like they're standing in a gully, a division of rock. (165″).	The balance of the thing. Standing right in between, as though this were a height, up at a great distance.	W FK Na
II 5. (20″) Looks like two people to me again, sitting with their legs touching and their hands with palms flat together.		W M,Fc,CF H
6. Somehow reminds me of blood, must be the color red. Looks as though it's very exact and solid.	That's why it looks raw, has something to do with the people. They're sort of peeled.	D C Bl
5.* They look like		

* It should be noted in explanation of the duplicate numbering of this response (and similar ones below) that the association in question represents an alternative to one already given. Such a response is not again scored. In the event that a subject continues a previous association after an interruption, the additional aspects are scored under the original response.

Response	*Inquiry*	*Score*
they're in furs or some very heavy material. Red like raw skin. Can see some part of bodies underneath fur cape. (130″).		
III 7. (5″) These look like two people; looks as though they're trying to catch—holding on iron pot. Must be very heavy. Stooped over and stretching a w a y from each other.	Here's the roundness of the oval of the pot. Round like a kettle. And the color perhaps.	W M,FC′ H P
8. The figure above the kettle reminds me of a tooth bridge. I can see two teeth in it.	Two teeth and the color of the gums.	D FC At
9. These o t h e r things look like m u s c l e s. That color looks very much like blood to me.	This is like a ligament.	Dd FC At
10. Maybe like a heart or something. (130″).	Heart and vessel leading to it.	D FC At
IV I don't know. Nothing. (130″).		
	Add: a) Two people— have hats on, kneeling. Leg or tail here.	(D M H)

Response	Inquiry	Score
	b) Two eyes here, though I don't know what on. Like cow's eyes, real gentle and soft.	(Dd F Ad)
	c) They're both joined onto something (referring to figures in *a*) like a growth or something, looks actually like part of the body.	(Dd F– At)
	d) This looks like opening into the vagina.	(d F Sex)
	e) Standing right above that would be ananother nude body. Neither man nor woman particularly.	(Dd F H)
V 11. (20″) I see two nude women, their faces up here. They look youthful. Looks like lying on their side. They're joined to something in the middle. Perhaps	This is too large for a bust and would have to be folded arms. And calf is too muscular for a woman's. Looks more like tails. Looks like sheepskin over their back, soft and fuzzy.	W M,Fc H

Response	Inquiry	Score
a man. Calf or lower part of leg over here.		
12. Man's top hat, one of those round ones, and face and shoulders.	Head and shoulder outline.	d F Hd
11. Perhaps those aren't women, perhaps they're boys like shepherd boys or Pan—that have a tail, I think. They have curly hair, both of them. (150″).	Don't know if boys are connected or not.	
VI 13. (12″) I see a bed-post. Looks just like one of the ones we have.	If there's a little light, it makes the round part shine.	D Fc Obj
14. Looks like feathers around it. The rest just looks like background. (85″).	Dark tips on the end, and the white and gray.	D FC′ A Obj
VII 15. (15″) I see two people leering at each other and their bodies are joined at the bottom, arms thrust backward. I don't k n o w whether they don't want to meet the whole way or they're trying but they're off balance. (75″).	Heads and chin jutted out, arm thrown backward grotesquely. Here is the breast, but chest looks caved in, stomach projected. Here they're joined. Maybe grown together like the other impression.	W M,m H

Response	Inquiry	Score
VIII 16. (40") I see two beings, I don't know whether animals or people. They're holding onto an arm.	More like animals. They have short legs; maybe something like a mole.	D FM A P
17. Sort of a disconnected thing (arm).	Arm goes clear up here. Whole arm. Holding them there. They look safe.	Dd M Hd
16. They're balanced on some sort of a stand as though they're climbing. Each one has a foot uplifted.	Here is rocky partition they're standing on, on top of something. Looks like height.	
18. I see two other little hands, too. (115").	Here. Just shape. And two molars. They go in in the middle like a single tooth.	S F Hd (S F At)
IX 19. (55") I see a face, eyes, nostrils, and neck, and breast, and hands.	This seems like a nipple here and here, and the hands look raw.	DdS F–,FC Hd
20. Then I see— seems like reindeer on the top, looking upward.		D FM Ad
21. Two pigs below them.		D F Ad
19. The face and the body are behind all those. (150").		
	Sex organs, female here and male here right	(Dd F– Sex)

Response	*Inquiry*	*Score*
	above it. Hands on either side on the breasts. The face doesn't go with it. The body part looks normal but not the face.	
X 22. (15″) I see, I guess, scorpions, black ones.	Their feelers are reaching up; they're standing on end.	D FM A
23. And two blue bugs of some sort.	Spiders or crabs or something like that.	D F A P
24. Two faces again, looks like there's two growths on their chins and chests. Reaching out. Joined together.	On their chests about this thing—whatever it is—that's grown there. Looks more like tissue than like something solid.	Dd F,cF Hd
25. I see two penises here in the green, and they're joined together by a face.	Impression of being joined together, or at least going toward one another. Not going down, going up. They'd be joined down here. They seem to be more important when they're standing up than in any other position.	D Fm Sex
26. Two women here, as though they're falling, with hair high above head and arms outstretched.		D M H
27. This looks like a mask here that joins the two penises.		D F (Hd)

Response	Inquiry	Score
28. This looks like a lot of muscle, like in anatomy books. Vivid colors.	These long things like veins or something. More the structure than the color.	D FC At
29. I see two people, too, two yellow people. They're going upward. (270″).	Two men. Dark part is hair.	D Fm– H

The essential features of this record as analyzed by scoring categories may be tabulated as follows:

Total number of responses:			29+7
Location:	Whole	(W)	5
	Large usual detail	(D)	17+1
	Small usual detail	(d)	2+1
	Unusual detail	(Dd)	4+4
	White space	(S)	1+2
Determinants:	Human movement	(M)	7+1
	Animal movement	(FM)	3
	Inanimate movement	(m)	2+1
	Shading as perspective (vista)	(FK)	1+1
	Form	(F)	9+6 (31%)
	Form with texture secondary	(Fc)	1+2
	Texture with form secondary	(cF)	+1
	Achromatic color	(C′)	1+1
	Form with color secondary	(FC)	4+1
	Color with form secondary	(CF)	+1
	Pure color	(C)	1
Content:	Whole human figure	(H)	7+2
	Part of human figure	(Hd)	8
	Whole animal figure	(A)	3 ⎫ (17%)
	Part of animal figure	(Ad)	2+1 ⎭
	Anatomy and sex	(At & Sex)	5+4
	Blood	(Bl)	1

Nature	(Na)	1
Object	(Obj)	1
Animal object	(A Obj)	1

Popular Responses: 3

Ratio of human movement
  to color: (M:ΣC)   7:3.5
    (Experience balance)

Ratio of other movement to
  surface shading: (FM+m: Fc+c+C')   5:2

Proportion of total responses found on last three cards: 45%

Aver. first reaction time to gray cards: 14″

Aver. first reaction time to colored cards: 27″

Ratio of whole to part
  human and animal figures: (H+A: Hd+Ad)   10:10

b. *Significant Results and Leads*

(1) The subject is very readily stimulated by environmental and emotional impacts (45 per cent of responses on last 3 cards), but uses these contacts to nourish her autistic, inner life (M = twice C); most of these emotional responses are probably of sexual import (color responses with anatomical content).

(2) Emotional repression (inhibition) is indicated by the lack of animal forms and animal movement (low A%; FM much lower than M).

(3) Capacity for intellectual control of impulse is relatively weak (F% = 31); in substitution she has resorted to the safer expression of emotion in fantasy with resultantly poor integration between drives and overt behavior.

(4) Marked concern over social acceptance and about adequacy in an adult role may be inferred (H% unusually high; human forms seen critically with too many Hd for H).

(5) She shows poor participation in everyday modes of thought (only 3 P) and some indulgence in being "different" (Dd's).

(6) Features of the response content besides the anatomical (concern over "growths" in two instances, followed by sexual content; hesitancy in deciding upon the sex of figures—as in #11, and in IV, add. e) confirm the importance of the sexual problem.

(7) The general quality of the record—rich perceptions and elaborations, including the presence of blended determinants—support the earlier assumption of superior intelligence.

(8) There are no evidences of malignant disturbance or severe psychiatric disorder; the record, rather, has features indicative of psychoneurosis occurring in a person of somewhat schizoid personality structure.

3. Rosenzweig Picture-Frustration Study

This technic was introduced because the Rorschach had suggested that the patient's complaints were largely in the realm of interpersonal relationships, doubts of her own social adequacy, and suppression of direct emotional outlets. It was judged that observation of reactions to frustration might provide further clarification of these patterns.

a. Protocol

Situation No.	Response	Score
1.	Oh, that's all right.	/M/
2.	Oh, what will she think of me.	I'/ /
3.	Let's move.	/ /i
4.	It wasn't your fault.	/M/
5.	I hope that we can fix it successfully this time.	/ /i
6.	I'm sorry. I didn't know.	/I/
7.	I don't think so.	/E/
8.	Oh, did she?	E'/ /
9.	Well, thank you.	/M/
10.	I certainly am not.	/E/
11.	That's all right. Goodbye.	/M/
12.	I'll get it tomorrow.	/ /i
13.	Oh. When will it be possible?	/ /m

Situation

No.	*Response*	*Score*
14.	Oh, how I love cold weather!	E′/ /
15.	Everyone does.	/M/
16.	I guess I wasn't thinking.	/I/
17.	Well, I didn't mean to.	/Ī/
18.	Oh.	E′/ /
19.	I'm sorry officer.	/I/
20.	She's probably jealous.	/E/
21.	I wasn't trying to be malicious.	/E/
22.	No. I'm all right.	Ī/ /
23.	Oh hell.	E′/ /
24.	Oh, that's all right.	/M/

The condensed record blank follows:

	O–D	E–D	N–P	Total	%
E	4	4	0	8	33
I	2	4	3	9	38
M	0	6	1	7	29
Total	6	14	4		
%	25	58	17		
GCR: 58%					

b. *Significant Results and Leads*

(1) She tends to avoid the direct expression of hostility (E per cent at first quartile for normal female group)—a result in keeping with her feelings of personal insecurity.

(2) As frustration continues, she is apt to be pushed by her suppressed aggression toward a more direct expression of it (trend away from M and toward E′ and I) but she still is not characteristically extrapunitive.

(3) While she has marked self-doubts (elevated I per cent), she is extremely sensitive to direct or implied criticism from others, and becomes defensive ($\underline{E} + \underline{I} = 25$ per cent; this figure is high).

(4) She makes few direct demands for help (no "e" responses); is likely to assume responsibility herself, act as if no fault exists, or accept events as an unfortunate but unavoidable burden (high I and E' per cent). These findings agree with the expectations for one who has not felt close to or secure with others (indicated by her history and Rorschach results).

(5) Her reactions are determined by personal needs and problems to a degree that involves some departure from the usual social patterns in reacting to everyday stress (GCR low, with confirmation of low P on Rorschach).

4. *Minnesota Multiphasic Personality Inventory*

This instrument was selected as the final one for inclusion in the test battery since it affords, in addition to its other merits, opportunity to determine the patient's subjective attitudes toward herself and her problems.

a. *Protocol*

She sorted the cards rapidly, not appearing to experience much doubt or hesitancy about the nature of her responses. When her choices were scored according to the established norms, the subject's standard scores on the various scales were as follows:

Hypochondriasis	64	Validating scales	
Depression	84	?	50
Hysteria	68	L	53
Psychopathic deviance	69	K	44
Masculinity	57	F	70
Paranoia	62		
Psychasthenia	74		
Schizophrenia	84		
Hypomania	45		

b. *Significant Results and Leads*

(1) It should first be noted that all the validating scales except K are within the normal range. The K score of 44 is, however, significantly low and raises the question of symptom-exaggeration.

(2) Deviant scores (T-score above 70) occur on the scales for Depression, Psychasthenia and Schizophrenia. Although the content of a few responses (e.g., that people can read her mind, they look at her critically, she hears strange sounds when she is alone, things sometimes seem not to be real) might lead to the interpretation that the high Schizophrenia score represents a true psychotic illness, other factors contraindicate such a conclusion for the present. The simpler and more probable explanation that hers is a neurotic reaction occurring in a highly schizoid type of person is based on the following observations:

(a) The K score, as already noted, is significantly low and implies possible exaggeration of symptoms through self-preoccupation.

(b) The majority of the T-scale scores are within the normal range; most psychotic individuals exhibit extensive distortion in other scales and have more elevated standard scores in general.

(c) The deviations associated with the high Schizophrenia score relate to depression and fear—a not uncommon setting for less malignant withdrawal and self-absorption.

(d) It is an accepted view that rather extreme emotional upset and florid symptomatology, which at any other age would necessarily indicate more malignant disturbance, may appear in the adolescent period. The patient's problems might be interpreted as belonging to "late adolescence."

(e) The other tests of the battery, especially the Rorschach, had led to a similar interpretation.

(3) The content of the responses served to confirm many of the conclusions and impressions derived from the projective technics.

(a) *Lack of security in social or personal relationships, absence of warmth or intensity in family ties* (as suggested in P–F and

Rorschach): Little love or companionship in family, quarrels, no one understands her, people disappoint her; shyness, over-sensitivity, criticism or scolding hurts her terribly; feels lonely even when with people.

(b) *Sexual concerns and guilt* (denial of drives already evidenced clearly in Rorschach): worried about sex matters, dreams and thoughts about sex, something wrong with sex organs, unusual sex practices; habits too bad to correct, bad thoughts run through mind.

(c) *Active fantasy life* (suggested in Rorschach): likes love stories and romantic themes; would rather daydream than do anything else.

(d) *Underlying aggression toward social world* (especially suggested in P–F): mistrust of other people's motives, would not feel bad if family were in trouble with law, would enjoy beating crook at own game, resents being taken in cleverly, easily becomes impatient with people.

From the significant results and leads that were afforded by the foregoing tests, a report in which the findings were combined on the *minimum hypothesis* basis was prepared.

REPORT OF PSYCHOLOGIC EXAMINATION

Behavior: The patient was a pleasant, cooperative girl who was very tense in her approach to the tests, perhaps because she was so determined to do well. She worked for several hours without observable reduction in interest or energy. Test results are considered to be entirely representative of her level and mode of functioning.

Intellectual Factors: Since the patient's educational and vocational histories indicated that she must have had better than average endowment, only a brief survey of her intellectual capacity and efficiency was made. Her vocabulary is rated at a superior level and her ability to analyze and reason abstractly is at a comparable one. She is thus well within the normal range for intellectual efficiency. While it is true that her personal concerns and needs sometimes interfere with her making the usually accepted interpretations of events, such interference is not apparent in relatively objective, impersonal problems.

Personality Factors: This girl is easily stimulated by the events and relationships of her environment but she cannot accept or integrate these experiences; they thus become tension-provoking. To relieve her discomfort she uses her personal contacts to nourish an autistic inner life which denies practical reality and fosters the unusual and different. She is so insecure and unsure of her status in her relations to other individuals that she avoids direct expression of hostility when she is thwarted. She is similarly afraid to make any direct demands for help. She is likely to attribute failure to her own weakness or to take the attitude that she is the victim of an unfortunate fate. While she is ready to blame herself, she cannot accept criticism from others and is over-ready with denials and excuses for her actions. Her hostilities hence find release in a rather diffuse rejection of personal ties. Because personal relationships are intrinsically threatening to her, frustration tolerance in social situations is low. She does not feel comfortable with others, has thought that she would enjoy hurting those whom she loves, considers herself less happy than most, and would rather sit by herself and daydream than do anything else.

Her excessive concern with sexual matters is readily apparent. Her thinking becomes increasingly inaccurate and unrealistic when she is preoccupied in this sphere. Although she is generally able to meet the demands of social adjustment in her own limited way, there are occasional "breaks" in which primitive, uncontrolled affect is displayed. It is evident that the basic problem with which this girl is struggling relates to the acceptance of her impulses and drives (primarily sexual and aggressive) as a healthy, organized feature of her larger social responsiveness, with a resultant lack of capacity to feel secure in other interpersonal relationships. The content of some of her test productions, in which she expressed uncertainty over the sexuality of figures and concern over unexplainable "growths," indicates the possible presence of some latent homosexual conflict.

Her responses to the personality questionnaire cluster about ideas of unworthiness and inadequacy. This depressive quality is coupled with markedly schizoid features. She stated that things do not always seem real, that she hears strange sounds when she is alone, that she is sure other people can tell what she is thinking, and that strangers look at her critically. On the whole, however, it appears unlikely that she is suffering from any psychotic disorder; in view of her general degree of integration and the postadolescent nature of her problems, it seems rather that she has a psychoneurotic disturbance on the background of a highly schizoid personality structure.

Summary and Conclusions: The patient appears to be of better than average intelligence. Her problems do not interfere with efficient intellectual functioning as long as her specific areas of concern and preoccupations are not involved. She is threatened and made insecure by interpersonal relationships. She is likely to adopt the attitude that her difficulties are her own fault but resents similar implied criticism from anyone else. Being so absorbed in doubts about her personal status, she is over-responsive to social stimulation and relationships; she can handle such contacts only by reorganizing them on an autistic basis at the sacrifice of practical reality and in favor of the unusual and different. Excessive concern with sexual matters is apparent and in this context her thinking becomes less realistic and less accurate. Her fundamental problem centers in her inability to accept her impulses and drives as a healthy, organized aspect of her larger social responsiveness. In this respect she resembles the adolescent who is attempting to make the transition to adult roles and responsibilities. However, she has several traits and attitudes that are characteristically schizoid and, while the over-all picture conveyed by the tests is that of a psychoneurotic disturbance, these schizoid aspects may have some bearing on the type of therapy that she can safely tolerate.

Chapter 10

A Child with Problems of Post-Encephalitic Origin

A YOUNG girl, the elder of two siblings, whose behavior and adjustment had offered no special cause for concern contracted measles at the age of nine and a half. Her illness was uneventful for the first week but she then developed a very high fever, was comatose and had to be fed intravenously. She was hospitalized for eleven days and returned home as soon as her acute symptoms had subsided. It was then that she was noted to be restless, irritable, agitated, worried over trivialities and readily moved to tears. These features were regarded as an abrupt departure from her customary behavior. A neuropsychiatric consultation about a month after the phase of her illness that was characterized by fever and coma brought up the possibility of encephalitis. She was therefore admitted to a hospital for observation during her convalescent period.

Psychologic testing was initiated shortly after her admission to aid in the general evaluation of her behavior and illness. Comparison with the results of a later re-examination in the course of her recovery was also anticipated. Both organic and emotional factors were to be considered. If her poorly controlled reactions were to be attributed directly to the encephalitic process, it was desirable to estimate whether and to what extent the changes were either acute and transient or chronic and permanent. It was also considered important to evaluate the possible traumatic effect of her sudden hospitalization.

The patient entered actively into the psychologic tasks set for her. However, she was readily distracted both by environmental stimulation and by her own ideas. Frequently she interrupted her performance to discuss completely irrelevant matters. While her initial approach to problems seemed to be systematic and well-planned, little concentration or effort was exerted when she encountered more difficult and perplexing tasks. As she became increasingly restless and overactive, she asked repeatedly to be returned to the ward, maintaining that she was too weak to participate in "the games." She became tearful and sullen when an attempt was made to discuss family relationships with her.

To measure the child's intellectual level the Stanford-Binet Intelligence Scale was selected as the first instrument since it is the best available test of its kind for young subjects and readily allows, by the nature of its administration, for the establishment of rapport.

1. *Revised Stanford-Binet Intelligence Scale, Form L*

a. *Protocol*

Year VI: Complete success. *Basal age of 6—0.*

Year VII: Succeeded in identifying absurd elements of pictures, in copying a diamond form, and in supplying an opposite analogy in an incomplete sentence. *Failed* to point out similarities between *apple* and *peach* ("A peach is more delicate than an apple; peach has a 'p', 'e', and 'a' in it."), *ship* and *automobile* ("Ship slower than auto"), and *iron* and *silver* ("Silver prettier than iron"). Unable to repeat five digits correctly. Poor social comprehension: If she broke something belonging to someone else she would "take it to the shop maker and let him fix it," and if he could not, she would "find the postmaster who will say 'Who broke this? Come and get it'." *6 months credit.*

Year VIII: Success on vocabulary, recall for facts from story read to her, practical comprehension and social judgment. *Failed* to identify the absurd aspects of two out of four sentences. Example: In commenting on the engineer who said that the more cars he had on his train, the faster he could go, she called him foolish because "he would have about 60 cars and get in a train wreck." Consistently gave several differences instead of a similarity and a difference between *baseball* and *orange, airplane* and *kite, ocean* and *river,* and *penny* and *quarter.* Was unable to repeat sentences without error. *6 months credit.*

Year IX: Succeeded in making simple change correctly and could reverse four digits. *Failed* completely to grasp absurdity of statements. Unable to visualize design made by cutting paper or to reproduce simple line drawing from memory. Could not supply rhymes, e.g., in attempting to give a number that rhymes with tree, she said "sixty." *4 months credit.*

Year X: Succeeded in recognizing pictured absurdity, in reading paragraph correctly (only one error) and in reproducing 10 memories from it. *Failed* vocabulary items and repetition of six digits. Named only 12 words in one minute of free association. Assigned poor reasons for social behavior; e.g., children should not be too noisy in school "because Sister might paddle them and she'd give them work after school." *4 months credit.*

Year XI: Failure on all items.

The credits when summed yielded a mental age of 7 years, 8 months. On the basis of the child's chronologic age of 9 years, 8 months, the I. Q. was computed to be 79.

b. *Significant Results and Leads*

(1) High borderline level of intelligence was demonstrated but was probably not optimal for these reasons:

(a) School progress prior to illness had been satisfactory up to fourth grade.

(b) Although most of the items she passed were below her age level, vocabulary was close to her age standard and reading was adequate at year X with good comprehension.

(c) Rapid dissipation of effort and interest were observed in the test situation.

(2) There were evidences of inefficiency in the test performance.

(a) Rote memory, requiring attention only, was poorer than memory for meaningful material.

(b) She could detect absurdities in concrete, pictured situations but became rambling and irrelevant when absurdities were presented orally.

(c) Erratic quality of performance: failed Comprehension at VII, passed at VIII.

(3) The obtained level was considered to reflect interference from the current illness. The chief difficulty seemed to consist in poor attention and in inefficiency due to distractibility. Poor performance on visual tasks (Designs, Paper Cutting) raised a question of organic defect and suggested further testing with visual materials; but the selective nature of the "memory disturbance" was a contra-indication. Incidentally it was noted that the child's projective comment about the reasons for not being noisy in school showed the threatening nature of the classroom situation for her.

2. Cornell-Coxe Performance Ability Scale*

This is an individual test of the performance type designed for use with children between the ages of $4\frac{1}{2}$ and 16. It is similar in many ways to the Arthur Point Scale discussed in Part II but was preferred for use in this case because it is somewhat briefer than the Arthur Scale; this child's distractibility and poorly sustained concentration made shorter testing time an important consideration.

a. Protocol

Assembled manikin with head placed correctly, but both arms and legs were reversed so that they did not fit closely into the sockets she used. Time: 20″. She was satisfied with the result though it was characteristically an impulsive and careless response and constituted her lowest weighted score. She completed the first two Block Designs, each consisting of four blocks, with relative ease. In the next, still consisting of four blocks, she had three units placed correctly and was willing to accept her solution. She com-

* Cornell, E. L., and Coxe, W. W. Yonkers-on-Hudson: World Book Co., 1934.

pletely failed the nine-block design, seemed unable to analyze it at all, and had no correct placements at the end of 3'30". Her weighted score on this group of items was next to her highest. In the Digit-Symbol test she completed just over one full row without error and thus obtained her highest weighted score. She had some difficulty in reproducing visual designs from memory, did none of them perfectly, but was able to recall at least some elements of all except the last. In attempting the Cube Construction test, which requires the subject to copy a block model with some painted sides and some unpainted ones, she had minimal success on the first two (4 out of 9 and 3 out of 9, respectively), and complained that she could not do this sort of thing. She stopped before the time limit on the last item had elapsed. Her placements on the Healy-Picture Completion board were erratic. She gave some responses that were relevant and meaningful but she inserted three pictures which were so unrelated to the scene that credits had to be subtracted from the total score. She spent 6'33" on this task; her variable performance did not, therefore, seem to be the result merely of quick impulsiveness. Credits were assigned and computed as follows:

	Raw Score	Weighted Score
Manikin	2	12
Block Design	13	26
Digit-Symbol	26	29
Memory for Designs	6	22
Cube Construction	9	23
Picture Completion	12	24
Total Weighted Score		136
Mental Age Equivalent		7–7

b. *Significant Results and Leads*

(1) There is close correspondence between the level here obtained and that on the verbal intelligence scale. This result suggests that whatever interference is present seems to be generalized and is affecting many aspects of performance with about equal severity.

(2) Apart from the exceptionally poor score on the first item (possibly reflecting initial anxiety in a new situation) the weighted scores are within a quite narrow range.

(3) The earlier question of special difficulty with visual space-form perception, suggested by the Stanford-Binet results, is not further justified; scores on Block Designs and Memory for Designs are in keeping with those on the other subtests.

3. Goodenough Draw-A-Man Test

The Goodenough Test was next employed since it is useful both as a measure of intelligence in children and as a projective indicator of certain emotional difficulties or social maladjustment.

a. Protocol

The patient drew a crude oval head in which she placed eyes, eyebrows, a schematic nose and a mouth; then she added hair along the outside edge. Next she drew a shoulder line and put a collar, tie, and row of buttons down the center. She made no outline for the side of the trunk but attached arms at the shoulder and legs at the bottom of the trunk space. (Her drawing is reproduced as Figure 5 and has been already discussed in Chapter 3.) She earned a total of 14 credits (1 each for head, legs, arms, shoulders, eyes, nose, mouth, nostrils, hair, clothing, fingers, two-dimensional limbs, eyebrow, and correct shape of eye), with a mental age of 6 years, 6 months.

b. Significant Results and Leads

(1) The rating is a little lower than those on the fuller measures of intellectual level; however, the character of the production suggests that emotional disturbance is probably responsible. The Stanford-Binet and Cornell-Coxe results at high borderline standard are therefore accepted as more representative of her present ability.

(2) The discrepancy between accurate attention to details, such as the eyebrows, shape of eye, nostrils, etc., on the one hand, and the

omission of the trunk delineation indicates a disorganized, confused concept of persons and is a characteristically disturbed response. The size of the drawing and its placement on the paper further suggests some anxiety. These points may be clarified by the later tests of personality and emotional reactions.

4. *Rorschach Method of Personality Diagnosis*

The Rorschach method was selected as the next instrument because it reveals both intellectual and emotional patterns of response and illuminates their interrelationships. It discloses the dynamic modes of thinking, not merely ability level, and may provide special information where neurologic damage is involved.

a. *Protocol*

Response	Inquiry	Score
I 1. (1″) A piece of bark, like.	Because it's colored gray.	W C′F Pl
2. Kind of looks like a policeman.	Cap. Look like they're holding that man too, in the middle. Two policemen.	D,W M H
3. Somebody that was kind of choked to death, like, and has no head. He has his arms showing, poking out.	Hands are up there. But if someone killed him by cutting him off he wouldn't be alive at all. If he was he'd probably see if he could grab something.	D M H
4. Looks like it's snowing something out. Black spots on it.	Everywhere, even on the men. You can see such teeny little white spots, too.	Dd FC′ Na
3 & 2. And then this man has a real black mark going way down to his feet. And		

Response	*Inquiry*	*Score*
this is a belt, I know. And these t w o policemen have such fat arms and skinny legs. One fat leg and one skinny leg. (165″).		
II 5. (1″) It looks like it's on fire.	Because it's all red.	D CF Fire
6. And they're dancing around like, with such skinny legs and such a big mouth, and tongue sticking out. Look like they're crying and making faces. His neck goes way down to there, down about to his shoulders. And he has two legs, one red one with those sticks. And they're holding h a n d s. This man's leg is longer than the o t h e r one's. (135″).		W M H
III 7. (2″) Looks like they're two men and they're cooking somebody and they have a sack. They have two sharp nails.	Only one leg and that's half way off.	W M H P

Response	*Inquiry*	*Score*
8. It's a chicken, too, because you can see it up here (see #10).	It sounds silly but it's a chicken in a pot, because you can see its sharp nail.	D F A
7. They have skinny legs, too, and they have these sharp toe-nails, too.	They're going to cook the little hen and eat it up.	
9. There's a bow here.	Right here.	D F Obj P
10. And two little chickens here and that's easy to tell because you can see the little head like and the little toenail.		D F A
7. And both these men have a—I don't know what you call that. Looks like a bone. (230″).		
IV 11. (5″) This man has such big shoes and big fat legs and such skinny arms with bone poking out, catching onto his hands. His tummy. The rest are the bones sticking out. It's not a nice word to say. And he has a fat stomach, too,	It's a man but he has no head. He would look alive if he had a head. Everyone would run away because he'd look like a killer if he had a head on, so strange looking.	W M H

Response	*Inquiry*	*Score*
with his ribs poking out. (Reiterates above details.) (165″).		
V 12. (2″) This one has such big long legs and he has no hands, and he has these big legs with the bone. I guess this is his tummy. He has bones sticking all over him. Even has a bone on his fat stomach, too. (150″).	Looks almost like a chicken but it isn't a chicken because he has a tummy, too. Looks like a man, but does look something like a chicken, too, because it's real fat. More like a chicken than a man.	W F– A
VI 13. (5″) This one has two feet with feathers and bones sticking out. No hands, but has arms, and he has no head. I guess these stand for his neck. This white line's going down a n d then t w o white marks and then he has two sharp points near his feet. Is this a bone? He has two bones covered with skin. (135″).	It's a man. That looks like a bunch of feathers but I know it's bones. Looks like feathers because it looks fluffy like.	W F– H (D Fc Obj)
VII 14. (15″) Two ladies, and they have — I think	Look like they're dancing. Hair white, can see the clearest part,	W M,FC′ H

Response	*Inquiry*	*Score*

that's a big long h a i r d o. Hair's white with stickers in it, and they both have hands, only one hand on each. Right here are their pants, and this white line going down here, I guess that tells where the different parts are. Look like they're making faces, too. (140″).

couldn't be black or gray. These are pants because they're in the right place.

VIII 15. (5″) This one's pink and yellow, like fire, and green and gray.

W C Cn

16. Looks like this m a n has sharp points all over him again. Here are two lines, I mean one line; I don't know how it could be a man again. And then he has bones all over him. His neck showing, and he don't have his pants on the right way.

This doesn't look exactly like a man, but I know it is, has to be. I never heard of anyone else wearing such pants, have stickers all over and all raggy and torn.

Dr F– H

17. These look like bears. I thought pigs at first, but

One big leg and one little leg.

D FM A P

Response	*Inquiry*	*Score*
pigs have longer tails.		
18. They **h a v e** their feet in this fire and they're climbing up this man. (195″).	It's yellow and orange and that's the only kind of fire I've seen. Orange with yellow flames in it.	D CF Fire
IX 19. (10″) Look like two witches here and they have such long fingernails. And it has something in front like a nail. Two of the fingernails don't have nails on them.	If that man starts to kill them they'll probably jab him.	D M H
20. Looks **l i k e** someone's catching them, going to kill them or something.		D M H
21. And here's some pink stuff they have their shoes on, so it couldn't be that, but it looks like strawberries or an apple. (170″).		D CF Pl
	Now I turned it like this and it looks something like George Washington.	(D F Hd)
X It's hard to explain.		

Response	Inquiry	Score
22. (20″) Two legs with two bones sticking out. At the bottom are shoes. Have a neck and something crawling—no, just their bones. He has both of his hands, and here are two more legs, which doesn't sound good. These men are hanging onto something. Looks like an old witch and a big man. (130″).	Not fat or pink like the other ones. I don't know.	DW F– H
	These look like beetles crawling up or something, but I guess it's ribs.	(D FM A)

The essential features of this record as analyzed by scoring categories may be tabulated as follows:

Total number of responses:			22+3
Location:	Whole	(W)	9+1 (41%)
	Large usual detail	(D)	11+3 (50%)
	Unusual detail	(Dd)	2 (9%)
Determinants:	Human movement	(M)	8
	Animal movement	(FM)	1+1
	Form	(F)	7+1 (32%)
	Form with texture secondary	(Fc)	+1
	Achromatic color	(C′)	2+1
	Form with color secondary	(FC)	0
	Color with form secondary	(CF)	3
	Pure color	(C)	1

Content:	Whole human figure	(H)	11
	Part of human figure	(Hd)	+1
	Whole animal figure	(A)	4+1 (18%)
	Plant	(Pl)	2
	Nature	(Na)	1
	Fire	(Fire)	2
	Animal object	(A Obj)	+1
	Object	(Obj)	1
	Color naming	(Cn)	1

Popular Responses:		3
Ratio of human movement to color: (*Experience balance*)	(M:ΣC)	8:4.5
Ratio of other movement to surface shading:	(FM+m: Fc+c+C′)	1:2
Proportion of total responses found on last three cards:		36%
Aver. first reaction time to gray cards:		6″
Aver. first reaction time to colored cards:		8″
Ratio of whole to part human and animal figures:	(H+A: Hd+Ad)	15:0

b. *Significant Results and Leads*

(1) As regards thinking disturbance:

(a) Her approach is characterized by marked perseveration, faulty perceptions, and loose associations (repetition of "man-bones, etc." in an unusual number of responses).

(b) She displays evidence of *impotence* and *perplexity* ("This doesn't look exactly like a man but I know it is"; "These look like beetles crawling up or something but I guess it's ribs.") which are characteristically "organic" features.

(c) The discrepancy between the good quality of some responses (e.g., #2, 3, 6, 7) and the poor quality of others confirms the impression of mental inefficiency and erratic approach noted in connection with the measures of intelligence. Moreover, the responses of good quality (especially M) strongly suggest that her native intelligence must be of at least average level.

(2) As regards personality structure and emotional adjustment:

(a) There are evidences of sexual curiosity, concern and anxiety. In the repetitive theme of the man she uses the word *tummy* as something distinct from *stomach,* synonymous with "a bone sticking out," and—in her own words—as "it's not a nice word to say." Also to be noted is her concern over "pants and where the different parts are" (responses #14 and 16). This finding adds weight to the surmise that her hesitancy in defining the body outlines of the man in her earlier drawing had an emotional basis.

(b) That conformity has been excessively stressed in her environment is suggested by the unusual predominance of human over animal movement responses. The reverse ratio is to be expected at her age and signifies, when present, a freer and less trammeled play of imagination in a child.

(c) Emotional expression appears to be impulsive and immature (0 FC, 3 CF, 1 C). The preference for uncontrolled over controlled affective outlet is indicated (by the occurrence of the responses to either bright or achromatic colors before others have been given; cf. I, II and VIII) and highlights the discrepancy between strong emotional pressure and more natural childish drives.

(d) Perhaps because her environment has failed to offer other satisfactions, she appears to have developed a strong introversive trend (experience balance markedly in favor of movement over color responses).

(e) The various clues related to an overly-rigid environment, sexual concerns and emotional immaturity made it advisable to study more fully the content of her needs and preoccupations. To fit this purpose the Thematic Apperception Test and the Rogers Test of Personality Adjustment were scheduled to complete the test battery.

5. *Thematic Apperception Test*

The pictures selected for use in this case were partially from the series published by Murray in 1943—designated by the appropriate Arabic numbers—and, for the rest, from an unpublished collection intended for the testing of children. The form of the verbatim record is explained in the section on the T A T, Chapter 7.

a. *Protocol*

1. (A boy is looking at a violin which rests in front of him on a table.)

I. (1″) He's playing something—don't know what it is—something like a little boat. He's just holding his hands up on his ears like—he isn't touching it or anything. He's just looking at it. And there's a light flashing there—from the paper like. [What is he thinking?] I guess he got this little toy for Christmas and is looking at it and thinking it's a swell toy. And this little boy—he's just looking at it. He has a piece of white paper there. [What will happen after this?] I guess he'll put that away and start another toy—if he got it for Christmas—looks like he did. (1′40″).

7 GF. (An older woman is sitting on a sofa holding a book. Close beside her a girl with a doll in her lap sits on the arm of a chair.)

II. (1″) Well, this little girl's holding a doll while her mother's reading to her. But she has her back turned to her mother—she doesn't seem to be paying attention. [What is she thinking?] Well, I guess she got this toy for Christmas, too, and she probably wants to play with it. I guess she doesn't want to hear any stories. [What will happen after this? How will it turn out?] Well, I guess she'll stop and maybe it will be bedtime—because mostly your mother says a bedtime story. She must be sleepy. When I can't go to sleep, my mother reads me a bedtime story. (2′15″).

(A little girl is reaching into the pocket of an overcoat while another leans over a banister and watches.)

III. (1″) These two little girls have braids—probably like me and my little sister. And this little girl, she just looks like my sister. She won't

be my sister very long—be my sister, yes, but won't have the name——.
And the big girl doesn't look at all like me. [Can you tell me a story
about this picture?] Yes, I guess I'll tell it. She's looking in the pocket
of the coat—or might even be her father's or something. I'm sure it's her
coat. [What is she looking for?] I don't know what—maybe it is her
coat and she might be looking for some money to get groceries for her
mother. [What if it is her father's coat?] Well, if her mother told her
to do it, it would be all right—but if she didn't, well, that would probably
be stealing—unless she knew her mother wanted her to do something.
[What happens then?] Well, she might be going for groceries or something or maybe even stealing. But I don't think she'd be stealing—because
her little sister's watching her and she'd probably tell her mother if she
were stealing. (3').

(A woman with a sewing basket in her hands is seated in a chair and is
looking to one side.)

IV. (2″) Well, here's a lady here—she looks kind of frightened. [What
led up to this? What is she frightened about?] Well, there's a big long
thing here—maybe she's scalded or something—hot, real hot—because she
has a lot of clothing on. [Who is she?] I wouldn't know—but she
doesn't look anything like my mother—I wouldn't know what she is.
[What is she thinking?] Probably thinking when will that heater stop.
Maybe she doesn't have another chair. That would be silly. [What will
happen after this?] Well, if the heater goes off, she'll be much happier.
[Anything else?] Well, she has this white robe or something on, with
black trousers. And she has white stockings that probably go with the
robe—and black shoes. (2'20″).

(A boy, dressed in baseball clothes, has his hand on the shoulder of a
smaller boy who looks up at him. There is a school in the background.)

V. (3″) Well, this little boy—here's a big man—looks like he's asking
him to play hooky—because there's a school up there. This little boy
looks worried, so that's the reason I think he wants to go to school. The
older boy looks mean-like—he has a baseball and he wants the other boy
to play baseball. Real mean, see—don't he look mean? I wouldn't do
that at all. The school is right in back of the tree. [What is he thinking?]
He wants to go to school—he's worried because he wants to go to school.
And the boy is only holding his shoulders on him, so he could run away.
[How will it turn out? What will happen?] Well, this little boy will
probably run and get away. And if the Sister [i.e., nun] saw him, she'd

probably think he was playing hooky—because these big boys can run faster than little boys. [Do you think he will get away?] Yeah, I do—if he ran this way. He'd probably say, "Let's take a little walk," and run near the school and probably kick the big boy. (3').

8 BM. (A young boy is shown on one side of the picture while on the other is dimly depicted a scene of what might be a surgical operation.)

VI. (5") This man is real sick. But it don't look like it—it looks like rough people around. But they can't be rough people—they look exactly like doctors. They're sticking a big needle in him—right in the stomach. I had one right in my back—it didn't even hurt. [Tell me more about the picture.] Well, the man's really getting pinched. The boy looks like his son—looks very sad-like. [What happened?] I wouldn't know— probably got in a traffic jam or something. [How does it turn out?] Well, he'll probably get better soon. [What is the boy thinking?] Well, he must be very sad—he doesn't exactly look sad though because he's got big lips. There are two doctors there. Looks like there's a gun there—I'll bet you he was shot. [Who shot him?] Probably some mean old man. But there is a gun there. There's a ladder there, too. This little boy couldn't have done it. I guess that's all. (3'20").

(A baby is lying on a bed and a woman is seated beside him.)

VII. (5") Oh, this is a very cute picture. Well, here's a little boy, here, and his mother seems to be crying—no, she's very happy with him. He has a didie on. [What is going on?] Well, the mother looks real happy. She's playing with the little baby. I wish I had a little baby—a little girl. The mother's holding a rattle in her hand and she's patting the baby. [How does the baby feel?] He looks—you know a baby can't smile very much when he's real young—but this little baby—he has his lips kind of down. So maybe he don't feel very comfortable—maybe he's cold or something. Maybe he wants his toys back—of course, that's not the way a baby would act. [What will happen after this?] The baby will probably be put to bed—just like I'm put to bed. I'm going to go to bed early tonight. [Anything else?] Except there's a little light on and I guess when the light's off, he'll go to bed. He's in a cradle, looks like. (3').

(A young man is seated on a bench looking at the ground while an elderly man with books in his arm stands beside him.)

VIII. (5") Well—one of these men staying here—he looks lazy. And there's a man selling books. He don't seem to want any books. There's a little cottage behind. And he's some—there are trees—he don't seem to be paying any attention to that man. [What is going on?] This man's selling books for sale and he doesn't seem to be paying any attention; he doesn't want any books. That's what my mother says, "Don't want any books." After—he'll probably go in his house and go to bed. Maybe he feels sick or something. This sort of looks like a doctor but I know it isn't. [What is he thinking?] I guess he just doesn't want any books and wants to go back in the house when the man's gone. (3′).

13 B. (A little boy is seated on the doorstep of a log cabin.) ·

IX. (1″) Well, this little boy's in a barn. It looks real dark in there. And this little boy's thinking about something. He's in his little bare feet—like in the summer when you go in the sprinkler. [What is he thinking?] Well, he's probably thinking—maybe he doesn't have any shoes and wants to get some new shoes. Maybe his mother's very poor. It's very dark in here and he doesn't like a house like that—it's just made out of wood. Maybe he has no mother or anything. [What is the outcome?] Well, this little boy—maybe he has no mother, and he'll have to stay like this, night or day, cold and winds, everything. [How does he feel?] He feels very sad because—I think I told you about that—maybe he'll have to stay out in the cold—maybe he'll have to go in this dark barn. (3′45″).

(A little girl dressed in pajamas has one hand to her eyes and the other on her stomach; beside her is a woman.)

X. (10″) This little girl looks like she's crying. But her mother's trying to gentle her up without crying. She's ready for bed. Her little dolls and toys are on the floor. And it will probably be bedtime soon. Her mother, I guess, will tell her a night-time story before she goes to bed. [What led up to this?] Well, probably, perhaps night-time came—because blinds are down and everything. And maybe it's time to go to bed. Maybe she's not going to have a night-time story—maybe that's why she's crying. Maybe her mother's telling her it's too late. (2′15″).

5. (A woman is looking through the partly-opened door of a room.)

XI. (5″) This mother looks angry-like—maybe someone is in her room. She looks very angry. She has a bookstand and flowers and the light is on—I don't think the light is on. But she seems very mad. I guess she thinks somebody was up to mischief. That is why I don't like to go to my bedroom—I get scared of stories. She looks very angry and she knows someone's in her room. The light must be on. [Who is there?] I

wouldn't know—maybe one of her children, sneaking something—something good to eat. [What happens then?] Well, maybe a burglar was
in her house or something. If the mother ever does find out who did it,
I know she'll be very, very mad—she'll just be very mad. That's all it ever
seems to be anymore—someone's in there; the light has to be on. This
mother looks angry-like, but it don't make me frightened—she just can't
see who's in there. Maybe she has a little son or girl; maybe she's sneaking
something. I never do that to my mother. (3′15″).

(A girl is feeding a baby at a table; a man is carrying a tray out of the
room.)

XII. (5″) The little baby's here. This little girl or mother's feeding him
something. He seems to want to eat hisself. He's a cute baby, a little boy.
The father's bringing something for the mother—because he has an egg
there and babies don't eat eggs. [Who are these people?] Mother and
father of the child and a little baby—I don't know—he's—I do think this
is the mother; she's sitting down in a chair. She does look like a little
girl though. [What if she were?] She'd be feeding the little baby instead
of the mother and she'd be a big helper—just like I'm going to help with
the beds. [Anything else?] The father has some—toast and cake there,
too. The little girl's feeding him something. On the table there's toast
and an egg on a tray. (2′30″).

(A man is sitting up in bed with a tray of food in front of him and a
woman is standing next to him.)

XIII. (5″) Oh boy, that looks good! Well, this looks like a sick father.
He has a paper and there are roses. And he has his food here—coffee,
sugar, cream, egg. The mother's standing by his side with a bathrobe on
and whatever she's supposed to wear under it. Man's wearing a "scapler"
[i.e., medal] around himself to make you better. [What is going on?]
Well, he's a very sick person—because you can tell when anyone has a
"scapler" on. But he's sitting up in bed like I used to do. And he's liking
his food. [What is he saying?] Well, they just seem to be very happy—
the mother and father are smiling but the father seems to be smiling best.
Probably soon he'll be out of bed. [Anything else?] And there's a paper
and candy there. And the mother is smiling down at him—just like an
angel, taking care. And he's about ready to eat as soon as he puts a napkin
on himself, so he won't spill. He has such a pretty wall. Looks like that's
all—but he has a pretty room and everything, just like I have a pretty room.
I have roses, too. (3′40″).

b. *Significant Results and Leads*

No attempt at a full or formal analysis was made since, for one thing, many of the pictures in question are unstandardized and, for another, the child—as is true of many others—was not always able to adhere to the test instructions. At times she was apparently evasive and at others she remained at a purely descriptive level. A qualitative interpretation provided the following leads:

(1) There is evidence of a clash between adult standards and the child's natural desires. (I. Boy being politely grateful but unenthusiastic about Christmas gift. V. Boy who "wants to go to school" but might still be accused of "playing hooky.") The similar clue from the Rorschach is thus confirmed.

(2) The mother-figure is viewed with ambivalence in a rigid family environment. (X. Mother may comfort or may reject little girl. II. Child rejects mother's attentions and expresses feeling that they are granted only at specified times. IV. Hostility and aggression is expressed against mother. IX. There is poignant recognition that security must come from the mother.)

(3) A search for warmth in an infantile, dependent role is prefigured. (VII. Subject identifies self with care baby gets; and in XIII, with attention sick father receives from mother.) Illness may temporarily have offered some of these satisfactions.

(4) There is some desire for affection from the father, perhaps in competition with mother for such favors. (XII. She puts child in mother's role. XIII. She identifies in illness with the father.)

(5) There are mixed feelings about her illness and the treatment she has received. (VI. She identifies doctors with rough people. VIII. Refuge of being sick and going to bed indicated. XIII. Being sick means getting attention.)

(6) Sexual curiosity is manifested. (XIII. "Mother with a bathrobe on and whatever she's supposed to wear under it." XI. The mother is in conflict with her child who is a forbidden presence in the bedroom of the former.) This result re-emphasizes the trend noted in her Rorschach.

6. *Rogers Test of Personality Adjustment* *

This inventory was included as the final member of the test battery to elicit information about the patient's attitudes toward home, family, school, playmates, etc. From it was sought concrete information that might help in effecting any necessary alterations in her environment as a preparation for her return home. It was in taking this test that she became tearful and anxious, and was so disturbed that she was unable to complete all the directions in detail. The results, therefore, had to be viewed qualitatively.

a. *Protocol*

Section One: Her three choices for the people she would like to be were: 1. A teacher (nun); 2. A housewife (mother); 3. A princess. She commented that her mother would be disappointed in her desire to be a nun since her mother wanted her to be a housewife like herself.

Section Two: Her three wishes would be: 1. To have my father and mother love me more; 2. To be bigger than I am now; 3. To be stronger than I am now.

Section Three: If she were going away to live on a desert island, the three people she would choose to take with her would be: 1. Mother; 2. Father; 3. Grandmother.

Section Four: In this portion of the test the child is instructed to rate himself in comparison with several imaginary children who are described as possessing certain characteristics or traits. The patient insisted on hurrying past this section. Since the comparisons are in terms of other girls, it was of interest that she commented here on the boy friends she had and got along with well. At the end of the section she was asked to pick that one of the mentioned girls whom her mother and father would like

---

* Rogers, C. New York: Association Press, 1931. This technic, not described in Part II, is similar in most respects to the Bernreuter and Minnesota Personality Inventories covered there. It is, however, somewhat more projective in character.

best. Instead she wrote her own name, saying, "My father doesn't like any girls. He loves me and myself."

Section Five: This section provides multiple choice answers to specific questions such as "How well can you play ball?", "How many friends would you like to have?", etc. Among her outstanding responses were the following: If she were going to a circus and had three choices of companions, she would like best to go with her mother and next best with her father. She refused to make a third choice because "It makes me sad that I couldn't go with Mother and Father. I wouldn't go at all." She said that she did not want to be grown up but to be just as she was. She denied all possibility of sibling rivalry, stating unequivocally that she was the one her parents treated "best of all." With reference to the sort of person she would like to be when grown up, and what her parents would like her to do, she reiterated, "I just want to be a mother."

Section Six: She refused to fill out a plan showing how many people there were in her family and whom she liked best.

b. *Significant Results and Leads*

(1) She apparently withdraws from active participation in her contemporary environment—as already indicated by the Rorschach findings. (Cf. the kinds of persons she would like to be; failure to mention contemporaries as desert-island companions or even as company at circus.)

(2) The importance of meeting adult standards is stressed for the third time in the repetitive statement "I just want to be a mother."

(3) There is reluctance to give up the infantile, dependent role, as evidenced in her need to reassure herself of her parents' love, her desire to remain at her present age, and her over-denial of sibling rivalry.

(4) There is marked emphasis upon needing the father's affection and attention.

(5) It appears that family and interpersonal relationships are

anxiety-provoking; her display of emotional disturbance in taking this test, which directly involves such relationships, was unique in her examination behavior.

From the results and leads that were available from the various tests, a report in which the findings were integrated was drawn up.

Report of Psychologic Examination

Behavior: The patient was a friendly girl of ten who entered with alacrity into the test situation. She was, however, readily distracted by extraneous stimuli and by her own promptings. Frequently she interrupted the test performance to talk about wholly unrelated subjects. While her initial approach to the problems was well planned and effective, her concentration and effort decreased as the tasks became more difficult and perplexing. She was restless and fidgety, sometimes aggressive and demanding, and repeatedly asked that she be returned to the ward; she was, she said, too weak to take part "in the games." When she was confronted with a test that required her to think of herself in relation to her family and friends and to make certain choices in that sphere, she became sullen and tearful. On the whole, the examination results are considered representative of her present level of functioning though it is doubted that the measured intellectual ability is optimal.

Intellectual Factors: The results of the intelligence tests reveal the patient to be functioning at the upper limit of the borderline level. There are, however, many indications that she is not using her full potentialities. It is probable that she was of at least average ability before her illness; she still copes readily with simple, everyday problems. Her thinking is likely to be concrete in nature; she has difficulty in making generalizations. The major obstacle seems, however, to be her ready distractibility. While this feature may prove to be related to her physical illness, there is no convincing evidence of specific defect in visual-motor coordination or new learning that would suggest permanent organic damage.

Personality Factors: The child's Rorschach record must be considered from two points of view: its representation of her personality reaction patterns and its delineation of her intellectual approach and functioning as these may have been affected by the encephalitic process. With respect to the latter, her productions exhibit rather severe disturbance with a tendency both to loose associations and to marked perseveration. She occasionally displayed the characteristic *impotence* and *perplexity* of organically impaired thought processes. It therefore seems likely that the distractibility, faulty attention, and tendency to become disorganized and irrelevant which were noted on intellectual tests are related to neurologic interference with mental efficiency. On the other hand, the adequacy of some of her responses indicates that her potential or native endowment is of at least average level.

There is also evidence from the various tests that her emotional development has been thwarted by certain problems. She responded frequently in the examination as would a child who has been forced to adapt to unrealistically high adult standards and interests in order to win acceptance. Apparently her environment has offered too little opportunity for normal childish behavior or fantasy and has set great value on being "good," "polite," and "grown-up." Since reality has thus given her little gratification for her normal needs and drives, there have been two effects now evident in her reactions. She has become a rather introverted child who retreats into her inner life from a rejecting and forbidding environment. She seems to be in some doubt and conflict with respect to the love her parents have for her, and her responses to direct questions on this point were not entirely consistent. At one time she stated that her first wish was to have her mother and father love her more; later she said that her father loved her more than any one and liked no other girls. She is, furthermore, immature in her emotional expression, responding as if she has been deprived of the opportunity to grow naturally in a stimulating and understanding atmosphere. There is some evidence that her fantasy life is fixated at a level that would permit her to assume an infantile role and be fed, clothed, and put to bed like a baby; presumably her illness has accentuated this trend. Despite these attitudes she seems to have adequate social awareness for her age—more, perhaps, than she should have.

The patient has much curiosity and some concern about physical sex characteristics and differentiating features. She described many of her human figures in the Rorschach as unclothed, and expressed particular interest in the male genital area; she also gave a number of responses for the blot-sections which often have symbolic sexual significance. When she described the clothed figures of women she expressed curiosity about the construction of their figures under the clothing. Her special interest in the father-figure as a love object and the suggestion of curiosity about the intimate relationship between parents contribute to the impression that there may be definite conflicts in her psychosexual adjustment.

Summary and Conclusions: This child was friendly and generally cooperative in the testing situation but she tended to be easily distracted from the tasks. She often launched into long stories unrelated to the problems at hand and sometimes complained of her physical symptoms when the tests became difficult or unpleasant. While it seems probable that her potential intelligence was originally of at least average level, she is now functioning at the upper limit of the borderline standard. Her responsiveness is characterized by many erratic qualities closely related to poor attention and distractibility. Her record on the Rorschach test also reveals some intellectual inefficiency that may be due to the encephalitic process. Re-examination of her intellectual ability during the course of her convalescence will be important in evaluating the permanence of her inefficiency.

Personality tests revealed emotional maladjustment. There are indications that her environment has been one which forces her to adopt adult patterns of behavior in order to win acceptance. She therefore sets undue value on being a "good" child, yet feels little security or satisfaction in her family relationships. She has, in any event, developed adequate social awareness for her age. The expression of her emotions is extremely immature and reflects a lack of opportunity for healthy growth in her environment; actually she would prefer to play an infantile role and to be cared for like a baby. She also expresses a considerable concern and curiosity regarding physical sex characteristics and differentiating features.

Since the child's behavior and general physical condition improved during the ensuing month, it was decided that she could go home. Several weeks later, in view of the fact that she was maintaining the progress she had shown earlier, she seemed ready to return to school. At this point a re-evaluation of her intellectual abilities was requested by the psychiatrist as a guide to setting realistic goals for her school work. She was brought to the examiner's office by her mother. The latter seemed rather anxious about the examination and asked many questions concerning it, expressing doubts about the child's abilities, especially in arithmetic. The patient appeared somewhat sobered by her mother's anxiety over her possible test results but quickly became more cheerful and friendly when left alone with the examiner. She asked the examiner not to tell her mother about any of her failures. It was apparent that she needed affection and reassurance, partly as a defense against the mother's criticism.

The child was eagerly cooperative during the first part of the session but, as the tasks became more difficult, she tended, as in the earlier examination, to become more distracted and to show less interest and attention. It was not clear whether this behavior was a function of fatigue or an evidence of her characteristic reaction patterns in situations of frustration. The test results are, at any rate, considered to represent fairly accurately the patient's present level and mode of functioning.

The *Revised Stanford-Binet Intelligence Scale, Form M,* was administered since *Form L* had been used on the previous occasion and this Scale provides one of the best measures of those skills closely related to school achievement. She had complete success on all tests at *Year VII;* her *basal age* was therefore 7–0. On *Year VIII* she succeeded on the social comprehension questions, was able to recognize absurdities in situations presented orally, understood problem situations and named the days of the week. She was unable to explain the similarities between *mosquito* and *sparrow* or *window* and *door;* nor could she supply opposite analogies in the sentence-completion problems. Her successes at this level earned her *8 months credit.* At *Year IX* she was able to reproduce one of two visual designs from memory, to organize dissected sentences, and to reverse four digits. However, she failed the verbal absurdities completely; for example, in explaining what was foolish about the young man with his hands in his pockets who was twirling a brand-new cane, she said, "If he was young, why should he have a cane unless he was crippled?" She was not successful in providing similarities and differences for the problems presented nor was she able to give rhymes for the words offered. Her performance on this group of tests yielded *6 months credit.* She recalled more than five ideas from a paragraph read to her and was able to name 15 animals within one minute when she attempted the tests at *Year X.* Failure occurred in counting the blocks of pictured structures and in explaining verbal absurdities at this level. She was apparently unfamiliar with abstract words such as *pity* and *curiosity* and was unable to repeat six digits correctly. She received *4 months credit* for her successes on this group of tasks. She failed completely on all the tests at *Year XI.* The totaling of the credits she had accumulated showed a mental age of 8 years, 6 months. This result, when computed against her chronological age, yielded an I. Q. of 87.

The outstanding aspects of this second administration of the Stanford-Binet Scale may now be summarized. There was, on the one hand, evidence of considerable improvement since the first examination. Her basal level was one year higher and her I. Q., 8 points greater. The range of her test variability was narrower and control of attention seemed more adequate in such activities as the repetition of digits, the explanation of verbal absurdities and the reproduction of designs. On the other hand, there was still evidence that her potential capacity was not being fully utilized. Her measured intellectual level was still not as high as was to be expected on the basis of her past history. There continued to be fluctuation of attention and flagging of interest during the examination. Finally, the quality of some occasional successes above her basal level gave proof of many associations and capabilities that were not regularly exemplified in her performance.

After the results of this second examination were related to those on the previous battery and were considered from the standpoint of her return to school, the following report was prepared.

REPORT OF SUPPLEMENTARY PSYCHOLOGIC EXAMINATION

The results of the patient's last test performance indicate that she is now functioning at the level of dull normal intelligence. While the degree of recent change is not outstanding, it marks a definite improvemen in her intellectual efficiency, especially since the interval between tests has been very short. Her basal age on the intelligence test is now a year higher than formerly, and her performance on most of the subtests is qualitatively more adequate than during the previous examination. She is now even more adept at tasks which require common-sense judgment and social understanding, but she continues to display difficulty in conceptual thinking. She also shows considerable ability to learn new material in an automatic or routine fashion. Capacity beyond her present level of efficiency is indicated by the occasional wealth of associations she shows and it is, in general, considered that these test results still do not measure her optimal intellectual level.

In considering her school placement it is important to note that the mental age level at which she is functioning is that of the average child in the upper third grade. She thus does not show the capacity for successful fourth grade work under ordinary conditions. Since she would now normally be in the fourth grade, she may have to repeat this grade next year. It is, in any event, undesirable for her to attempt making up by any extra effort the work she missed on account of her illness. It should be added that in an understanding school environment that gave her sufficient freedom and encouragement, she would have a reasonable chance of completing the fourth grade satisfactorily this year.

Chapter 11

An Adolescent with Episodes of Manic Excitement

THE PATIENT was an 18 year-old boy who had experienced four episodes of disturbed behavior (manic-depressive, manic) at brief intervals during the preceding ten-month period. He was the only child of parents married when they were both quite young—close to 20. The father was an intelligent and ambitious man who had received training as a metallurgist though he had not completed the work for his college degree. He was generally considered to be "happy-go-lucky and full of fun." About 13 years before the patient's hospitalization his father had undergone a personality change that made him irritable and argumentative. This condition was later traced to a thyroid disorder for which an operation was performed. Soon thereafter he separated from his family. During his last year in the home, he was a definite source of fear to the boy, who was then about six years old.

The patient's personality was described as being much like his father's—happy, friendly, energetic and conscientious. Since the age of 12, he had worked at odd jobs during summers and after school, insisting that he pay a large proportion of his own expenses. A few months after his sixteenth birthday he was graduated from high school, where he had maintained an honor average grade until his last year. He was described as seeming at this time to be more frivolous and less studious. Activity in athletics also began to assume a larger part in his life and in several of his summer jobs he served as swimming instructor or lifeguard. He soon entered the university as a premedical student on a partial scholarship; offers from his mother and an uncle to help pay the remainder of his tuition expenses were refused by him.

His interests at this time were rather rigid. For reasons of religion and of athletic training neither alcohol nor tobacco were used by him. He had few and only superficial associations with girls, and became quite concerned that some of his friends were bringing their "dates" to the fraternity house. As his illness progressed this idea became incorporated into his disturbed thinking.

The acute onset of symptoms occurred at a football game during his freshman year in college, when he was a member of the second team. His school was losing and he had to be forcibly restrained from going onto the field. This excited episode constituted the first of a series during each of which he was arrogant, irritable and absorbed with many religious and moral ideas. Between these periods he was quieter and was quite apologetic to his mother for his previous behavior. He was hospitalized for a few weeks at a time, on one occasion with a brief series of electroshock treatments. His adjustment did not, however, become stable enough to permit his return to school and although he attempted to work, he could not keep a job for more than a week or two. During this time he was rejected by his draft board—an event that seemed to precipitate the episode leading to his last hospitalization.

This young man was referred for psychologic examination on two separate occasions. He was first tested about a month after his admission to the hospital as part of the general evaluation of his personality and illness. He was examined again three months later, when it seemed likely that he would soon be ready to return home and when aid was sought in planning for his educational and vocational future.

First Psychologic Examination

1. *Wechsler-Bellevue Intelligence Scale*

The Wechsler-Bellevue was administered first because its relative objectivity made it a natural "ice-breaker" for this patient who had good confidence in his skills and was accustomed to intellectual work. The specific purposes were to check the appropriateness of his academic ambitions in relation to his abilities, and to gage whether his illness had affected his mental efficiency.

a. *Protocol*

Information: The patient succeeded on the first 21 items unhesitatingly but failed the four remaining ones. *Raw score: 21.*

Comprehension: He was able to answer seven of the problems completely and two others partially. As an illustration of his occasional confusion of thought his response to the item which requires an explanation for the fact that land in the city costs more than land in the country is appropriate: "In rural sections land isn't as populated, doesn't have as many buildings, tax assessments aren't so high; therefore, land in the city costs more because of advantages such as sewage disposal, school buildings, and theatres. Also because the buildings in the city hold more because they're skyscrapers." *Raw score: 16.*

Digits: He was able to repeat six digits forward but failed seven on both trials. He was similarly successful in reversing six digits but required two trials; he was unable to reverse seven digits. *Raw score: 12.*

Arithmetic: Correct responses were given to the first eight problems in rapid order. *Raw score: 9.*

Similarities: His generalizations were stated very well on six items and to a degree warranting partial credit on three others. He failed on the three remaining comparisons, an example of which is: "Just rewards for one's actions. If one does something meritorious, he deserves *praise;* if he does evil, he must receive *punishment.*" *Raw score: 15.*

Picture Arrangement: Full credit could be given on all tasks and additional credits for rapid time were earned on two of them. *Raw score: 19.*

Picture Completion: He succeeded on all but one of the items. *Raw score: 14.*

Block Designs: He was able to complete all the problems successfully and received additional credits for rapid time on five of them. *Raw score: 28.*

Object Assembly: All three forms were assembled correctly. *Raw score: 21.*

Digit Symbol: He completed 55 items in the allowed time of 1½ minutes without errors. *Raw score: 55.*

The scattergram of his weighted scores is shown in Figure 17. The total Verbal Score was 63, with an equivalent I. Q. of 121; the total Performance Score was 68 with an I. Q. of 116. The Full Scale I. Q. was 125.

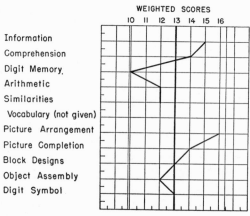

WEIGHTED SCORES

Fig. 17. Scattergram for Wechsler-Bellevue Scale, *Case in Chapter 11.*

b. *Significant Results and Leads*

(1) A superior intelligence level is indicated by the I. Q. of 125. There are only five points of difference between the Verbal and Performance I. Q.'s—an insignificant discrepancy.

(2) The pattern of the patient's scores suggests no special disabilities or other evidence of psychiatric disorder. His average weighted score of 13.1 has a 3.3 point range of expected variability. None of his deviations exceeds this margin. There is therefore no evidence that his illness has affected his intellectual efficiency.

(3) A suggestion that an attention difficulty is present is found in the slightly inferior scores on digit repetition.

2. *Rosenzweig Picture-Frustration Study*

Since the intelligence test gave such uncomplicated results, attention was next turned to the evaluation of personality reactions. The P–F Study was introduced to gain an understanding of the patient's behavior and attitudes in tension-provoking situations of everyday occurrence.

a. *Protocol*

Situation No.	Response	Score
1.	Please be more careful and avoid such mistakes.	/E/
2.	I'm sorry. Perhaps I could have it mended or replaced.	/ /i
3.	Neither can I.	E'/ /
4.	Well, accidents can happen.	/M/
5.	Would you care to replace it with another one?	/ /i
6.	Excuse me; I was not familiar with the rules of this library.	/I/
7.	I'm not trying to be.	/E/
8.	I would like to go but I have to work.	E';M'/ /
9.	What will I use for an umbrella in the meantime?	/E/
10.	That's a bad statement to make unless you can prove it.	/E/
11.	You're excused; I've done the same thing myself.	/M/
12.	I'll take his then and exchange it when we get back to the office.	/ /m
13.	If I'm to be your lawyer you had better keep your arrangements.	/E/
14.	In weather like this the buses from her home are always late.	/M/
15.	We'll make up for your error in the next game.	/ /m
16.	I'm sorry fellow but you were blocking traffic by going so slow.	/E/
17.	I always carry an extra set in case of such an emergency.	/ /i
18.	How soon will it be before you get a new supply.	/ /m
19.	I'm hurrying to the hospital for an emergency operation.	/I/
20.	Perhaps she only has some relatives visiting her.	/M/
21.	Oh, I'm sorry that such an accident happened.	I'/ /
22.	No, I'm all right.	I'/ /
23.	How long is that going to take.	E'/ /
24.	That's OK; I'll buy another one.	/M/i

The condensed record blank follows:

	O–D	E–D	N–P	Total	%
E	2.5	6	0	8.5	35
I	2	2	3.5	7.5	31
M	.5	4.5	3	8	33
Total	5	12.5	6.5		
%	21	52	27		

GCR: 71%

b. *Significant Results and Leads*

(1) There is no outstanding difference between the patient's characteristic patterns of reaction, as measured by this Study, and those of the normal group with which his results can be compared. The percentages for all the scoring categories are close to the average.

(2) He appears to meet situations of everyday stress with the conventional modes of behavior—as indicated by his GCR rating of 71 per cent.

(3) No evidence of variability in reaction to his own earlier behavior is to be noted.

(4) In general, the record suggests nothing unusual and, if interpreted at its face value, would indicate adequate frustration tolerance and socially accepted patterns of reaction. There remains, however, the possibility that the subject in his approach to the test, as in his approach to life, attempted to give the responses approved by his rather rigid standards instead of expressing more projectively the underlying personality patterns that might be suspected from his social and psychiatric histories.

3. *Thematic Apperception Test*

Since the P–F Study had not revealed any consistent patterns of maladjustment and thus gave results as uncomplicated as those already

obtained from the intelligence scale, it was decided to probe somewhat more deeply for the origin of the patient's difficulties. It was
assumed that his problems were bound up with the particular events
and relationships of his personal world. To explore these aspects of
his experience the Thematic Apperception Test was used since it elicits
information of an implicit kind regarding the typical figures, trends
and conflicts that preoccupy the person. Pictures from the series published by Murray in 1943 were selectively employed. The verbatim
record is reproduced below in the form already familiar.

a. *Protocol*

1. (A boy is looking at a violin which rests in front of him on a table.)

I. (5″) Well, in this picture the boy is looking at the violin, contemplating the lesson he's supposed to take during his practice period. He's
thinking how he'd like to go out and play but due to his mother's desire
for him to learn music, he's confined to his room and won't be allowed out.
So he's sitting here contemplating the hours he must practice. He's thinking of ways to get out of it. He's thinking of the futility of studying the
violin—what it will all amount to—what's the purpose of it. I don't believe
the boy particularly likes the instrument. I'd say he dislikes it very much.
I'd say as he sits here looking at the reflecting of his face on the shiny
surface of the violin, he's wondering how soon the hour will pass and
he can go back outside—back to other chores. He's dreaming of the future
—wondering whether he'll be a violinist or a football or baseball star.
Maybe he'll work his way through college as a musician. He's wondering
what use he'll make of the violin. So as the boy sits here wondering, contemplating the origin of the violin and his own personal history, slowly
but surely minutes pass by and the hour ends or the practice period ends
with very little practice occurring. But the boy is a student of music;
he has both dreams—and the instrument has helped to build the boy
because it helped him with the future, even though only in his dreams.
(3′37″).

2. (A country scene showing a young woman with books in her hand and,
   in the background, a man working in the fields; an older woman is
   leaning against a tree.)

II. (12″) In this scene it appears—it takes place on a farm in the United
States, perhaps Ohio or Pennsylvania. It appears to represent a family—
three people: a young woman, an older woman who seems to be the mother

of the girl, and a man that may be the girl's father—but I'd say her brother. It seems to show the dawn of the young farm girl. Instead of being the usual farm girl growing up on a farm, marrying a farmer and raising her children as farmers, this girl has found a zeal or zest for knowledge. The man and the horse are farming a place in the ground—agriculturalist, farmer; whereas the girl is looking for new horizons—a new future. And with the books in her hand she is either going on for some profession such as teaching or perhaps she is already a teacher and is going on in educational fields. This is probably a big event in her life. The mother seems to be looking at the girl with the corner of one eye, hoping that with some parental tie she can keep the girl in her own group, yet hoping that the girl can make a career for herself. And I'd say she's going into a career as a teacher because that's what lots of farm girls have done in the past. The brother is taking over the duties of the father—to keep up the farm and provide a living for himself and his mother. I think it's necessary because here the man is young and the elder woman appears to be his mother. He has his right hand pointed toward her and he's looking at the sun—all the evidence points toward his being her son. Perhaps he, too, wants to go out. I'd say the father is dead, but he may not be. So that's the decision of these three people—that he should stay here and the daughter get the opportunities. And it will be up to her to elevate the family from a common farm—with intelligence (no, scratch that out) (pause)—with her desire for knowledge or education. (5').

4. (A woman is grasping the shoulders of a man who is turned away from her and apparently trying to pull away.)

III. (8″) Well, this picture—the man seems to be torn between two loves. That of the faithful lover, this woman, and the love of the lower woman who appears in the picture—the rash, brazen type with low morals, which appears on his right-hand side. Perhaps in some way this fellow may have taken to drink or some other adequate start which turned down his character. Perhaps he started to go with the lower woman and, trying to keep faith with the girl who seems to love him very much, he's got himself into the lowest degradation. He can't seem to bring himself out of it. Try as he might, he can't seem to bring himself out. So this girl has come to his rescue—trying to win him back—to bring him out of the depression he's in; give him moral and mental strength. He'll perhaps marry her, lead a new life, and watch his children become stable, upstanding people. (pause) I think mentally he's confused, torn between his love of the lower woman, and he doesn't think he's worthy of this girl.

And I think for her sake and his own he'll try to prevent their having a joint happiness. (3'50").

3 BM. (A human figure is huddled on the floor against a couch. Beside him is an object often described as a weapon.)

IV. (20") This woman seems to be in a state of deep depression. Perhaps something tragic may have happened to her family, such as an accident may have killed a member of the family. Or perhaps she's been ostracized from her family because of some injury or some wrong she may have done to a member of her own family, but she—I'd say it's a woman, yes—in a deep state of remorse—sobbing, leaning on a low studio couch, pitying herself for (pause) for having done an injustice to her family. Or in case someone of the family has been killed, she's just deeply heartbroken. She's lost—the news is such a tragedy. But in case she has been dismembered from her family or extranged from them, I think she's pitying herself, trying to make new resolutions, trying to better herself and win the respect of her family again and become a member of her own household once more. There's something here—it looks like a razor and then a pipe; if it's a razor she may be contemplating suicide. It may be an ash tray or a cigarette—if it's that—deep smoking, depression, deep sorrow show the degradation she is in. She's like in the sea; she can't swim and there's nothing to catch on to. That's why she's sobbing, grieving, hoping that by this method—crying her heart out, as the expression is—she'll be able to reinstate herself—either in her own person or her family, as I said before. (5'8").

6 BM. (An elderly woman is standing with her back turned to a young man who appears perplexed.)

V. (3") This looks to be a picture of a mother and son who has matured and, I believe, desires to leave home. His expression of knitted brows—he's deeply troubled, he has news—he has something he wants to say to his mother—and yet he knows if he should tell her the conflict in his mind—her face is in trouble and he knows the news he's bringing.—He's been outside, you can see by his coat. Perhaps something happened—perhaps in an automobile accident—and perhaps friends of his or members of his own family—I'd say members of his family were injured; and I believe the cause of the accident was upon him. I believe it's his responsibility. He's very troubled; he doesn't know how to explain it to this woman who is his mother—or she might be someone else's mother—he doesn't want to tell her this because it might cause some illness within her—might cause a heart attack or the news might cause shock that's liable to affect her very deeply, perhaps resulting in death. But he's undecided, knows he has to tell his mother. I believe he's also ashamed to face her; for a son he seems to act strange here. He's deeply troubled—by his eyebrows and the way he's nervously fingering his hat. I think he has a deep love for his mother. He's afraid if he tells her he's responsible for injuring some other person that—(pause) the outcome from this accident—he may be sentenced, tried for violation of the law, held responsible for the deaths resulting from the accident. The grief that would come upon his mother might result in her death. He has such deep love for his mother, he doesn't want to shock her with the news but he knows he must and wants to get it off his chest. So I imagine in one fast sweep he tells her he was responsible for an accident, some particular party was killed and it may mean imprisonment for him. And I imagine that the mother, after it was a great shock to her, slowly regains herself—and, as a mother always does, tries to console and encourage him. Later, together they try and rectify the accident and try and prove he's innocent if possible—to prevent him from being imprisoned. (6'57").

7 BM (An older man is gazing at a younger one who is staring into space.)

VI. (7") There seem to be two men at work who seem to be discussing some subject such as music or art or poetry. It shows two schools of thought: the older man firm in his own belief, his own method of teaching the subject—let's say painting—and talking to the younger man who has listened but is not listening directly to the teacher. He's thinking of his own development, modernistic perhaps. He's listening to the old scholar who is telling him how he likes to picture life in his paintings—philosophy. He's trying to pass on some of his art to the student. He hopes some of his words will help the younger man to surpass his own achievements. The younger man is critical, listening with the expression of one ear open and one ear closed. Rather than be a copy, he's trying to pick out the finer points in this man's life, thinking how he himself can find success among his modernistic contemporaries. The reason I say he's modernistic is because his dress and tie is a lighter shade whereas the older man, besides being older, is wearing drab clothes. So it's reasonable to think the younger man is modernistic if both are artists. I think there's a fondness, a warm companionship between the two because both are artists, and I think the younger man of the modernistic school has a warm devotion to the older man. But he knows that among his own age or era of paintings he is confronted with different problems and he must present his ideas differently from his companion. So he listens as a son to his father, taking in advice and knowledge and wisdom of the older man, so that he might, with his own ability and philosophy, become an outstanding artist of the modern age and, in that way, achieve success for himself and repay his teacher or his friend for his kindness in giving him a start—in giving him his knowledge and his success. (7′7″).

8 BM (A young boy is shown on one side of the picture while on the other is dimly depicted a scene of what might be a surgical operation.)

VII. (7″) This seems to be a young boy, perhaps of teen age. I imagine he's still in school. By his personal appearance he seems to be a very conscientious boy, perhaps of a studious nature, who desires to be a great man. And these visions which seem to be in the background are his dreams. They appear to be thoughts of a doctor or surgeon. Perhaps this young boy, like many other young boys at the present time, is confronted with the problem of war—because that seems to be the subject here. He doesn't know whether to help humanity and help people or whether he must take up the rifle and kill. And judging by the appearance of the boy, I'd say he's the type that would make—that if he were—if there is such a thing as war causing the appearance of the rifle in it—perhaps not a natural war but war within the boy's mind; that would be the boy dedicating himself entirely to his life's work, expecting very little in return but longing and desiring to give his all for his fellow men. I think that's this boy's dream. I think that's what he'll do—go ahead and study to be a doctor or a surgeon and be a great humanitarian. He'll refuse this—it might be draft or what most students are confronted with—thinking of selfishness, using their profession to serve their own purpose rather than its original objective of serving others. But this boy has his back—I believe he will refuse to accept any dishonorable (pause) action or advice, and will go on to find his own profession—that of medicine, a true obsession for himself and a life for others. (5′55″).

13 MF (In the foreground is a young man who stands with his head buried in his arms; in the background is the figure of a woman lying in bed.)

VIII. (23″) This appears to be a scene where a man has committed a sin. He has either—we'll say he has misled this woman and after the action has taken place he can see where his pleasure was only a farce— was only a minute enjoyment. And now he feels the weight of this sin upon his mind; he knows he has dishonored himself and also this woman.

He doesn't know where to turn now. If this is just a woman he has met—a companion, a friend—rather, a sudden acquaintance, and he has utilized her for his own pleasure and, as I have said, dishonored himself—and he doesn't know what to do now. He's perplexed. He knows—he feels in his own mind that there's nothing he can ever really do that will convert her opinion of him and he knows he must do something. (pause) He feels deeply responsible for having abused her. He will either beg forgiveness of his—of the woman; or perhaps he'll put on a false affection and propose genuine love to this girl and perhaps ask her to marry him. Because he feels so—he knows he has wronged—that this is something that will always be in his mind and he can only make up for it by actually loving the girl or trying to love and trying to win her affection for him by sincerity, and have a beautiful romance in place of this clandestine, illicit love and courtship. (6′30″).

16 (Blank card.)

IX. (10″) I have in the right hand corner of the picture a little boy around five or six in the usual clothes of a small striped shirt and little short trousers. Round on the floor, on the bottom of the picture—it's a living room with a radio—the usual furniture of a home, but more toys. There's a light on the boy's face; his eyes are sparkling. And behind him there are visions also. It appears to be—they are mature men, groups of men participating in—they're dressed as football players. (This is really going to be corny.) And they're engaged in a football game. (That's enough description.) Well, we have the boy in this corner by himself with nobody in the room. His parents aren't in the picture. Perhaps his mother is in another part of the house but his father isn't there. As little children usually do when left by themselves, he took the toys and is amusing himself. He has a ball in his hand, a football in this case. His father is not home to play with him so he's playing with himself. He's thinking in this picture of the stories his father has told which reflect back to his father's days in college and his father's participation in college football. While the boy is not lonely at the present time—not lonely for playmates at the present, he's still longing for his father. And waiting for his father to come home and play parlor football with him. Or to romp with him and to hear his father's descriptions of his football fame. And the boy knows it's about time for his father to be coming home so he's holding the ball in hand and thinking of his father as his father would appear dressed in football garb and actually playing—playing football. And all the anticipation of his father's arrival is expressed in his eyes and his deep

love for his father are expressed—also in his eyes and in this vision of his
father as a youthful college football star. (8′16″).

18 BM (A man is being clutched by three hands that belong to invisible
antagonists.)

X. (13″) Well, this looks like a man that's a little bit under the weather
from drink or something. His clothes are untidy; his hair is down in
his face; he's very ill-kept, tousled; his tie is wrinkled. It all seems to
show he's intoxicated. I'd say he's so intoxicated that these hands which
are upon him are of policemen, officers, sweeping him away from the gutter
or the taproom—wherever he was—into a patrol wagon which is to take
him to jail. (2′10″).

18 GF (A woman has her hand around the throat of another whom she
seems to be pushing over a stairway banister.)

XI. (10″) In this scene, these two women seem to be quarrelling over
something—say jealousy of a man whom both are in love with. And the
one woman has made some—made a statement against the—this man, to
try and (pause) to test the other one's love for him. And the other, the
second woman, who's deeply in love with the man, also, refused to let
the other woman frustrate her. She refuses to display her emotions or,
rather, her opinion of the man. But, however, she does betray herself by
seeking—by grabbing this other woman about the neck and attempting
to strangle her, thus displaying her own emotions and love for this man.
(Whew!) And by strangling this other woman she no longer has to hear
these words said about her, and because of her jealousy for this man's
affection for this other woman, she may strangle the other woman, thus
having a free field for the man's affections. But I don't think she will
strangle her—I think she's only warning the girl—this other woman—not
to speak of the man in her presence, not to talk about him. And also
warning her to turn her attentions to another man. But I don't believe
she'll strangle her. (6′16″).

b. *Significant Results and Leads*

The interpretation of this protocol is not here presented in detail
because of space limitations. After the assimilation, descriptive analysis
and statistical evaluations had been completed, the following topical
generalizations were made.

(1) *Identification:*

Central character is a boy or man who is depressed, perhaps to the point of suicide (4, 3BM, 6BM, 13MF). He feels that he is torn between good and evil but unworthy of the good, and that he owes a great duty to his family whom he has in some way harmed (2, 3BM, 4). He emphasizes a deep love for his parents (6BM, 16). He is a conscientious boy, ambitious and dreaming of the future, but prevented by others from achieving his goals (1, 2, 8BM). Sometimes he feels that he is made to do things against his will by an over-ambitious mother (1, 2). There is expression of conflict as between identification with the mother-figure or the father-figure (16, 18BM, 18GF).

(2) *Figures:*

Family is represented as a unit to which the central character owes an obligation that he must fulfill (2). He feels that he has harmed them in some way and may be ostracized from their circle (3BM).

Father-figure is usually portrayed in a very sympathetic light. He is said to be a kind and helpful man who plays with his son and gives him good, though possibly somewhat old-fashioned, advice (16, 7BM). He is also identified with a football player (16). In one story he is shown as a reprobate (18BM).

Mother-figure is presented as an ambivalent object. On the one hand, she is said to be domineering, over-ambitious for her child, and eager to keep him tied to her (1, 2, 6BM). On the other hand, she is described as troubled over her son's problems and as a source of help to him (6BM). The son shows concern over the effect of his misdeeds on her (6BM).

Other women are portrayed in various lights. One is said to be good and wanting to give the hero "moral and mental" strength. Another is, however, in conflict with the first and is "rash and brazen, with low morals" (4). Still another is said to be "an acquaintance" seduced by the main character; he must fall in love with and marry her to redeem them both (13MF). All are shown as sexual objects. The first two may symbolize his general conflict between good and evil (4).

(3) *Trends:*

The major theme of the stories involves the central figure's sense of guilt and unworthiness. This orientation is attached to some wrong he believes he has done his family (3BM, 6BM), is ascribed to sexual misconduct (4, 13MF), or is attributed to other anti-social behavior (18BM). Though he expresses doubt as to the possibility of atoning for his sins, he feels that he should at least try (3BM, 4, 13MF). He speaks of himself as being involved in a conflict between good and evil, symbolized by the need for choosing between a good and a bad woman (4) and by the opposition between the ideal of serving mankind and the necessity for war, killing and selfishness (8BM). Some ambition is shown, though it is of an autistic character and liable to be frustrated by others (1, 2, 8BM). Resentment is expressed toward a dominant, over-ambitious mother-figure (1, 2). Strongly repressed homosexual tendencies are suggested (16, 18BM).

(4) Dynamic clues including sequence:

There is considerable conflict in evidence regarding the expression of aggressive impulses, especially in relation to the mother-figure. Where guilt for aggressive behavior is not overtly expressed, there is a tendency to change the theme from one of outward aggression to one of self-blame (1, 6BM). *Blocking* occurs on three cards, two of which involve stories with unusually strong feelings of guilt (3BM, 13MF; also 18BM). There also appears in the sequence of the stories considerable conflict over the relationship to the father and about the choice of parent for identification. After the portrayal of an idealistically "good father" (16), a football player, the response to a card which often elicits homosexual trends is unusually brief (the shortest in his series) and describes a man who is a reprobate (18BM). This story is succeeded by one in which there is marked identification with the mother against another woman who seeks to alienate the father (18GF). The transition from an adolescent, homosexual adjustment to a mature, heterosexual orientation is perhaps indicated. The tendency to symbolize conflicts (4, good and bad woman; 8BM, good and bad ways of life) is also noteworthy.

(5) Endings:

Six of the stories end happily, two have unhappy endings, and three are indefinite or conditional. An optimistic attitude toward the future is characteristically adopted. It should be noted, however, that such optimism is of two types: in some cases the central figure must assume responsibility for solving his problems and may be allowed to atone for his sins (2, 3BM, 13MF); in other cases, the solution is more autistic, a faith in the future with no particular basis (1, 7BM, 8BM).

(6) *Formal features:*

All the stories are told on an interpretive level with little attempt to formulate involved plots. The vocabulary used is well above average but involves some awkward and ambitious neologisms. Considerable confusion in expression is apparent and there are occasional instances of illogical or unusual, perhaps manic, associations (2, "sun" = "son"; 8BM, "war" becomes "war within the boy's mind").

The composite generalizations which may be made from the preceding topical ones yield the picture of a young man who is overcome by a sense of unworthiness and inferiority. He feels that he has harmed his family in some way for which he must make amends and he has rather mixed feelings about both his parents. There is more evident concern about the relationship to the mother than to the father. While he, on the one hand, accepts her as a protecting and helpful person, on the other, he tends to resent her attempts at controlling him. The aggression that he expresses toward her is, however, hard for him to accept. Of the father-figure he has a sympathetically idealized picture which is doubtless based upon wishful fantasy. An undercurrent of resentment against the father is present and in this context identification with the mother against the deserting male parent appears. There is, moreover, manifest vacillation over whether identification should be with the mother-figure or with the father-figure. Similar conflict is indicated in regard to the expression of aggressive impulses. Superficially hostility does not appear but at a deeper level aggression has been turned upon the subject himself. Sex is equally problematic for him. He seems to be caught in the transition from a youthful, homosexual stage of adjustment to a mature, heterosexual one but can reconcile himself to neither of these orientations at present. Homosexual trends are unconsciously repressed, heterosexual ones, consciously rejected as sinful. The struggle here involved is portrayed in a sense of engulfing conflict between good and evil forces of which he is the victim. He regards the outcome of this warfare within him as doubtful but he expresses an optimistic attitude with an added touch of idealism. A need for atonement is expressed and is depicted as a bridge for returning to a healthy social life. There are indications of confused thinking and of unusual verbal expression that bespeak his adolescent, intellectual ambitions. A tendency to symbolize personality conflicts in conceptualized fantasies is also apparent.

The integration of this picture with the known facts of the social and psychiatric histories is not difficult. This young man, who has not had the benefits of a normal home life, is evidently experiencing a conflict of identifications that is making his psychosexual development a more than averagely difficult problem. The relationship to the mother is, therefore, more than usually complicated by ambivalence and the nature of his relationships to men more problematic than it would ordinarily be. That he wishes for independence is evident from the facts of his having worked since the age of 12 in order to contribute to the support of the family and of his refusing to accept financial help toward his education from mother and uncle. But he is, at the same time, inevitably dependent upon his mother and deeply resents his father's desertion of her. There are perhaps, in addition, aspects of personality structure or organization that make for unstable vacillation from one extreme to another in his struggle with good and evil. His rigid standards, already evident from the history, would here find their place as a basis for his acute sense of guilt and unworthiness; his manic episodes might represent the excessive demands upon the ego that his very early attempts at independence have entailed.

REPORT OF FIRST PSYCHOLOGIC EXAMINATION

Behavior: The patient was friendly and eager to do well. He seemed fairly confident of his ability on the intelligence scale but anxious about the quality of his stories on the Thematic Apperception Test. The latter procedure was administered two days later than the others, at a time when he happened to be in a somewhat more depressed frame of mind.

Intellectual Factors: The results of the tests indicate that the patient is functioning at the level of superior intelligence. No special abilities or disabilities are apparent from his performance. The measure of his intelligence is probably optimal though the scores may have been adversely affected to a slight degree by a minor difficulty of attention that was observed.

Personality Factors: The most striking aspect of his performance on the personality tests was his overwhelming sense of guilt and unworthiness. This approach is particularly apparent in the sphere of sexuality. He is in evident conflict over the change from an adolescent-homosexual to an adult-heterosexual orientation. He seems to be struggling against homosexual impulses but at the same time thinks of heterosexual activities as sinful and immoral. He expresses guilt also about his relationships to his family whom he feels that he has harmed in some way. His mother is a strongly ambivalent object for him. At times he identifies with her; at others, he strenuously resents her domination. In general, however, he appears to consider aggression against her or other members of his environment to be wrong. He accordingly controls his aggressive impulses in a superficially adequate manner though it is likely that at a deeper level these tendencies become symptom-provoking. In this context belongs his marked sense of struggle between good and evil forces to which he is prey. Though he expresses considerable doubt about the eventual outcome of this struggle, his outlook is, in general, optimistic. He apparently believes that he can in one way or another redeem himself and achieve a normal adjustment.

Summary and Conclusions: This young man is functioning at the level of superior intelligence and his efficiency appears not to have been impaired by his illness. Considerable guilt and anxiety are evident in the personality test results. This orientation relates chiefly to his psychosexual development, with homosexual impulses apparently constituting a definite problem. He is highly sensitive to his inner conflicts but his outlook on the future is optimistic. There are no indications in the test results that any psychotic thinking or emotional disorder still persists though the patient's deep concerns over his personal problems undoubtedly absorb his energies and reduce his chances for successful adjustment.

SECOND PSYCHOLOGIC EXAMINATION

Three months after his first psychologic examination the patient was re-tested to fulfill a three-fold purpose. It was desired, for one thing, to confirm the measure of his intellectual capacity obtained earlier and to determine whether his ability was sufficient for a college education. A second objective was to sample specific vocational skills as a basis for helping him select the best general area for his studies and ultimate employment. Finally—and fundamental to the other two goals—there was the need for evaluating further his personality adjustment and patterns in order to determine, in terms of his total potentialities, the educational and vocational objectives that were suitable for him.

1. *Psychological Examination for College Freshmen—American Council on Education* *

The A. C. E. Psychological Examination for College Freshmen was selected for use in the re-examination because it is intended to appraise aptitudes with special reference to the requirements of the college curriculum. Furthermore, this test provides separate norms for the combined results of three linguistic subtests that have proved to correlate highly with success in liberal arts courses and other norms for three "quantitative" tests that appear to be closely related to scientific and technical courses.

* Thurstone, L. L., and Thurstone, T. G.   Washington, D. C.: American Council on Education, 1943. This instrument and the two following ones described in this section have not been discussed in Part II. The present test— the A. C. E.—is a paper-and-pencil measure of intellectual capacity designed for group administration and is, therefore, similar in a general way to the Otis Self-Administering Test that has been outlined earlier. Of the other two tests, one is a measure of clerical skill, the other an instrument for assessing visual-motor capacity broadly related to mechanical aptitude.

a. *Protocol*

The patient did slightly better on the linguistic than on the quantitative subtests; he placed at the 84th percentile on the former, at the 76th percentile on the latter. The percentile rank for his total score was 84.

b. *Significant Results and Leads*

(1) The results indicate that he has greater ability for college work than most freshman students attending 4-year colleges.

(2) Confirmation of his superior intellectual capacity, as previously measured, is here obtained.

(3) He has slightly more ability in verbal than in quantitative skills but—as was true on the Wechsler-Bellevue Scale—the discrepancy is not significantly great.

2. *Minnesota Vocational Test for Clerical Workers* *; *Revised Minnesota Paper Form Board Test* **

These two vocational tests were regarded merely as a brief sampling of the patient's aptitudes for particular kinds of work. Since he had already made a vocational selection (physical education instructor), the aim was only to touch upon the areas of his special abilities and interests as these supplemented his personality characteristics. The present two tests will therefore be summarized briefly.

On the *Test for Clerical Workers,* which rather narrowly measures aptitude for filing and similar office activity, the subject is in the superior range (80th and 90th percentiles) of a mixed adult male population but in an inferior one (15th and 50th percentiles) of employed male clerical workers. It is therefore apparent that he is not likely to experience success in this type of occupation.

On the *Paper Form Board Test*—a paper-and-pencil test for the measurement of "mechanical" ability—the subject achieved a score

---

* Andres, D. M., and Paterson, D. G. New York: Psychological Corporation, 1934.

** Likert, R., and Quasha, W. H. New York: Psychological Corporation, 1941.

of 47, which gives him an A rating, at the 92d percentile, in comparison with males 16–25 years of age; a B rating, at the 85th percentile, as compared to freshmen in liberal arts colleges; and a C rating, at the 70th percentile, on the norms for engineering school freshmen. It is therefore apparent that he might be expected to do better than the average individual enrolled in an engineering course. Great success is not indicated but some sort of occupation connected with engineering or mechanics would, at least, represent a reasonable choice for him.

3. *Strong Vocational Interest Blank for Men*

To determine the similarity of the patient's interests to those of workers in various occupations the Strong Vocational Interest Blank was employed.

a. *Protocol*

In filling out the face-sheet he noted that he had a preference for Physical Education and that he had previously considered both Engineering and Medicine. His ratings for the various groups of occupations are as follows:

Group I   A (Artist, Psychologist, Architect, Physician, Dentist)
Group II   B+ (Mathematician, Engineer, Chemist)
Group V   A (Y.M.C.A. Physical Director, Personnel Manager, Y.M.C.A. Secretary, Social Science Teacher, City School Superintendent, Minister)
Group VIII C+ (Accountant, Banker, Purchasing Agent, Office Manager)
Group IX   C (Sales Manager, Real Estate Salesman, Life Insurance Salesman)
Group X   B (Advertising Man, Lawyer, Author-Journalist)

The individual occupations for which his patterns were at an A level were: Dentist, Y.M.C.A. Physical Director, Mathematics-Physical Science Teacher, and Musician.

b. *Significant Results and Leads*

(1) His interests conform well to those of individuals in the kind of occupation to which he aspires.

(2) Although he has some skills that indicate probable success in engineering, the interests he reveals in this area are not as marked as are those associated with physical education.

(3) His low interests for the groups of occupations involving business life may have some relationship to his previously noted poor clerical skills.

4. Rorschach Method of Personality Diagnosis

To determine the relationship between the patient's vocational aptitudes and interests and his personality patterns as a whole, it was considered advisable to administer the Rorschach technic. Earlier personality tests were, of course, also available but this additional instrument was expected to throw important light upon the chief directions of his interests and the organization of his personality.

a. Protocol

Response	Inquiry	Score
I 1. (5″) Man's face; exceptionally long nose, mouth, chin.	Nose, chin, eyebrow, protruding jaw.	Dr F Hd
2. Center p a r t looks somewhat like mask; eye, mouth, place for nose; upper part of head missing.	Jack-o'lantern. Mostly the eyes and open mouth. Pieces cut out.	DrS F Mask
3. Hat placed on head with crown of hat misplaced.	Whole thing, if black extended o v e r top. (Same face as #2)	W F Hd
4. Silhouette of woman's body.	An "Oscar"; little statue, just lower part.	D F Hd
5. Looks like it could be a vase, holding maybe a candy dish. (125″).	Chinese, four-legged base, top comes off; whole thing.	W F Obj

Response	*Inquiry*	*Score*
II 6. (5″) Black part looks like two dogs or lambs touching noses. Central part has no connection.	Shaggy because of edge. Might represent hair of lambs.	D FM A P
7. Red blotch at bottom something like butterfly.	Just the center part; design of body and wings.	D F A
8. Upper red look like seals sitting up, or sea lion. (70″).	Body curved, head up.	D FM A
III 9. (2″) Skeleton model of pelvis and abdominal regions.	X-ray because can see shape of bones.	Dr F At
10. Distorted face of owl.	Shape, eye, etc., general outline.	D F Ad
11. Center is some representation of a bow tie, the red.	Shape. And color makes it look more realistic.	D FC Obj P
12. Animated cartoon of waiter holding something in his hand. Tuxedo.	Tuxedo because of dark color. Looks like tuxedo because waiter.	D M,FC′ H P
13. Upper blotches are an external view of the stomach. (90″).	Just shape.	D F At
IV 14. (10″) Lower part looks like person sitting on a chair. (Upper part obstructed.) But	Like a photo with feet out closer than rest of body.	Wˣ M H

Response	Inquiry	Score
large man with feet extended.		
15. Stump of tree.	More behind, man sitting on it. Seems round in shape. (Demonstrates).	D Fc,FK Pl
16. Or even a scarecrow.	Scarecrow propped against stump; no strength to it, relaxed.	W F,m (H)
17. Lower part looks like a statellite (stalactite) built from the roof down, like in a caravan (cavern).	Just shape.	Dr F Na
18. Or a large chandelier like in theatres.	Form.	D F Obj
19. Upper parts look like distorted arms hanging very relaxed, pointing down. (170″).	Loose, finger pointing down.	d Fm Hd
V 20. (9″) Two outer parts look like calf-muscle of leg from knee to ankle.	Shape.	d F Hd
21. Center looks like a rabbit only he seems to have wings. Cartoon maybe.	Sitting on hind legs perhaps, front paws up.	D FM A
22. Very general form of person's face; mouth, nose, chin. (72″).	Not a real person; just general shape.	D F Hd

Response	*Inquiry*	*Score*
VI Egad! Don't see much of anything.		
23. (20″) Upper part gives effect of lighthouse on a mound, tall tower, beacon.	These give lighted effect because of their shading.	D FK Arch
24. A newel post.	Shape, and light spot could be a reflection of light on it, glossy finish.	D Fc Obj
25. Or a sceptre.	Cross on top; decoration.	D F Obj
26. A c r o w n, rather odd shape though.	See it in perspective, four prongs show.	Dr F Obj
27. Snowflakes or ice formations.	Light shining on it, like on rainspout.	D Fc,C' Na
28. Butterfly or moth.	Wing, antenna, leg.	D F A
29. Rug pattern. (155″).	Looks like the weave of cloth, plain color.	Dd Fc Obj
VII 30. (5″) Couple of l i t t l e gremlins, i m p s, fairy-tale characters; facing each other; feather in cap, paw or arm extended.	Leering at each other, small bodies, feet tucked under. Coat open, flapping.	W˟ M,m H
31. Layout of an island on a map. Darker in center, lighter at edges.	Built up, higher on right.	D Fk Geo
32. Crouched back, paw, and face of cat or lion, if let imagination go.	Just the shape, though color may have brought it out, like perhaps a black cat.	D FM,FC' A

Response	Inquiry	Score
33. "Arms" look more like deer's hoof. (140").	Long toes, very vague. Just the way it's poised.	Dd FM Ad
VIII 34. (10") Two animals, something in cat family from the body and the leg stretched. But the head looks more like a cat, mouse, or guinea-pig.	(Describes in detail specifying "inner" and "outer" legs.)	D FM A P
35. Dark spots like in newsreel you see ships or islands taken from high altitude with light blue background.	Color looks like ocean. Color most important at first, then irregular formation with small darker spots.	D CF,Fk Geo
36. Spinal column.	Linked together, vertebral sections with spinal column.	D F At
37. Mask. Two large eyes, orange and darker orange. Like Greek masks in theatre. (165").	If it were all the same color I wouldn't have noticed it. Contrast between orange and pink.	D F Mask
IX 38. (40") Another mask, more like face of skeleton. Inset eyes, apertures for nose, dark brown shading.	Eyes with dark rim make it look hollow.	D Fc,FK Mask
39. Claws of lobster or crayfish.	Shape. I guess maybe also color.	D FC Ad
40. Caricature of face with tuft of hair, nose, chin.	Shape. Nose, tousled hair, chin, eye.	D F Hd

Response	Inquiry	Score
41. Submarine, conning tower and deck.	Rounded like conning tower, and long narrow deck.	Dd F Obj
42. New-born bird, large head, protruding eyes. (285″).	Shape first, then color, too.	D FC A
X 43. (7″) Easter decoration. Don't put that.	All the color, yellow, green, etc. No shape to it.	W C Sym
44. Rabbit's head, two long ears. If animated, I'd say wearing a wig.	I said the wig for a joke.	D F Ad P
45. Dog, bird-dog, or Irish setter sitting back on haunches, front legs extended.	Shaggy, because of the edge. Color makes it like bird-dog or spaniel.	D FM,FC A
46. Two other animals, terriers because of coloring of hair, or deer if shaped a little different.	White with dark spots like wire-haired. Running, leaping.	D FM,FC′ A
47. Two kidneys.	Shape.	D F At
48. Or a governor on an engine.	Shape.	D F Obj
49. Two faces of insects, like grasshoppers.	Facing each other.	D F Ad
50. The two large blue are faintly like a crab.	Too many arms, but general shape.	D F A P
51. Exaggerated outline of Africa.	Shape.	D F Geo

Response	*Inquiry*	*Score*
52. Another face, nose, chin, eyebrow.	Here. Shape.	Dd F Hd
53. One on inside too. Large wide mouth.	Laughing.	Dd F Hd
54. Snail, something like.	Without the shell. Shape of head.	D F A
55. Rabbits. (285").	Back view. Color important but shape more so. Sitting up.	D FM,FC A

The essential features of this record as analyzed by scoring categories may be tabulated as follows:

Total number of responses:			55
Location:	Whole	(W)	6 (11%)
	Large usual detail	(D)	36 (65%)
	Small usual detail	(d)	3 (5%)
	Rare detail	(Dd)	10 (18%)
	White space	(S)	+1
Determinants:	Human movement	(M)	3
	Animal movement	(FM)	9
	Inanimate movement	(m)	1+2
	Two-dimensional perception of perspective	(k)	1+1
	Shading as perspective (vista)	(FK)	1+2
	Form	(F)	30 (56%)
	Form with texture secondary	(Fc)	5
	Achromatic color	(C′)	+4
	Form with color secondary	(FC)	3+2
	Color with form secondary	(CF)	1
	Pure color	(C)	1

Content:	Whole human figure	(H)	4
	Part of human figure	(Hd)	9
	Whole animal figure	(A)	13 } (33%)
	Part of animal figure	(Ad)	5
	Anatomy	(At)	4
	Object	(Obj)	9
	Mask	(Mask)	3
	Plant	(Pl)	1
	Nature	(Na)	2
	Architecture	(Arch)	1
	Abstraction	(Ab)	1
	Geography	(Geo)	3

Popular Responses:		6
Ratio of human movement to color: *(Experience balance)*	(M:ΣC)	3:4
Ratio of other movement to surface shading:	(FM+m:Fc+c+C′)	10:5
Proportion of total responses found on last three cards:		40%
Aver. first reaction time to gray cards:		9.8″
Aver. first reaction time to colored cards:		12.8″
Ratio of whole to part human and animal figures:	(H+A:Hd+Ad)	17:14

b. *Significant Results and Leads*

(1) Abstract thinking is definitely less in evidence than would be expected of an individual at his general intellectual level (low W); on the other hand, excessive attention to details, including unusual ones, appears (D and Dd numerous).

(2) Freedom of emotional and imaginative expression are limited and not in keeping with his presumed potentialities (F% high).

(3) There are indications that he resorts to immature fantasy in preference to the more productive thinking appropriate to an adult social role (FM much higher than M).

(4) He appears to be over-responsive to external stimulation

beyond his inner personality resources (40% of all responses on last three cards; 6 of 9 FM on colored cards).

(5) There is evidence of considerable anxiety (many Fc and additional C′ responses).

(6) He uses neologistic expressions of an ambitious sort as he did in the T A T.

The results of the various procedures included in the second battery were integrated and referred to the earlier test findings with a view to the better understanding of the patient's educational and vocational problems. The following report was then prepared.

Report of Second Psychologic Examination

Behavior: The patient was much interested in the new tests and their results. He understood that they were to help him with his vocational choice and he displayed a thoughtful and constructive attitude toward this problem. It was apparent that he was exerting his best efforts. The results of the tests are considered to be representative of his abilities.

Intellectual Factors: It had been determined during a previous examination that the subject is of superior intellectual capacity. The A. C. E. Examination, additionally administered, shows that he has greater ability for college work than most freshman students of 4-year colleges. He should therefore have no difficulty in completing a college course with better than average grades. All the tests indicate that he has somewhat greater facility with words than with problems involving quantitative understanding. A test of ability for clerical work reveals that he is superior to most men in this skill. However, his scores do not compare favorably with those of employed clerical workers and thus do not warrant his consideration of this vocational field. His "mechanical" ability is superior to that of most engineering school freshmen. Though this rating is not exceptionally high, it does suggest that he could do creditable work in engineering school or in some mechanical occupation.

Personality Factors: His expressed vocational interests, as tested, are similar to those of men in social service and scientific occupations. He enjoys working with people but expresses distaste for selling and business, preferring employment in which he can teach or help others. His attitudes are much like those of Y.M.C.A. physical directors in agreement with his own avowed choice of physical education instructor. He does not have the same interests as engineers.

At the present time, however, the results of the Rorschach method disclose that the patient is turning much more of his interest and thought toward himself than toward his environment and its members. He feels overwhelmed by his emotional problems and expresses a marked sense of insecurity. His difficulty in accepting an adult social role, noted previously, apparently persists. These attitudes, and his related efforts to constrict his spontaneity, operate as an intellectual handicap for him. Though he is well able to adjust in obvious and conventional ways, he can not now solve problems demanding original or creative work. On the whole, he is not at present able to use his superior intellectual ability to best advantage. He does not see situations clearly and avoids productive generalizations, resorting instead to unimportant details and immature fantasy.

Summary and Conclusions: The patient's intellectual capacity is superior to that of most freshman students and on this basis he should have no trouble in completing a college course. His ability in clerical work is not sufficient to warrant his seeking such employment but he gives evidence of considerable mechanical aptitude. His expressed interests and attitudes are like those of men in social service and scientific occupations and justify his own choice of physical education instructor. From the results of the Rorschach method, however, as well as from those of the previously given personality tests, it is apparent that the patient is still too involved in his own problems and anxieties to undertake any strenuous intellectual endeavors at present. His emotional conflicts and his feelings of inadequacy seriously interfere with the full use of his intellectual abilities. It would, therefore, seem advisable for him to spend considerable time in psychotherapy before returning to school. Employment during this period should be of a comparatively simple and undemanding character, possibly of a mechanical nature and preferably among congenial associates. If he becomes less engrossed in himself and his problems and better able to deal with the latter, he might well follow his own present choice of occupation.

The patient's institutional treatment lasted for five months. At the end of that time he returned home but he continued psychotherapy by occasional visits to the hospital. A year after his discharge he was working regularly in a shop which manufactured meters and instruments. He had become engaged and was making plans to be married. His behavior exhibited no signs of abnormal variability or excitement.

Part Four
A VARIETY OF APPLICATIONS

Chapter 12
The Province of Clinical Practice

IN ITS MOST complete form psychodiagnosis includes not only tests, psychometric and projective, but social history and psychiatric study as well. This fact has been illustrated throughout the volume. Even in the presentation of the protocols for the individual tests included in Part II, social history and medical data were at least briefly introduced. In the evolutionary studies of Part III, the importance of such sources was brought out more fully. In the portion of the book now at hand the effort will be made to carry the demonstration a step further and to integrate even more closely than before the findings which, when taken in their entirety, provide an intelligible picture of the total individual. Here, as always, the art of psychodiagnosis is recognized as involving a multiple approach to the complex unity of the person. Not only is over-simplification thus avoided; not only are the tentative gropings and unstandardized methods by which they are gleaned thus checked and rechecked; but, even more intrinsically, such a diverse method of attack makes it possible, by the repetition and reinforcement that it entails, to comprehend the individual in his own terms—one of the essential bases of the psychodynamic point of view.

The attempt will also be made to present in this section a greater variety of personality problems than that provided in Part III. The cases are examples of those encountered in the work of the psychiatrist and clinical psychologist whether in private practice, in the out-patient clinic, or at a mental hospital. In these discussions psychodynamics rather than psychiatric diagnosis will be stressed.

The order in which the case studies in the succeeding chapters are presented is based upon the following rationale. The first two reports indicate the limits, both positive and negative, which characterize psychologic tests in their practical application. The first demonstrates what can be learned from tests alone in situations where, for research purposes perhaps, it is desirable to do "blind diagnosis," integration with other data being achieved later. The second reveals the relative impotence of psychologic testing when uncooperativeness presents a stumbling block. At the same time it is shown in this latter instance how evasiveness itself is both psychobiologically and psychodiagnostically significant. The next three cases have in common some neurologic or organic aspect; mental deficiency, general paresis, and a psychosis of senescence are included. A psychosomatic presentation follows and paves the way for the two final chapters in which are considered functional problems focusing upon personality dynamics. Here will be found studies of hysterical amnesia and of murder determined by unconscious psychopathology.

Chapter 13

Psychotic Reaction to Military Service

ONE OF THE incidental gains of World War II was the opportunity it afforded the clinical psychologist to prove his professional competence in dealing with problems of personality and of interpersonal relations. While the psychologist contributed significantly to induction and selection procedures during World War I, especially in the application of intelligence tests, his role during the second conflict was more diversified and much more closely integrated with the efforts of the social worker and the psychiatrist. In other words, the clinical psychologist was recognized as commanding tools beyond the intelligence test and achieved a part in full-scale psychodiagnosis, including problems of personality, and in psychotherapy. It is in considerable measure to this military background that the present growing prominence of clinical psychology among the professions must be attributed though there had, of course, been ample preparation in antecedent peace-time progress.

The psychodiagnostic tools employed by the psychologist were of value at induction, at points of selection during service, and in connection with various treatment procedures. In view of the ubiquitous impact of modern warfare and the continual uncertainties of peace, the psychologic problems of military life retain their relevance. An illustration of the manner in which psychologic tests may aid in the understanding of the reaction of an individual to military life is hence introduced.

The organization adopted in this case report is intended to delineate somewhat more closely than in the succeeding chapters the design of test selection and the relationships of psychodiagnostic results to psychiatric analysis. The presentation is therefore characterized by the rather independent accounts of the psychologist's study and of the psychiatrist's investigation. An illustration of "blind diagnosis" by psychologic tests administered and interpreted on a minimal anamnestic basis is thus afforded. The section that follows demonstrates how integration can be achieved in successful instances.

The patient was a 34 year-old Roman Catholic single male, born in a small Ohio town, the youngest of six siblings. He was educated through the ninth grade and was a printer by occupation. His father, a pottery-maker, died ten years before the patient's illness. His mother was living and well. Both parents were native-born. There were two older sisters and three older brothers, all married. The patient enlisted in the army about a year before war was declared by the United States, but after serving for only a few months, he became mentally ill and was given a medical discharge with a diagnosis of Dementia Praecox.

PSYCHOLOGIC EXAMINATION

The eight tests to be discussed were selected to evaluate intelligence and other aspects of capacity and, more especially, to elicit information about psychodynamics. For the latter purpose the projective technics, including particularly the Rorschach and Thematic Apperception Tests, were employed.

SUMMARY OF PSYCHOLOGIC TEST RESULTS

Wechsler-Bellevue Intelligence Scale
Verbal Scale: I.Q. 89
Performance Scale: I.Q. 103
Full Scale: I.Q. 96

Interpretation: Average intelligence. Not optimal.

Wells Memory Test *
Memory Quotient: 76

Interpretation. Memory loss. Not optimal.

---

* Not described in Part II but similar in essentials to the Wechsler Memory Scale included there. See F. L. Wells (20), Chap. VIII.

Shipley-Hartford Retreat Scale
Vocabulary Age: 12.3 yrs.
Abstraction Age: 11.5 yrs.
Mental Age: 11.5 yrs.
Conceptual Quotient: 92 (unreliable)

Interpretation. Qualitative results indicate efficiency loss in Vocabulary and Abstraction.

Rorschach Method of Personality Diagnosis

Interpretation. Introversive (autistic). Disturbance of conceptual thinking. Disappointed ambitions.

Thematic Apperception Test

Interpretation. Maternal domination. Pseudo-artistic inclinations. Disappointment in life. Sexual maladjustment.

Word Association Test
Group Contact Score: 53 per cent

Interpretation. Good contact.

Rosenzweig Picture-Frustration Study
Extrapunitive: 25 per cent
Intropunitive: 42 per cent
Impunitive: 33 per cent

Interpretation. Exaggerated intropunitive tendency. Trend from impunitiveness to intropunitiveness.

Davis Personal Problems Test *

Interpretation. Conflictful insight regarding sexual maladjustment.

ATTITUDE

The patient was passively cooperative in attitude during nearly all of the tests. Attention, however, was variable and persistence irregular. He was frequently preoccupied and was slow to respond. He grimaced

---

* Not described in Part II but similar in essential respects to the Bernreuter and the Minnesota Multiphasic Personality Inventories included there.

without external cause again and again, shook his head as if in response to his own thoughts, and occasionally sighed. He spoke with a certain affectation resembling an educated British accent. He sat in a slouched position, kept one hand in his pocket most of the time, and was probably masturbating during some of the tests. Nevertheless, the results may be considered representative of his best efforts at the present time since variability of attention, preoccupation, and slowness are constant factors in his condition.

INTELLECTUAL FUNCTIONS

The results of several tests in this area pointed to a present functioning level of average intelligence. Loss of efficiency was indicated. On the Wechsler-Bellevue Scale this loss was brought out by the inconsistencies within, as well as among, the various subtests. The Shipley-Hartford Scale confirmed the presence of deterioration. The Wells Memory Test showed a clear memory loss, noticeable chiefly in respect to new associations. The Rorschach findings, discussed in the next section, supported and extended the foregoing interpretation of the subject's capacities.

1. Wechsler-Bellevue Intelligence Scale. The Full Scale I. Q. of 96 indicated a functioning level of average intelligence. There was a significant difference between the ratings of the Verbal (I. Q. 89) and the Performance Scales (I. Q. 103). A difficulty in conceptual (verbal) thinking was suspected. Although there was wide scatter within and among all the subtests, there was less variability in the Performance Scale, and this fact may account in part for the higher performance rating. The inconsistencies in the various subtests indicated a moderate loss of efficiency. The original intelligence level was probably somewhat above average.

The Information score was above the mean score range. The long-range memory required in this test had been better preserved than any of the other verbal functions, but some inconsistencies and illogicalities occurred. Although the performance on numbers forward was adequate, he had considerable difficulty with reverse digits because of a perseverative trend and short attention span. A significantly low total score for Digit Memory resulted. The Similarities score was also low. Here again the performance was erratic and confusion of thought was evident. Both the Picture Arrangement and the Object Assembly scores were high and showed a good grasp of social relationships and essential details, respectively. However, the awkward position of the subject's fingers and the slight tremor of his hands interfered with the fitting of the blocks in the latter test. An inferior result on the Digit Symbol items indicated poor visual-motor coordination. On the Block Design his score was high.

2. *Wells Memory Test (Worcester Revision)*. The Memory Quotient of 76 was a resultant of considerable variability. His scores were above the current norms for school knowledge, repetition of the alphabet, counting backward from 20 to 1, and repetition of numbers forward. He achieved at the average level for sentence memory. His scores were very low for "old" personal information, new learning, repetition of numbers backward, and naming of common objects. His difficulty in the last groups of items was chiefly a matter of retardation rather than of inability to recall. His attempts to learn new associations, however, were almost a total failure. As a consequence, he became somewhat facetious and lost the goal of the test completely. In their entirety the findings were more indicative of inefficiency in present memory function than of any actual loss of memory and confirmed the Wechsler-Bellevue results.

3. *Shipley-Hartford Retreat Scale*. On this scale the patient was very slow and finished neither the vocabulary nor the abstraction sections within the time limits. The vocabulary results were inconsistent, containing a number of early failures among the successes. These inconsistencies, as well as slowness, strongly suggested an original vocabulary level above the present rating of 12.3 years. Thus, the Conceptual Quotient of 92 could not be considered reliable. The mental age of 11.5 years was, however, consistent with the rating on the Wechsler-Bellevue Verbal Scale. Loss in functioning efficiency was clearly implied.

PERSONALITY STRUCTURE AND DYNAMICS

Tests in this area revealed marked intellectual and emotional disorganization much of which centered in sexual conflicts and disappointed aspirations. The Rorschach did not yield a completely typical psychotic picture but the signs of maladjustment were, nevertheless, numerous. Some superior intellectual ability was indicated but there was evidence of its being largely dissipated in fantasy. Intellectual disorganization and affective repression were disclosed. The Thematic Apperception Test emphasized the part which family relationships had played in the patient's faulty personality development. The mother was represented as a crude, dominating, and censoring figure who had influenced both his sexual and vocational adjustments unfavorably. The father, with whom he seemed to have identified, was represented as weak. A clear tendency toward homosexuality was revealed. The patient had apparently been driven, though almost completely in the realm of fantasy, by high aspirations, few of which he had been able to realize. He was now attempting defensively to deny ever having had these ambitions. Another way in which he reacted to his failures was by withdrawal, guilt feelings, and a strong sense of inadequacy.

4. *Rorschach Method of Personality Diagnosis.* Interpretation of this test had to be made with particular caution because of the patient's underproductivity (15 responses). The protocol reflected an individual of good intelligence, probably of superior level. Intellectual control seemed fairly adequate (high percentage of good form-clarity) though maintained with difficulty. The introversive orientation was marked (movement responses) and was strongly autistic. Intellectual ambitiousness, probably disappointed, was indicated (comparison of whole and movement responses) as was also vague anxiety of a "free-floating" type (shading responses). Repression of affectivity was manifested in the almost total lack of color responses. Although an unusually long reaction time for all cards was found, the especially long delay for the color cards suggested color shock with implied emo-

tional conflict. Features of the record which corresponded to the pattern usually found in schizophrenia were as follows: loss of contact with reality (low number of popular responses, insufficient normal detail responses, and the presence of vague abstractions); difficulty in conceptual thinking (pseudo-abstractions, contamination tendency, inconsistent poor form-clarity, whole and unusual detail responses exaggerated); irregularity in tempo and in number and quality of responses; affective blocking. The presence of anxiety responses, the suggestion of color shock, and, in some measure, the number and type of the movement responses gave evidence of an active restitutive process.

5. *Thematic Apperception Test.* The patient sat in a huddled position throughout this examination and spoke in a low voice. He reacted strongly to the stimulation of the pictures, perhaps because they nourished his already existing preoccupations. At times he seemed to be so carried away by his emotions and thoughts that it was necessary to recall him to the task at hand. There were indications that he was secretly masturbating and this behavior seemed to vary according to the emotional stimulation of the particular picture. His facial expression was then one of absorption, he stared blankly, and failed to answer the examiner's questions.

Analysis of the stories, card by card,* follows. *Card I* (1——boy with violin) revealed a tendency toward self-absorption and self-directed criticism. Insight was revealed in the subject's statement that emotions may interfere with practical adjustment. *Card II* (2——country scene) brought out attention to unusual details and a tendency to characterize reality in a symbolic way. The family was described as intellectually disappointing. The story expressed conflict among the "mental, emotional and physical aspects of life" and, by implication,

---

* The pictures used were, with one noted exception, from the series published by Murray. In the present interpretive analysis the statements, apart from the picture descriptions, which are given in parentheses, are based upon the subject's gross behavior; those that stand without parentheses represent the contribution of the stories themselves.

in the subject. The relationship between mother and father was depicted as not smooth and the father played a relatively minor role in the family conflicts. *Card III* (6 BM——elderly woman and young man): army life was described as disturbing. There was recognition of the hero's lack of self-discipline. Feelings of guilt with a need for punishment were expressed. The hero showed impulsivity, rebelliousness, and an inability to face problems rationally. The son was a disappointment to his mother, and she could not understand him. The relationship between them was portrayed as problematic. (At this juncture signs of increased preoccupation were manifested.) *Card IV* (14——silhouette of man in dark room against bright window) indicated the repression of anxiety. The matter-of-fact treatment and relative brevity of the response supported this interpretation. However, in *Card V* (=o——woman's head against a man's shoulder) the repressed anxiety became partly manifest. The patient included the death of a son in the story. Although the woman was being comforted by her husband, she was the dominant figure. The man "is gaining strength from the mother's weakness." (Evidence of tension in the subject became more pronounced at this point.) In *Card VI* (3 BM——huddled form of a boy on floor, head against couch), the anxiety was openly expressed in a suicide theme. The subject spoke of "a girl who has had a child." Sexual problems and unhappiness were coupled in the narrative. Art was presented as a possibility for sublimating unacceptable sex drives. (Preoccupation here markedly increased. The patient seemed to have difficulty in responding to the examiner's questions.) *Card VII* (16——blank card) yielded what seemed, by available criteria, to be largely autobiographic material. Heterosexuality was rejected in the story. Platonic friendship and art were goals to be pursued. The hero's emotional turmoil, fear, self-disgust, feelings of inadequacy, and need for punishment were reflected. Disillusionment was expressed, and some insight by the subject into his own state of mind was shown. *Card VIII* (Picasso painting of nude figures, contained in an early, unpublished Harvard Psychological Clinic series): An initial effort to minimize the sexual aspect appeared but presently an incestuous situation was described. (The obvious sexual aspect of this picture seemed to rouse the subject from his preoccupations. He became more alert, perhaps defensively.) The nude figures were characterized as brother and sister. A maternal figure was depicted as chastizing and censorious. *Card IX* (7 BM—— gray-haired man and adolescent boy): Restlessness and conflict concerning the choice of an occupation were revealed. The subject's identification with the father was suggested. *Card X* (18 BM—— man clutched from behind by three hands): The story described a very dissipated individual who had strong guilt feelings. (The subject again gave evidence of preoccupation.) The word choice suggested a homosexual theme. *Card XI* (8 BM——adolescent boy in scene of surgical operation): The difference between aspiration and achievement was stressed.

The impression of somewhat superior intelligence was conveyed by the vocabulary employed in the stories. The extent of the patient's subjective participation in the responses is shown by the way in which his total behavior seemed to vary with his productions. The mother figure was described as having very high standards. She was concerned about her son but did not understand him. She represented the "emotional" aspect of the family situation. She was characterized as dominant and disapproving. The patient was critical of the relationship between her and his father. The father was described as weaker than the mother. He was reserved and unconcerned about the family, although he dominated the father-son relationship. The son was more or less identified with him. There was a suggestion of incestuous inclinations toward a sister. Heterosexuality was rejected as leading to trouble and unhappiness. A homosexual trend appeared. Lack of success in life was ascribed to sexual excesses and unconventional behavior. Aggression seemed to be turned inward with accompanying emotions of guilt, self-blame, and remorse. Frustration was represented as met by indecision, withdrawal, and thoughts of suicide. The need for punishment was clearly expressed in the endings of the stories and in the constant themes of discouragement, despair, submission, and dissipation. High but disappointed aspirations were revealed. Introspective self-criticism, suggestive of insight, was outstanding. The patient seemed to be recognizing his own emotional instability. For him art was the way of salvation.

6. *Word Association Test.* The patient was slow in understanding the directions for this test. Additional explanation, however, resulted in his full cooperation. The reaction times to the words varied from I to 15 seconds, with a median of 3.5. Reaction times of 7 to 10 seconds were found for the words *command, attack, smooth, tongue, luck, hard, cottage, pity, thirsty, couple,* and *different.* Extremely long response times were found on the words *love* (15 seconds) and *blame* (14 seconds). Unusual responses which may be of significance were as follows: *fruit-children, justice-unjustice, mouth-Mississippi, suck-honey, swallow-man, home-soon.* The complex indicators revealed a definite sexual problem, possibly homosexual (*love, swallow, tongue, suck, different, couple, hard,* etc.). Anxiety and guilt were also disclosed.

7. *Picture-Frustration Study.* From the total scores for extrapunitiveness, intropunitiveness and impunitiveness, it appeared that the patient characteristically turned aggression upon himself (42 per cent intropunitiveness) in situations of frustration, with accompanying feelings of guilt and remorse. He was particularly limited in his capacity to externalize aggression. While his record began with impunitive responses, he soon had swung sharply to the intropunitive mode which was presumably more idiomatic for him.

INDICATIONS OF INSIGHT

Evidence of the patient's insight into his condition was obtained incidentally from several of the foregoing tests, e.g., the Thematic Apperception Test. From such findings he appeared to have considerable awareness of his problems, perhaps even being morbidly preoccupied with them. In order to evaluate insight more directly a personality inventory was administered.

8. *Davis Personal Problems Test.* To indicate his worries, in accordance with the instructions, the patient underlined only a few words, all of which he evaluated by an intensity number of 1. Nevertheless, he constantly referred in conversation to the other intensity numbers. Once he asked the meaning of "acute anguish." The words underlined were: *temptation, cravings, excesses, nervousness,* and *unnaturalness.* Anxiety concerning sex and mental illness was thus evasively admitted. He apparently had some awareness of his difficulties but was not able to face them straightforwardly.

PSYCHIATRIC FINDINGS

The family history of the patient contained no other example of nervous or mental disease except for a temporary facial tic in one sister. The father was a steady worker, sociable and sober, who died of "cirrhosis of the liver and spleen." The mother, still living, was inclined to drink too much. All the siblings were in good health.

The patient's early development was normal except for a fracture of the right forearm at four and of the right femur at five. While he was in the seventh or eighth grade at school, a tic, still present, developed in the muscles around the right eye. Not caring for school, he was often truant during the last few years. He went to work in a printing shop and continued this occupation until his enlistment, except for short periods during the depression when he delivered groceries or worked for the Civil Works Authority. He was not ambitious nor was he greatly concerned about the amount of money he earned. Cleanliness was important to him. He went to Mass nearly every Sunday. In his spare time he was content to sit with his friends, talking and drinking wine, or to read newspapers and current magazines such as *Reader's Digest* and *News Week.* Always quiet, he preferred reading to company. He had little interest in moving pictures, was not athletic, never traveled, and had no hobbies. Although he enjoyed dancing, he had no steady girl friend and never contemplated marriage. According to his mother, one girl who liked him called him up and wrote to him but he paid little attention to her.

He stated that the sex relations he had, mostly with prostitutes, did not give him much "kick." Neither venereal diseases nor homosexual contacts were reported.

At the age of 30 the patient volunteered for service in the U. S. Army. He did not wait to be inducted because he wished to choose his own branch of "defensive" service. At first there was no complaint from his instructors in the Engineering School Provisional Battalion, where he was working in the printing shop. However, in about two months, he came one day to the orderly room demanding to see the Major. He said he was a conscientious objector and wanted a transfer to the infantry. When on KP over the weekend, he thought spies had been posted to watch him. After a few days in the station hospital he seemed quieter and was returned to duty. A few days later he reported for sick call, bringing a postal card to "Dr. Quack of the Quack Quack Hospital." Again admitted to the station hospital, he stated that since discontinuing sex relations three years ago from fear of syphilis, he had striven toward "intellectual intercourse." He wanted to be a man but wished to avoid hurting his mother, to whom he was very close although he had never kissed her. He was afraid that when he had spoken in one of his letters of being a "tower of strength," he may have been misunderstood. His mail, he thought, was being intercepted and read. He believed he had a mission in reference to Negroes, who should not do menial work. The army had, in his opinion, a "spiritual function." He expressed the fear that his friends would think him a pervert because after paying a prostitute he did not have intercourse with her. At the end of about four months he was given a medical discharge from the army and sent home.

Back with his family he stayed in the house most of the time, frequently sitting and laughing to himself and slapping his knee with his right hand. Although now untidy about his appearance, he took showers so often at all hours of the night that the water had to be shut off. He gradually became more and more preoccupied, talked to himself incessantly, and appeared suspicious of everyone.

Early in the following year he was admitted to a state hospital.

There he was quiet and cooperative but asocial and preoccupied, with a speech mannerism resembling an English accent. He claimed to have been commissioned by the Virgin Mary to travel throughout the world and report conditions to her. He conversed continually with the Virgin by means of a generator ray, a practice which made him irritable and weak. He was able to have sexual intercourse by air or telephoto. Realizing he had been mentally sick, he attributed his illness to poisoning. Not liking army life, he said, he could not adapt himself to it. He now thought himself to be well.

A diagnosis of Schizophrenia, Paranoid, was made and electroshock treatment was attempted without improvement. He was then transferred to another hospital for special study, and it was there that the present investigation was made.

In his new environment he sat with his arms and legs folded as though to take the smallest possible space; walked close to the walls of the corridors, and often stood jiggling rhythmically and peering with an empty smile into a vacant room. He replied to questions politely, in a pompous, vaguely evasive manner. He became fleetingly irritable when asked about his mannerisms but his florid delusions were no longer evident. He admitted only that he felt a warm ray continually playing on his back, which he believed was put there by the doctors in order to help him. Although he denied hallucinations, he was seen talking to himself at times. He ate poorly and paid no attention to his personal appearance. In spite of good memory for past events, he did not keep track of the date or show interest in current happenings. He was indifferent to his present condition and to his future.

Physical examination revealed an asthenic body build but disclosed no contributory pathology; his urine, blood, and serologic tests were normal.

CONCLUDING INTEGRATION

From the psychiatric findings and the psychologic test results an intelligible portrait emerged in the following terms. The patient had always had a withdrawn personality, given to fantasy and pre-occupied with himself. This schizoid trend, seen through the life course, might be regarded as the developmental background of the psychosis.

He appeared to have experienced little in the way of normal family life. He felt dominated by his mother, whose place was sometimes taken by his oldest sister. The mother was undependable and frightening. The father was a weaker person with whom the patient may have identified in terms of submission to the mother. The sister's temporary facial tic and the patient's persistent one may have a psychologic relationship, but further information on this point is lacking. Socially the patient's life was that of the average small-town fellow. His adult recreations consisted in drinking and loafing around on the street corners. He did not have much to look forward to and was not completely satisfied with so unpromising an existence.

Conflict over sexual adjustment existed perennially. An undercurrent of homosexuality was probably present. Most of his recreations were with men. He visited prostitutes in the company of other fellows without ordinarily having intercourse. His drinking with the boys may also have expressed some latent homosexuality and his artistic inclinations and psychotic affectations were interpreted in the same way. Domination by the mother could to some extent be responsible for the sexual maladjustment.

While military enlistment perhaps to some extent represented an effort to break away from his drab and unhopeful existence, in another sense it was an escape from anxiety about the army itself. He stated that he enlisted in preference to being drafted because he believed he would then have some choice regarding his branch of service. He could not tolerate the thought of being assigned to an "offensive" rather than a "defensive" line of duty. His statement at the onset of the psychosis that he was a conscientious objector is thus understandable. The enlistment which might therefore at first glance seem to be an assertive act appears instead as a form of escape. It is not surprising that on this basis army life proved to be intolerable and precipitated a mental breakdown in which loosely organized delusions of grandeur autistically compensated for his almost equally autistic former ambitions. The erotic content of his delusions indicated the part which his unsolved sexual problems played both before and during his military experience.

Whereas the interpretation up to this point has been largely developmental and psychiatric in emphasis, it is desirable now to stress the contemporary personality picture. The psychologic tests have at points confirmed or supplemented the foregoing account. Their distinctive contribution stands out more clearly in the following.

Taken in their entirety, the tests revealed an individual who was originally of somewhat superior intelligence but had ambitions that extended far beyond his possibilities of achievement. He was functioning during his illness at the level of average intelligence, according to his test results, but a significant degree of deterioration was apparent. The decline was evidenced particularly by impairment in memory function and by defects in the ability to think in abstract terms. His emotional problems centered largely around disappointed ambitions and profound sexual conflicts. Both these sources of maladjustment seemed to have been unfavorably influenced by his early family situation. His mother had dominated him; his father represented a weak model with which to identify. That he never managed to make an adequate sexual adjustment was probably in part a result of confusion about homosexual conflicts which he found impossible to resolve without anxiety. His typical reaction to frustration and failure was one of self-blame and withdrawal from reality, and he at times even went so far as to entertain thoughts of suicide. He had a high degree of insight into his maladjustment and was attempting to preserve his personality integration with some slight measure of success. That he was also failing appeared in the manneristic affectation of his voice, the grimacing and other lapses of attention noted during the tests, and the more objective indications of deterioration in the various findings.

It was concluded from these studies that the army represented for the patient a challenge to which he was not equal—an opportunity for comparing himself with other men that left him with an increased sense of inadequacy; a disciplinary life which interfered with his habits of daydreaming; and, perhaps, an excessive strain on his homosexual tendencies which in a more mixed civilian environment received less stimulation. With his originally better-than-average intelligence and his current insight it seemed possible that re-education could restore him to at least a moderate degree of successful adjustment; but counter-indications were the long-standing faulty reactions of withdrawal, the marked sense of failure and patterns of excessive self-blame, and the evidence of existing intellectual impairment.

Chapter 14

Psychotic Evasiveness

IN A CERTAIN sense many psychotic reactions represent an evasion of reality. Since the relationships between patient and psychologist are themselves a part of the very reality which such patients have renounced, they are apt not unnaturally to prove resistive to psychodiagnostic technics. There are, of course, many exceptions to this generalization since few psychotics have consistently divorced themselves from the environment and many others, after they have made an institutional adjustment, become accessible. Nevertheless, the problem of psychotic evasion constitutes a stumbling block for the clinical psychologist—one which skill can sometimes overcome and which systematic knowledge about "uncooperativeness" as a positive rather than a negative phenomenon may help to surmount. It has therefore seemed desirable to include one presentation in which evasiveness stands out both in the symptoms of the patient as a psychobiologic adjustment and in his relationships to the procedures of psychodiagnosis. The natural limitations of the psychodiagnostic approach in such cases will thus be better appreciated.

The patient was a 32 year-old married man, the youngest of ten siblings, who, perhaps because of his position in the family, had always been pampered. When his father, a farmer of limited education, died, it became necessary for him to leave high school in the second year and go to work. He was employed first as a restaurant helper, then as a cook. At the age of 18 he married, and at the time of his illness had six living children, ranging in age from two months to 13 years. His wife was Catholic, the patient, Protestant, but no evidence of any concern over religion was apparent until after the onset of his psychosis.

His maladjustment was of gradual and insidious development, the first symptoms appearing about three and a half years before his hospitalization. He had had to close what had been a successful restaurant business because the highway on which it was located was abandoned. He brooded some over this failure, but soon went into a hotel venture. When this, too, proved unsuccessful, however, he refused to accept bankruptcy proceedings, and wanted to assume full responsibility for the debts he had incurred.

From this point on he was satisfied with assembly line jobs and factory work, and for one period of five months was on unemployment relief. At about the same time he joined the Rosicrucians and invested their activities with much importance until he was dropped from the membership because of his peculiar behavior. A few months later he took his children out of the public school system and insisted that they be sent to parochial schools. He began to assign special significance to little actions of his wife, believed that the policeman on the corner was there purely for his personal protection, and worried that the men he worked with were plotting against him. The following spring he received an induction notice from his draft board. He quit his job and, though rejected for military service, did not return to work. He stated that the army wanted only dishonest men with racial and color prejudices and that his failure to display these attitudes was the reason for his rejection. Three or four months later he was acutely disturbed and exhibited much manneristic behavior. For example, he insisted on wearing a red sweater as a signal that it was dangerous for the neighbors to approach him. He was also convinced that he was being followed, that his wife was going out with other men, and that attempts were being made to poison him. There soon ensued a period of over-activity in which he turned on all the lights in the house and sat talking loudly to himself, and he then had to be removed to a hospital.

In the institution he became moderately cooperative and, on the whole, less boisterous than at the time of his admission. He was, however, prone to episodes of argumentative, obscene, and threatening talk.

There was no essential improvement in his condition for the next eight or nine months, during which time several types of attempted treatment proved ineffectual. He was finally transferred to another institution for long-term custodial care.

The psychologic examination served as part of the initial evaluation of the case when the patient was first hospitalized. He was tested about two weeks after admission—as soon as his behavior had become sufficiently stabilized to ensure cooperation. The battery of procedures was designed to be exploratory in nature—to provide a general evaluation of his responsiveness rather than to answer any particular question. It was hoped by the psychiatrist that, since the patient had not been very communicative, further information about him might be elicited by the tests.

The patient was examined on two successive days. On both of these occasions he was friendly and participated in the testing situation with a superficial willingness and effort to cooperate. However, he displayed little interest in the results, and it was judged that he was withholding information throughout the procedures. Although he exhibited no overt signs of anxiety, he remarked occasionally that some of the questions were out of his field or were unanswerable. He seemed able to gage to some extent what tasks were within his capacity range.

He was first administered the Revised Stanford-Binet Vocabulary on the premise that it would provide an indication of his original endowment level. He defined 23 words correctly, and these were rather consistently in the easier portions of the test. He did, however, fail a few of the early items because of his tendency to give very brief responses and his refusal to elaborate further. For example, he stated that a *muzzle* was a muzzle for an animal, but did not clarify this definition further. His score of 23 was equivalent to a mental age of 17 years (Babcock norms), indicating a "bright normal" intellectual endowment.

On the Wechsler-Bellevue Intelligence Scale, employed to evaluate his present mental level and modes of thinking, he showed little interest or persistence, responding rather quickly and without much insight into the correctness of his solutions. His performance was therefore erratic and involved failures randomly interspersed with successes. The Full Scale I. Q. he obtained was 94 (low average level), the Verbal Scale I. Q. being 98, and the Performance Scale, 89. His average weighted score on the ten subtests was 8.2, with an expected range of variability between the limits of 6.2 and 10.2. Since he had achieved a weighted score of 13 on Digit Memory, his performance on that subtest was outstandingly deviant; at the other extreme was his weighted score of 4 on Picture Arrangement. A score of 10 on Object Assembly seemed also to be worthy of further interpretive attention.

Taking in their entirety the intelligence test results indicate that the patient's original level was higher than his present low average rating. This interpretation is supported by his school history and by the clear inefficiency of his observed approach to problems. He displayed especially poor judgment in understanding the significance of social situations and in anticipating the causal relations of events correctly (low Picture Arrangement). In pointing out similarities between concepts his thought processes proved to be markedly concrete; e.g., a dog and a lion, he said, both have four feet, head and tail; a wagon and a bicycle both have wheels. The ease with which he was able to repeat digits suggested further that his thinking was most adequate to automatic tasks not requiring the application of past experience or discriminative judgment between the relevant and the irrelevant. It is possible also thus to account for his relatively good score in the assembling of disarranged objects; once he had recognized the meaningfulness of these concrete things, all of the elements necessary for the completion of the tasks were provided in the immediate test situation.

In brief, then, his native intelligence, as measured by the scales, was above average; acquired abilities and social intelligence were of limited availability. These findings could be readily related to the nature of his illness and to his evasive orientation toward the examination.

Similar findings are of fairly common occurrence among schizophrenic patients.

In investigating the patient's personality and emotional reactions, the first of the instruments administered was the Picture-Frustration Study. One basis for starting with this rather than with one of the other projective technics was the hope that its somewhat more structured character would elicit readier cooperation from him. This surmise proved to be correct since he responded promptly, completing the Study in 11 minutes. However, he gave his characteristically brief and equivocal replies in a number of instances and found it impossible to respond at all to two of the items. Only 20 of the situations could accordingly be scored. Nevertheless, the record was sufficiently complete for some interpretation. It appeared that he could express aggression against the environment only with difficulty and that he was more apt to turn it upon himself in an ineffectual fashion (40 per cent intropunitiveness, 30 per cent obstacle-dominance). Moreover, he seemed to lack the usual resources for defending himself against criticism so that he frequently became blocked in situations of interpersonal stress. His Group Conformity Rating was only 42 per cent and indicated a distinct deviation from conventional patterns of behavior. Taken in their entirety the results, once more, emphasized the patient's tendency to evade the painful aspects of experience by withdrawal or misinterpretation. It was not, however, possible from his brief and rather unproductive record to penetrate back of the scored responses into the domain of his inner feelings and emotions.

The patient's Rorschach record confirmed and elaborated somewhat his reaction patterns of evasiveness, negativism, and asocial trends. He gave only 11 responses, rejecting three blots as entirely meaningless to him. On the whole his reactions were vague and ill-defined. Three were based on the white portions of the cards (which usually serve as the backgrounds rather than as the main figures of the pictures)—a kind of behavior indicative of negativism. He managed to produce three concepts that are considered popular but strongly resisted any suggestions with reference to other popular responses which he had not spontaneously given. He was equally resistant to attaching any meaning to the color of the blots—the areas that tap capacity for meaningful emotional expression. His only departure from a rigid, though inaccurate, adherence to purely factual and formal interpretations of his world was through the medium of human movement responses—representative of inner fantasy life. When, however, as in this case, such responses occur in the absence of others that attest the possibility of environmental contacts and practical living, an isolative introversiveness typical of paranoid individuals is apt to be indicated. Since there were no redeeming features of richness or flexibility, he appeared to have few personality reserves that might serve as a basis for recovery or future adjustment.

Though the patient's lack of productiveness had set obvious limits to the effectiveness of the tests thus far employed, it still seemed worthwhile to attempt a technic that might throw light on the content of his personality problems. The Thematic Apperception Test was accordingly administered. Unfortunately the results were again meager. He gave very brief stories and held none of the pictures for more than three minutes. His productions were largely descriptive rather than interpretive, and encouragement toward further elaboration was met with his customary evasions. For example, to questions such as "What are they thinking and feeling?", he responded, "That I wouldn't know", or "Looks don't always reveal feelings." Similarly, when he was asked about the possible outcome of some of the stories, he replied, "That I couldn't say; usually a picture ends up all right"; or simply, "I give up."

Despite these limitations certain trends were discernible, especially in terms of his *selective evasion* of certain commonly given responses. For example, blocking and noncommital reactions were more in evidence when pictures that are usually interpreted as portraying heterosexual relationships or as involving the expression of aggression were the stimuli. (His avoidance of aggression here was, of course, consistent with the results of the Picture-Frustration Study.) He was also much more guarded in describing mother than father figures, attributing no positive traits to the former though investing the latter with some warm and sincere qualities. The outstanding aspect of his productions, however, was the absence in them of any sustained capacity to understand or interpret the feelings of the characters in his stories—lack of any real evidence of emotional ties or experienced identification with figures having certain values and playing certain roles.

In summary, then, the patient was superficially pleasant during the tests but seemed to be withholding responses throughout. He appeared to be functioning at the level of low average intelligence but there were indications of inefficiency and interference suggesting that his original level was significantly higher. He demonstrated a concrete attitude in his thinking and a lack of ability to understand the significance of social situations. Personality tests yielded a picture of evasiveness in all spheres. He proved constricted in his emotional reactions, with probable conflicts of a specific nature regarding sexual adjustment. He largely avoided any expression of hostility but had apparently not found adequate means of sublimating aggression. The over-cautiousness, constraint, and negativism apparent in his symptoms were borne out by the test findings, and the results throughout were consistent with a schizophrenic diagnosis, especially of the paranoid type. While predictions about future adjustment were limited by the restricted nature of his test responses, there was no positive evidence of any underlying richness or flexibility that would warrant optimism.

In this case the psychologic examination, however meager in its outcome, served to reflect the modes of response that the patient had apparently adopted in his illness. While this picture may have been to some extent equally characteristic of him throughout his life, his productions were so restricted and made evident so little of his latent reaction patterns that conclusions about either his "pre-illness personality" or future adjustment would be hazardous. Evaluation of his intellectual capacity and method of function was somewhat more adequate, perhaps because of the impersonal nature of the instruments; but even here he seemed to be responding minimally. This report thus illustrates how the productivity of the patient can set limits to the effectiveness of psychologic tests and how, further, unproductiveness may itself be an expression of an evasive adjustment to life. What lies back of such evasiveness in cases of this kind will still, of course, remain largely problematic but the palpable modes of function can be brought to light by the test procedures and lend confirmatory evidence, at least, to the data available from psychiatric interviews and observations.

Chapter 15

The Evaluation of Limited Intellectual Capacity

FOR MANY YEARS mental deficiency has been a field in which psychometric practice has been most fully and comfortably entrenched. Since lack of intellectual capacity has been the basis for segregating and managing the so-called feebleminded, measures which could objectify the judgment of the psychiatrist were very naturally welcomed. The value of intelligence tests was hence early accepted here and the Intelligence Quotient has held an unchallenged place in the diagnosis and disposition of the mentally defective. It is therefore highly significant of the current trend in clinical psychology that even in this traditional area the psychometric is gradually yielding to a psychodynamic approach—a shift of emphasis which, incidentally, brings the contribution of the psychologist closer to the best in psychiatric and social work practice. It is being recognized that a complete understanding of a person with less than normal intellectual endowment involves study of the interrelationships of this lack with the whole personality. The patient is no longer regarded as having an isolated defect which is something apart from the rest of him. Instead it is appreciated that the mentally defective individual functions as a unit with his own inner personality organization and special relationships to the environment. While the negative aspects of such a person's life are bound to obtrude themselves on the "normal" perspective, from the point of view of the patient his world, too, has its natural structure, demands and possibilities of fulfillment. Needless to say, the placement, education and guidance of the mentally deficient can enter upon a new epoch if such a view is fully implemented, and the role of adequate psychodiagnosis in this context is self-evident.

The case to be presented in this chapter illustrates the orientation in question in more or less obverse fashion. The subject of the study was a mentally defective individual who, instead of being denied scope for self-expression, was through ignorance being subjected to excessive demands that distorted her growth to the point of an apparent personality maladjustment. The essential relationships between level of capacity and expression of personality thus come to view.

This patient was a sixteen year-old girl who came to an out-patient clinic because her family considered her nervous, withdrawn and difficult. The family stated that for a long time, but especially in the last three years, she had bitten her fingernails and shown other signs of nervousness, lacked interest in her appearance, and objected to taking baths; she had little interest in school or other activities and made few friends. This behavior had been especially apparent since she had entered high school, that is, during the year before she was examined.

The patient was the youngest of four siblings; she had two sisters and one brother. Of her parents little is known. All the siblings were married and out of the home, presumably making a normal adjustment, though the whole family was considered in the community to be "of dull mentality." One sister, of whom the patient was especially fond, was unable to accumulate sufficient credits to graduate from high school. The patient's birth and early development were apparently normal, but at the age of two years she had poliomyelitis. She made a good recovery from this illness, however, and the only noticeable after-effect was a slight limp and drag of the left foot. At the age of five she had her tonsils and adenoids removed. The operation resulted in severe hemorrhages from which she nearly died. It was noted that since the age of six or seven she had had occasional "seizures," described by the family physician as "mock epilepsy," which occurred three or four times a month and lasted about three minutes. During these attacks she trembled and complained of pains in her abdomen but she did not lose consciousness. The patient herself said that the seizures were most likely to occur when she was excited.

When the patient was aged 13, her mother died of cancer, after being ill a year and in bed a month. The patient stayed with an aunt, her father's sister, during the last three weeks of her mother's illness, and after her mother's death she and her father went to live with this aunt, a single woman. A year later the father became ill with arthritis and had to give up his job as fitter at a steel-car company. He had two operations and at the time the patient was seen was still confined to bed. Having spent all his savings on his wife's and his own illness, he applied for an Aid-to-Dependent-Children grant from the Department of Public Assistance. This agency then referred the patient to the clinic because of her deviant behavior at home and at school.

Although the patient's poor school progress was not one of the main complaints at the time of her referral, it was noted that she had been having trouble in this area. She achieved satisfactory grades only with considerable difficulty and was described by her aunt as a dull student. On an Otis examination which she had taken during her freshman year in high school she had made a score of 44, which is equivalent to an I. Q. of 90. Her grades were at the low average level—C's and D's. In spite of these facts, the patient's family, and apparently she herself, were anxious for her to finish her commercial course in high school, and she was about to enter the sophomore year when she was seen at the clinic.

A physical examination was essentially negative; her physical condition at this time was considered good. The examination included an electroencephalographic study which yielded no definite evidence of cerebral dysrhythmia.

In the opinion of the doctor who saw the patient in the clinic her history and behavior raised the question of a schizophrenic reaction. The psychologic examination was requested to evaluate the presence of such a disturbance as well as the possible influence of limited intellectual endowment upon her behavior.

From the tests available four were selected for a battery with which to answer these questions. It was judged that the Wechsler-Bellevue Intelligence Scale would give the best measure of her intellectual level. This test was chosen not only because it is the most widely used intelligence test for adolescents but also because its various subtest scores can be analyzed to reveal specific abilities and disabilities. It was also considered important that much work has been done with Wechsler-Bellevue patterns from a diagnostic point of view. The Rorschach method fulfilled two purposes in this battery. It is useful both in revealing the quality of present mental function, in contrast to more formal measures of intelligence, and in evaluating personality reactions. The Picture-Frustration Study was employed specifically to assess the patient's responses to situations of a frustrating nature and her capacity to accept and adapt to problems and difficulties. A personality inventory was included in order to get a better understanding of what she thought about her relationships to her environment and what she considered to be her major problems. The Rogers Test (see p. 229 ff.) was selected for this purpose because it has special application to the problems of younger individuals.

In the testing situation the patient was friendly but seemed shy and withdrawn. She cooperated fully but with the passive obedience one might expect in a schoolroom. This attitude was particularly evident on the written tests, where, incidentally, she appeared to be much more at ease. She repeated every question that was asked her in what seemed to be an effort to concentrate, but she frequently forgot the question and then sat quietly staring into space. She appeared to have little insight, not even recognizing her most incongruous failures, and seemed vaguely disinterested in those problems that she could not handle. The test results are judged to represent fairly accurately her present level of functioning.

The results of the tests may now be reported. On the Wechsler-Bellevue Scale the patient achieved a Full Scale I. Q. of 64, which rated her at the high-moron level of intelligence. She showed somewhat better ability in handling verbal than nonverbal problems (Verbal Scale I. Q., 80; Performance Scale I. Q., 56). Though her scores on the Information and Arithmetic subtests were very low, that on Comprehension was her highest, suggesting that in spite of extreme difficulty in remembering facts and skills usually learned in school, she made surprisingly adequate use of what she did retain in grasping the general inferences of routine situations and in dealing with common-sense problems. However, poor scores on Picture Arrangement and Picture Completion indicated that she had difficulty in distinguishing essential from nonessential details and was almost completely unable to plan ahead in situations requiring the understanding of relationships in a logical sequence of events. Two of her best scores were on the Similarities and Vocabulary subtests but the quality of her responses showed that she was able to form verbal concepts only on a concrete and functional level. A *cushion,* for example, was said to be "something to lay on," while *gamble* was defined as "to play poker." While all of her scores on the Performance Scale were fairly low, she was especially poor on Object Assembly, earning full credit for none of the three items and requiring a long time for even inferior performance. Thus it was apparent that her ability to deal with items involving visual-motor coordination was very poor; when she resorted to trial-and-error methods in solving such problems, her efforts proved aimless. The fact that her score on Digit Memory was one of her highest while that on Arithmetic was one of her lowest made clear that though she was able to maintain attention, she had marked difficulty in concentrating planfully for any length of time.

The patient's Rorschach record was brief—only 16 responses—and contained no human movement associations. Only twice did she react to a blot as a whole, both times on cards where this sort of response is easy and obvious. In general, she made little effort to organize parts of the cards into larger meaningful concepts. Her perceptions were inaccurate—only a third of her pure form responses were of good quality—and her associations were markedly stereotyped, almost all of them involving animal content. Her record was thus characteristic of those produced by mental defectives and suggested that her native endowment was not essentially higher than her measured level of intelligence. Specific indications of the suspected schizophrenic disturbance were not found in her Rorschach record. Her responses were of uniformly poor quality, with none of the variability which would be expected if her intellectual inadequacy were due to functional impairment. There were no signs of bizarre thinking, contamination, confabulation, position responses, or impulsive reaction to color, and thus no evidence of a schizophrenic process superimposed upon her original deficiency.

The personality picture that did emerge from this test provided an initial basis for understanding her psychodynamically. Since there were only two animal movement responses in her record and human movement responses were completely absent, it appeared that she lacked inner compensations and could indulge in only immature and meager imaginative activity. Moreover, she seemed to be insecure in her relationships with other people and to withdraw from contact with them, inhibiting all emotional responsiveness; these tendencies were especially brought out by the absence of human content in her responses and by the avoidance of color in her associations.

Since intelligence testing had suggested that the patient was probably experiencing frustration in most of her daily living experiences, the Picture-Frustration Study was considered to be particularly appropriate. Her responses in this test indicated that her insecurity and partial awareness of her own inadequacy caused her to be defensive and particularly sensitive to criticism. She reacted to the frustrating situations with some excess of impulsive aggression, by blaming others for the difficulty involved, and obtained an extrapunitive score of 52 per cent. As her sense of frustration increased, she expressed guilt and anxiety about the hostility she had already expressed and tended to adopt a more conciliatory manner; that is, her responses showed a trend toward accepting the blame herself or avoiding the question of responsibility. She was, however, unable to maintain this seemingly adequate adjustment for any length of time and finally reverted to an open expression of aggression. Her reactions to situations presented in this test were seldom directed toward solving the problem at hand, and almost never did she assume responsibility for finding such a solution herself. In consequence, her social adjustment to frustrating situations was judged to be unadaptive and inadequate; she gave only half of the expected and conventional responses.

On the Rogers personality inventory her score for Social Maladjustment was high and implied that she herself perhaps recognized her problems as most severe in the area of social relationships. From the content of her responses it was clear that she felt she was unpopular; she expressed the wish to be prettier and to have more friends. There was evidence of a strong sense of inferiority about her scholastic record in which she felt her family to be disappointed. She resented authority and manifested antagonism toward her family, especially her father. Her responses on the Daydreaming scale of this test showed that she had not resorted to fantasy for the satisfactions she was denied in real life, but tended instead to retreat from situations where she would be inadequate.

These test results may be summarized under several headings. In regard to the patient's intellectual ability, it was clear from the results of the Wechsler-Bellevue that she was functioning at the level of defective intelligence. While she was relatively more facile with verbal than with nonverbal material, she was unable to think in abstract terms. She had especial difficulty with problems demanding information and skills usually learned in school, and in spite of comparatively good common-sense judgment in routine matters, she was quite unable to use foresight in her planning. These findings were substantiated by her Rorschach record which was in other respects also typical of those produced by mental defectives. There were no indications in the Rorschach that the patient's native endowment was essentially higher than her present level of performance.

This limited intellectual capacity had important implications for her social adjustment. She was already misplaced in school and her plans for continuing with a commercial high-school course were far beyond her abilities. She was accordingly being subjected to constant failure and frustration. The Rorschach record gave evidence that as a consequence of her inadequacy, she was insecure in her relationships with others. She tended to withdraw from social contacts and to inhibit all emotional responsiveness. The Picture-Frustration Study revealed that in situations of a specifically frustrating nature (which constituted a large part of her daily life) her sense of inadequacy caused her to be defensive and sensitive to criticism. She tended to react to her difficulties with impulsive outward aggression. In spite of the guilt and anxiety such expression of hostility aroused, she could not adapt in a conventional manner to her problems and was almost entirely unable to provide solutions for them. The results from the Rogers inventory indicated that she was aware of her difficulty in regard to social relationships and felt consciously inferior to her contemporaries. The resentment against authority which was manifested on this test confirmed the defensive attitude and sensitivity to criticism brought out in the Picture-Frustration Study. Findings from the Rogers and the Rorschach agreed in showing that, in spite of her tendency to withdraw from situations with which she could not cope, she did not resort to daydreaming to achieve her unrealized desires and, in fact, had no other inner compensations.

Finally, it is important to note that the patient's basic personality structure cannot be considered pathologic in any strict sense. Though her history and behavior suggested the possibility of a schizophrenic disorder, there was no evidence in either her Rorschach record or her Wechsler-Bellevue pattern to substantiate this hypothesis. The personality picture was, instead, that of a girl of defective intelligence, immersed in an environmental situation far too difficult for one of her ability.

In the light of these findings the psychiatrist concluded that psychotherapy was not indicated. He recommended that certain environmental changes be made to bring the patient's activities within her limited range of abilities.

The importance of the psychologic examination in this case lay in clarifying the discrepancy between the patient's native endowment and the demands of her environment. No essential personality mal-adjustment or disturbance of function was psychodiagnostically re-vealed. The apparent personality problem in cases of this sort is merely a reflection of inappropriate environmental pressures. Had the patient, for example, been living in an institution for persons of limited mental capacity, there would have been no such discrepancy and she would presumably not have been a misfit. Had her limitations been recognized earlier and some effort made to adjust the environment to her ability, it is likely that no personality peculiarities would have appeared. In other words, this girl had the potentialities for being a well-adjusted person of limited mental endowment. As a member of an averagely endowed social group, she could only fail to conform.

Chapter 16

Defect of Function from Neurologic Damage

AS KNOWLEDGE regarding the integrated functioning of the nervous system has advanced, it has become increasingly clear that neurologic damage is frequently significant not only in its local manifestations but also in its impact upon the total adjustment of the afflicted person. The patient is not only deprived of certain specific capacities that he had before but is faced with the problem of restructuring his entire psychologic life. His new limitations affect both the organization of his personality and his relationships to the physical and social worlds of his experience.

This newer approach to neurologic damage has broadened the horizons of the clinical psychologist by indicating the availability of psychologic test procedures and psychodynamic concepts with patients who would, on more traditional grounds, be considered of strictly organic interest. Recent inquiries into conceptual thinking and reactions to frustration among brain injured individuals are especially significant in this context and are exemplified in the following case study.

The patient was a 44 year-old married man, admitted to a hospital with a diagnosis of Psychosis with Syphilitic Meningo-encephalitis. The illness had been manifest for about six months previous to his hospitalization.

The family background of the patient may be summarized briefly. His father, now retired and in good health at the age of 70, had previously been employed as a fireman by the city. The mother, described as a sickly person, had died of a cardiac condition at the age of 36 when the patient was 12. She was said to have died in his arms from a heart attack that occurred while the family was trimming a Christmas tree. The patient was the third of five siblings. The two older ones were dead; a sister and a brother, respectively four and eight years younger than he, were living and well.

Little was known of the patient's early years. In addition to the usual childhood diseases, he had typhoid fever at the age of nine or ten. He attended parochial school, completed the eighth grade, and was thought to be "very smart" in his studies. For many years he was employed by the local electric power company, first as a ground man, then as a truck driver, and finally as a cleaner of street lights. He worked until the onset of his illness.

He was married at the age of 25 to a woman two years older than he. Two children were born. The elder, a son, died in early childhood; the younger, a daughter, was now 14 years of age. Marital relations were normal until the patient became disinterested about two months previous to his hospitalization. He and his wife were always happy together and it was therefore very difficult for her to accept or understand his irritability when he first became ill. His personality had always been easy-going and extraverted. He was interested in bowling, liked to play cards with his daughter, was fond of picnics, and enjoyed the radio and movies. He was devoted to his home and his work, was outgoing, mixed well, and had many friends. However, he was somewhat secretive and never discussed his personal affairs with outsiders.

The first signs of his mental illness coincided with an attack of influenza after recovery from which he kept complaining of fatigue. Three months later a personality change was noted. He became irritable over little things and very fussy about his personal appearance. He showed loss of memory and complained a great deal about pains in his head and back. Pneumonia developed and he was admitted to a general hospital. There he was noted to be confused and to have ideas of grandeur. He was then transferred to a state hospital where positive blood serology, positive spinal fluid, and a typical paretic colloidal gold curve were found. He received antiluetic treatment without improvement. Several months later he was transferred to the hospital where the present personality study was made.

A mental status note made shortly after admission recorded that the patient was in good general contact and amenable to ward routine. His speech was clear and his general mood one of indifference. There was no evidence of hallucinations, but he was overheard talking to himself much of the time. He maintained that while he was in the hospital he had seen a notice in the newspaper to the effect that his wife had divorced him. He was unable to recall much about the acute stage of his illness though he did remember that he had been accused by some voices of "bringing women into this country on the monopoly game." Though he did not admit that he was now mentally ill, he conceded that he might have been so previously. He knew that he was in a hospital for mental disorders but considered this fact an accident.

Treatment for paresis by injections of malarial blood was soon instituted. After approximately 47 hours of high fever, his behavior grew more controlled and he was moved to a quieter ward. However, he resented his hospitalization and was angry at being treated for paresis, which he denied having. Evidence of confused and delusional thinking was clearly present. He stated that he had divorced his wife five years ago for infidelity; then, contradicting himself, he said that his wife was now starting divorce proceedings against him. He emphasized that he had had no sexual relations with her for five years and believed that she had stolen and sold all his property. Of a son 19 years old he spoke with affection and expressed himself as intending to give the boy a university education. (This is the son who had been dead for many years.) He felt that he had been railroaded into the hospital and that he had been cheated by the nurses, attendants, and doctors. They had stolen his cigars, cigarettes, and money. He said, "I belong to the F.B.I., same as the rest of them do, and I'll have them put in jail." He considered himself perfectly well but as having been "framed" for syphilis.

For two more months he received antiluetic drug treatment but he showed no improvement and continued to be confused. At this point, with serology and spinal fluid tests still positive, the psychologic examination was administered.

The aim of psychologic tests in this case of known organic etiology was to define as accurately as possible the inroads of the disease upon the patient's thought processes and emotional reactions. A measure of general intelligence was used as the starting point in order to indicate whether his present level of functioning was significantly different from his estimated pre-illness level, and whether the pattern of scores and qualitative features were suggestive of any specific intellectual impairment or defect. The Wechsler-Bellevue Scale was selected for this purpose. Investigation was then made of three specific areas in which organic defect is frequently exhibited—memory function, conceptual thinking, and space-form perception by means of the Wechsler Memory Scale, the Object-Sorting Test, and the Graphic Rorschach method.* Finally, an evaluation of personality and emotional reaction patterns was made with the Rorschach technic and the Picture-Frustration Study.

The patient was not entirely cooperative at first but he soon became interested and quite willing to take the tests. He continually said that he might not be able to do certain tasks and required considerable encouragement; his demurral had the quality of childishly expecting praise rather than of insightfully recognizing his limitations. He lacked understanding of his failures and considered many incorrect responses acceptable. He was frequently reminded by the test material of events in his past life and indulged in rambling and circumstantial reminiscences which had a grandiose character.

The results of the examination may now be reported. On the Wechsler-Bellevue Scale his I. Q. was 91, with very close correspond-

---

* This technic, not described in Part II, requires the subject to draw his impression of the ink-blot in clarification of his verbal interpretation. A complex scoring analysis rates the correspondence between his expressed concept and the characteristics of the ink-blot. See J. R. Grassi and K. N. Levine, The Graphic Rorschach Manual. *Psychiat. Quart.,* 1943, 17, 258–281.

ence between his scores on the verbal and performance parts. Factual material, well learned, was competently retained, and his highest scores were on Information and Arithmetic. He was able to attend and concentrate effectively, an unusual condition in cases of organic brain disease. Memory function seemed unimpaired, with an M. Q. of 96 on the Wechsler Memory Scale. He had difficulty, however, in perceiving relationships, was unable to distinguish essential from non-essential details and could not cope with common-sense, everyday problems (low scores on Comprehension and Picture Completion). Tests revealed that he thought in extremely concrete terms. For example, he could grasp only the first two items in the Similarities series, and he defined words almost entirely in terms of specific situations, e.g., *cedar:* "poles that are used for light poles," and *cushion:* "made of feathers and cloth to sit on." His thinking disability was more clearly exhibited in the specialized tests. On the Object-Sorting Test he displayed marked impairment of conceptual or categorical thinking, and was able to form only very narrow groups organized in terms of use. Moreover, he had difficulty in grasping abstract principles even when they were demonstrated for him, and showed only limited comprehension of most of the concepts involved. His total score was far below the expected normal standard. He also exhibited a concrete approach in his Graphic Rorschach productions. He exerted maximal effort to reproduce the blot exactly as he saw it but included features both relevant and irrelevant to his concept. His drawings were distorted and asymmetrical but he failed to recognize his disability and quite enjoyed the task, saying several times, "I'm doing better than I thought I'd do."

The results of the Picture-Frustration Study indicated marked incapacity for adequate adjustment to problems of a frustrating nature; he exhibited only 46 per cent of the usually given responses. He became blocked in the situations and deliberately attempted to misinterpret their import in an effort to conceal his excessively hostile attitudes. However, when in the inquiry he had to face the situations realistically, his aggression was expressed in an impulsive and uncontrolled manner. He placed blame directly on other persons and received an extrapunitive score of 79 per cent. (Seventy-five per cent of normals have less than 50 per cent E-score.)

The patient's Rorschach record showed over-ready responsiveness, with poor mental control and faulty efforts at inhibition. There was evidence of some basic personality integration, however, and a few high quality responses were still given. For example, in Card II he described two bears with their paws tied together, and in the upper red of Card III reversed, he described two dancing girls standing on their tiptoes. But in general, his responsiveness was unselective and often inappropriate. He believed that the blots were intended to represent specific objects and that he must recognize them. He asked for reassurance from the examiner, gave responses even when their accuracy bothered him, and puzzled over irrelevant blot areas. Under "emotional" stimulation he became disorganized and finally merely named the colors of the blots.

The psychologic examination was summarized at the time as follows: "This patient's intellectual functioning is at a low average level, and there is no clear evidence that it has ever been essentially higher. Impairment appears in terms of an altered mode of approach rather than in measurable deterioration. Memory function seems adequate for his level. Well-learned information is retained, but he has difficulty in analyzing or organizing situations so as to discriminate between essential and nonessential details. He cannot apply abstract conceptual principles, and he responds to all problems in concrete terms. Mental impairment is reflected also in poor visual-motor productions and in faulty space-form perception.

"Emotionally he reacts over-readily and indiscriminately and applies little conscious control in the face of direct stress. He makes an effort to evade problematic situations, but if he fails in this attempt, aggression is openly and impulsively displayed.

"The total pattern of response, both intellectual and emotional, is characteristic of organic brain disease."

The aim of the psychologic examination in cases of this sort where no problem of psychiatric diagnosis exists is to provide details as to the nature of the altered functioning. The first question is whether an emotional or personality disorder is present in conjunction with the organic pathology. If such a disturbance is demonstrated, one is faced with the further question of whether it is a more or less direct consequence of the brain damage or whether it constitutes the patient's reaction to his illness. In this case there was little doubt that the emotional maladjustment was largely a consequence of poor control due to organic damage. In the light of the patient's history it was thus readily possible to understand portions of his delusional content (e.g., his fantasies about his dead son, and his sexual defensiveness) and the inhibited traits that the neurologic damage released. The essential illness was, however, on the psychologic side more a matter of formal deficit than of personality maladjustment. In other types of organic disturbance, a personality disorder may result from the patient's reaction to the threat of his illness, or test patterns may reveal evidence both of impairment and of reactive anxiety.

Chapter 17

Maladjustment in Later Maturity

ONE OF THE MOST recently developed fields of guidance is that which deals with the adjustment of the older person. In view of the increasing longevity that medical science and better social conditions have now made possible, it is, of course, not surprising that the problems of the elderly should have come to the fore in an unprecedented way. The terms *gerontology* and *geriatrics* have been coined to designate this important new area of research and treatment. While the early part of the present century saw the beginnings of the child guidance movement, the second half seems destined to bring similar advances in the understanding, education and adjustment of those who have reached later maturity. The case study reported in this chapter may serve to exemplify the role of psychodiagnosis in this field of orthopsychiatry.*

The patient was a 68 year-old woman who had been in and out of mental hospitals for the past seven years with a variety of neurologic and mental symptoms. The discussion of her problem will be oriented from the standpoint of her placement in a boarding home at a time when she was about to be released from the last of these institutions on indefinite visit. The psychologic examination will be considered in the light of its value to the psychiatrist and social worker in planning for her disposition.

This elderly woman was one of three siblings, the others being a brother and a sister who were both still living and well. The formal education of the patient ceased at the age of 18 when she was a senior in high school and had to leave because of typhoid fever. She appears never to have received her diploma. She then worked in a millinery

* The reader may find of interest the following article which includes a description of the same patient but from the social case-work point of view: Steinlein, C. R., Case work in a psychiatric hospital: some hostility factors. *J. psychiat. soc. Work,* 1947–48, 17, 75–83.

shop for about five years, until her marriage at the age of 23. Though she had no children, her marital life was described as happy, the relationship between husband and wife having always been a very congenial one.

The patient's father and mother reached nearly 80 before their deaths. The latter had been afflicted with tic douloureux for several years toward the end of her life and had apparently presented a number of senile symptoms that her relatives classified as "childish." The patient had nursed her mother during the latter's last five years and was much affected by her death. It may be significant that the patient herself developed tic douloureux in the following year, when she was 50; the psychiatrists who examined her at various times have considered the possibility of a psychogenic basis for this complaint—identification with the mother whose neuralgia had also been on the right side of the face. For her tic douloureux morphine was prescribed and was periodically administered during the intervening 18 years, sometimes throughout the day every few hours. She had also been treated for her ailment by nerve block injections of alcohol on some five or six different occasions with relief lasting from two weeks to a year in the various instances.

When the patient was 65 her husband died. Just as she had previously been deeply disturbed by her mother's death, her reaction to this event was again intense. She became disinterested in life and generally depressed. Her tic douloureux increased in severity and she had to take increased doses of morphine. In addition, she smoked excessively, resorted to alcohol whenever she could get it, and used other sedatives. It was largely in consequence of such behavior that it was found necessary to admit her at the age of 67 to the mental hospital where the present study was made.

On admission she was described as having no hallucinations or delusions but as showing signs of memory loss and of emotional instability and irresponsibility. She was considered incapable of caring for herself or of being provided for outside of an institution with her limited means. Mentally her symptoms were those of a depressed person who has lost interest in life. She indulged in aimless behavior, resorted to the use of sedatives and alcohol irresponsibly, and had once or twice frightened housekeepers, who were taking care of her, by erratic and threatening behavior. She was querulous and complaining about her neuralgia and insomnia. She described herself as an orphan, abandoned and not wanted, and was dependent and demanding at the same time, insisting especially that she be given medicine for her pain and for her sleeplessness.

Physically she presented a variety of symptoms. In addition to the tic douloureux already mentioned, she had some hypertension and arteriosclerosis. She appeared undernourished and anemic and had a limp due to the shortening of her right leg which had resulted from a fracture. A cane helped her to overcome her limp. Toward the end of her hospitalization she developed tachycardia and, still later, had several attacks of congestive heart failure. The provisional psychiatric diagnosis was Psychosis Associated with Organic Changes of the Nervous System; the final one, Psychosis with Arteriosclerosis.

The psychologic examination in this case first served the purpose of determining the degree of intellectual impairment, especially with respect to memory. It was of importance to know how far and in what ways the arteriosclerotic and other organic changes had affected her thinking processes. With respect to her possible placement outside the hospital, it was necessary to determine further the nature of her personality patterns as these might influence her chances of social adjustment. Some of the tests that were employed to answer these questions had been administered within a few weeks of the patient's admission to the institution; these were the Babcock-Levy Measurement of Efficiency of Mental Functioning and the Goldstein-Scheerer Cube Test for the evaluation of conceptual thinking ability. Two others—the Wells Memory Test and the Rorschach method—were given about five months later and well before plans were actually formulated for the patient's placement. In considering the disposition of the case, the entire test battery could therefore be consulted.

The patient was friendly, a little jocular, and submissively cooperative throughout the administration of the tests. She exerted obvious effort to carry out the instructions though she complained occasionally about the difficulty of the tasks and required praise and encouragement on the more complex items. She seemed to comprehend the requirements of the test situations readily and concentrated without obvious difficulty. She was clearly interested in the outcome of her efforts. Some of the more difficult problems aroused anxiety which she verbalized in comments like "I'm getting fussed" and by such motor manifestations as facial twitching and trembling of the hands. She had some insight regarding her degree of success and occasionally questioned the examiner about the correctness of her responses. Persistence was adequate. The pattern of her behavior in general—her childish dependence on the examiner, her quick flashes of easily dispersed irritability, lack of ability to judge her own responses, and somewhat jocular manner—was noted as characteristic of certain organic patients in the test situation. On the whole, the results appeared to be representative of her present functioning level.

The first test administered was the Babcock-Levy. On the Vocabulary section she defined 19 words correctly and was accordingly classified at year XIV (average intelligence). Her responses were somewhat rambling and erratic. Her definitions were loosely given and, to some extent, she failed items in an unpredictable fashion, i.e., regardless of difficulty. As compared with the year XIV level of achievement expected from this portion of the examination, her results on the other six sections ranged from year V to year XII and yielded an Efficiency Index of —6.6. She did best on items concerned with personal identification, familiar information, and well-learned rote material; poorest on tasks involving initial learning. The findings were interpreted, in accordance with the norms for this instrument, as giving clear evidence of deterioration.

The next procedure used—the Goldstein-Scheerer Cube Test—was intended to provide qualitative information about the process of conceptual thinking. This instrument has been found to be particularly instructive when employed with patients who have brain lesions or other organic nervous changes. It is based on the Kohs Block Designs (incorporated as a subtest into the Wechsler-Bellevue Scale) but has been modified for the purpose here in question by simplifying the steps that the examinee must make in order to afford him more concrete means of arriving at correct solutions. Under these circumstances it becomes possible to note more exactly the stages from concrete to abstract thinking as these are experienced by the particular subject.

The patient found it practically impossible to assemble successfully any of the designs in their original form, i.e., without the special aids provided according to the Goldstein-Scheerer modification. Her constructions were frequently loose, with open spaces and tilted blocks, and did not conform to the pattern she was supposed to be following. However, she seemed unaware of the discrepancy or was, at best, uncertain as to the correctness of her work. When aids which made it possible for her to copy the designs from models of identical size were provided, success was readily achieved—an indication of the concrete approach to which she was limited. But when she was then returned to the earlier situation in which she could not benefit from these aids, she became once more confused and unsuccessful. Such inability to profit from experience provided further evidence of the impairment of abstract thinking capacity frequently found among organically deteriorated patients.

The results of these two tests—the ones that she received soon after her admission to the institution—were considerably poorer than the findings on the two that were administered at a later date. It is possible that she had gained ground as a result of the care and treatment she had been receiving in the interim. In any event, the later results were interpreted as more closely representing her optimum level.

On the Wells Memory Test * she achieved a total Memory Quotient of 87. However, the Memory Quotient computed for "old recall"—under which heading are included items of personal identification, current information, well-learned school knowledge, etc.—was 93, and not significantly deviant from her present general intelligence level. On the portion of the instrument devoted to "new recall,"

* See footnote for page 272.

however, she achieved a Memory Quotient of only 79, reflecting the same difficulties that had appeared on the initial learning items of the Babcock-Levy procedure. She found it difficult to repeat the story read to her and to differentiate pictures which she had previously been shown from those which were introduced for the first time during the recognition trials. She likewise became confused in attempting to repeat digits backward and here expressed a certain amount of irritability. Taken in their entirety, the test results indicated a distinct, though not marked, impairment of memory. The findings were not, however, as poor as might have been anticipated from her performance on the Babcock-Levy and Goldstein-Scheerer and did not to the same degree contraindicate the possibility of her getting along in a boarding home.

The final technic employed was the Rorschach and was selected with a view to providing a more complete picture of her present mode of intellectual functioning as seen in conjunction with her emotional and general personality patterns. In this test her already noted impairment of memory interfered somewhat in providing a reliable record: she was not able to recall her responses when she was reminded of them as a basis for her elaborations in the inquiry phase of the procedure. Nevertheless, she produced 19 scoreable reactions. Interpretation afforded a picture of an essentially outgoing individual, susceptible to environmental stimulation though now becoming somewhat more withdrawn and egocentric than she had previously been. Clear evidence of effort and persistence in overcoming difficulties and a fairly well preserved grasp of social reality were reflected. Her perceptions were remarkably accurate and six popular concepts—indicative of ability to think in the conventional terms of her social world—were elicited. Some impulsivity and irritability were reflected. There were, however, no signs of unusual intellectual deterioration for her age or of psychotic personality disturbance. As seen in the more complete and interdependent fashion which the Rorschach method permits, the defects that had been revealed by her earlier tests assumed a far more benign appearance. The test results as a whole provided no basis for believing that she could not adjust in a protective noninstitutional environment.

The psychologic findings were of value to the psychiatrist and social worker in confirming their own observations that the patient's mental impairment was not so severe as to preclude the possibility of a boarding home placement. Moreover, the Rorschach method indicated that she had reasonably good emotional potentialities for living with others in the community.

But the patient had other ideas. She had made such an excellent institutional adjustment that a serious problem was encountered when the boarding plan was suggested to her. She was so comfortable in her surroundings that she preferred to remain there for the rest of her life. She had an income of $25 a month from Social Security and $1,000 in bonds from her husband's estate and was willing to turn over these funds to the hospital in return for her keep. Since, however, she had responded well to treatment and could no longer be regarded as suffering from any manifest psychosis, the plan for boarding her out was pursued and an attempt was made to bring about her emotional acceptance of this step. In the course of this process she wrote letters to her friends and relatives, painting a sorrowful picture of a person with no home who was being turned out into the cruel world. Despite this initial resistance, the physician and social worker were able in due course to help her accept outside placement, and a suitable boarding home was found. In that environment she at first had minor problems of adjustment because of her submissive but demanding attitudes and her complaints that the lady of the house was giving more attention to her room-mate than to herself. These and similar difficulties were gradually resolved and at the time of writing she was making an adequate adjustment without hospital supervision.

Chapter 18

Somatic Complaint as an Expression of Personality

WHILE IT HAS long been understood by the family physician that physical illness is never something separate from the total personality and experience of the patient, it has been only within the present century that a systematic approach to illness from this comprehensive point of view has emerged. The new impetus has stemmed largely from the understanding of unconscious processes in behavior as revealed by psychoanalysis. The increased knowledge of mental disorder which has resulted from psychoanalytic explorations is being gradually integrated with previous knowledge of physical disease to achieve a body of concepts under the designation "psychosomatic medicine." Problems of illness from this broadened standpoint are essentially matters of adaptation, growth and defense and include not only physical factors but psychologic and social ones as well. While the psychologic overtones of a fairly specific physical injury or illness ("somatopsychics") are highly significant, it is from the domain of internal medicine, where physical disease is closely bound up with the functioning of the autonomic nervous system, that arise the more involved and sometimes highly symbolized complaints in which both psyche and soma play their part.

Such a comprehensive view of illness and of injury inevitably challenges the clinical psychologist in his psychodiagnostic role. The projective methods, in particular, have proved valuable in this connection since they are, in a sense, psychologically neutral, prefiguring mode of function regardless of the tenuous distinction between conscious and unconscious processes. While some of the cases which are of psychosomatic interest involve abstruse formulations dependent upon intensive psychoanalysis, it seemed advisable to select for presentation here a simpler problem representative of those found not uncommonly in general practice.

The patient was a 16 year-old boy who was in his second year of high school at the time of his admission to a general hospital. He was the elder of two sons whose father was a college graduate and an engineer. The patient's life had been relatively uneventful until the age of ten. At that time his parents were contemplating separation because of an extra-marital relationship in which his mother was involved. The boy was aware of both the parental discord and its source. A few days before the separation was to be effected, the mother committed suicide. She was then 33 years of age.

Following this event the father made a brief and unsuccessful attempt to maintain a home with the aid of housekeepers. Subsequently the boys were placed in boarding schools whence they were able to pay the father infrequent short visits in the furnished room in which he lived. Because the brother was the younger an effort was made to keep him nearer home, the patient being placed in more distant schools. It should also be noted that shortly after the mother's death, the brother displayed some behavior disturbances and was seen at a child guidance clinic for a fairly long period. He was found to have a minor heart murmur which, while it necessitated no restriction of his activities, may have earned him some additional attention.

The patient's school record had been extremely variable. He had sometimes achieved placement on the honor roll, at other times he even failed. The father stated that he had not consciously stressed academic accomplishment or professional goals for the boys, but he admitted that he might have "taken these things for granted" in his attitudes. In any case, the patient was apparently working toward a career in engineering. It is also important to observe that in one of the schools he attended, he became a disciplinary problem and was involved in destructive mischief; it was requested that he not be returned the following year.

He was next placed in a school close to the city in which his father was residing. His initial adjustment here was rather good but during the first winter he received a knee injury while playing basketball and had to be hospitalized. There was some evidence that his complaints were prolonged beyond the point at which they had any clear physical basis. In any event, he was absent for so large a part of the school year that he could not be promoted.

When he returned to repeat the grade his behavior became somewhat seclusive and apathetic. He attributed these attitudes to his lack of ease with the younger boys with whom he now found himself and to his inability to participate in active sports. He spent much of his time roaming through the woods and surrounding country in solitary fashion. After six or eight weeks of school, at a point which happened to coincide with the first series of examinations for the year, he developed severe and persistent abdominal pains that required hospitalization. His complaints continued throughout his period of observation, and the pains appeared to become more vague and diffuse. When thorough examination failed to reveal any discernible physical basis for his discomfort, psychiatric consultation was requested. At the advice of the consultant he was transferred from a general to a psychiatric hospital for further study.

The application of psychodiagnostic technics in a case of this sort will depend somewhat upon the stage of the illness at which examination is made. In this instance the patient had been under medical observation for several weeks and the presence of physical disorder that might account for his symptoms had been ruled out. Moreover, he had already been examined by a psychiatrist with the finding that there was sufficient evidence of personality disturbance to warrant admission to a psychiatric hospital. The task confronting the psychologist was therefore different from what it would have been if he had been called on to examine the patient at the time of admission to the general hospital. Instead of having to determine whether emotional factors were present, it was the function of the psychodiagnostician to confirm the hypothesis of their presence and, further, to evaluate and define their degree and direction of impact.

The boy was seen approximately three days after his admission to the psychiatric hospital. He was pleasant and friendly and seemed no more ill-at-ease in the testing situation than any adolescent might be. He conversed freely but without taking his attention from the tasks set before him. He became absorbed in the procedures and expended evident effort in carrying them out. He seemed to enjoy them as an experience closely related to his familiar school routine and was very willing to return for a second test session on the afternoon of the same day on which he had had his initial appointment. It seemed clear that his condition in no way interfered with his doing the best of which he was intellectually capable; later analysis of the test results afforded no reason to believe that he had ever functioned at a significantly higher level.

The first test administered was the Wechsler-Bellevue. He earned a Verbal Scale I. Q. of 110 and a Performance Scale I. Q. of 96. His total rating of 105 placed him in the average range. He achieved the highest score on arithmetic problems but his performance in tasks involving factual knowledge and vocabulary was also very good. A pattern of this kind is often found among individuals who attempt to compensate for feelings of social inadequacy by a display of well-learned factual information that requires no particular flexibility or adaptiveness to produce. A similar rigidity was noted in his undue concern with details throughout the scale—a tendency that, nevertheless, helped him in identifying the missing details of pictures. Consistent with these findings is the fact that it proved very difficult for him to adopt the flexibility of attitude required for finding general similarities between concepts; he quickly resorted to a helpless "I don't know" in a series of such items.

His poorer general performance on the manipulative tasks seemed based upon a tendency to "blow up" in the face of difficulty with recourse to impulsive, illogical, almost purposeless behavior. Such evidence appeared twice, at points where he was suddenly confronted with tasks of greater complexity than he had heretofore encountered. He failed these initial tasks completely, not even earning partial credit, but he then proceeded to do the next and more difficult item of the same kind perfectly. In one instance he even earned additional time credit on the harder item.

The discovery at a later date that this boy had an abnormal brain-wave pattern is of interest in this context. The possibility exists that the failures just noted could have been due to brief lapses from consciousness of a subclinical, petit-mal nature. There was, however, no directly observable evidence of such interruptions and the points at which the failures occurred would still significantly support the foregoing interpretation of his reaction patterns.

At the conclusion of the Wechsler-Bellevue examination, then, some clues as to the patient's problems existed. There was a discrepancy between his ability and his goals. With merely average intelligence the training of an engineer was probably beyond him. Not only did it seem likely that he lacked the capacity for completing a college course with any degree of ease, but the specific types of activity most closely related to engineering were just those in which he exhibited the readiest breakdown and disorganization. It therefore became advisable to investigate further the sphere of his relationships with his father—to see whether his plan to follow in his father's footsteps was an expression of his own emotional needs or merely of passive submission to his father's needs. Another direction of possible inquiry concerned the implications for personality structure of the gap between his goals and his abilities—a gap that might signify an unrealistic adjustment to his environment on a schizoid basis.

Among the personality tests he was given in order to evaluate these hypotheses was the Rosenzweig Picture-Frustration Study. His reactions to these situations of mild stress and conflict were not grossly different from the expected normal behavior. He tended to be outwardly aggressive, blaming others readily but not excessively. A more significantly immature type of response appeared in his insistence on prompt satisfaction from others. However, he was not highly dependent or helpless in his reactions and seemed capable of taking steps toward reaching a constructive solution of problems himself. Moreover, he proved to be sensitive to conventionalized modes of behavior in socially stressful situations and could gloss over difficulties tactfully on occasion.

These findings gain in meaning from the results of other test procedures several of which indicated that, though his aggressive reactions to frustration were, on the whole and on the surface, adequately controlled, this pattern was more complex than at first appeared. His responses to the Word Association Test, for example, tended, in general, to be prompt, but he had extremely delayed reaction times (twelve to twenty-three seconds) to the words *fight, bite, suck,* and his response to the word *love* was "hit." Moreover, those stories on the Thematic Apperception Test which involved either a sibling rivalry theme or a woman in the role of wife were attended by strong expressions of outer aggression and were occasionally followed by reactions of self-punishment.

Another aspect of his personality that grew clearer from the other technics administered was his orientation toward an independent adult status. His stories on the Thematic Apperception Test indicated that one of his major conflicts concerned independence from parental domination. While such an attitude is common enough in adolescence, the trend is complicated for this boy by his recognition that in becoming less dependent he will have to assume adult responsibilities. Though in interviews he tended to deny any such conflict, the projective technics gave other evidence, especially as regards his educational and vocational goals. A contrast between a professional status expected of him by his family and a simpler position in life more agreeable to himself could be readily discerned.

His manner of coping with this conflict of ideals was further defined by the rather individualized relationship to his environment brought out by the Rorschach method. While he proved to be quite alert to the demands of reality, with no evidence of pathologic withdrawal, he did not appear to choose a socialized approach by preference. In confirmation of the Wechsler-Bellevue results reported above, he showed here, too, a high degree of rigidity, clinging to his own idiosyncrasies beyond the limits of effective adjustment. In his 28 reactions to the ink-blots he offered only two percepts commonly identified by normal persons. Moreover, he denied the pertinence of other popular responses when these were suggested to him as possibilities in "testing the limits." His performance in the Word Association Test was similarly lacking in common responses. The Rorschach further yielded indications of negativistic thinking and showed little capacity for meaningful personal relationships or warm ties with others. From these findings it appeared that the patient had managed an adjustment to a protective environment that permitted him the expression of his own special interests, but that he viewed his social surroundings in a highly individualized fashion. A somewhat schizoid pattern of adaptation seemed to be characteristic of him.

The content of some of the patient's productions considered in relation to his life experiences throws additional light upon his problems. His Rorschach responses were largely anatomical and he interrupted this test at one point to mention that he was reminded by the material of his brother's cardiac condition. This comment, which occurred early in the examination series, gave rise to the hypothesis that his somatic complaints might be related to sibling rivalry and might, in particular, be unconsciously intended to win for him the attention and affection that his brother had received on similar grounds. When the patient later interpreted one of the TAT pictures as representing a boy who has been sent away from home, is homesick, and consequently becomes physically ill, the hypothesis seemed in some measure verified by his thus relating parental rejection to physical illness.

Since this boy was passing through a period of normal emotional upheaval and growth attendant upon adolescence, it was important to note any features which might prognosticate his ultimate adjustment. There was evidence that his hesitancy regarding an independent adult role had specific reference to the unattractiveness of heterosexual relationships. As has already been pointed out, he expressed marked aggression toward women nor could he think of the marital situation as a happy one. The roles of adulthood would hence be more difficult for him than for the average adolescent to assume, and a tendency to withdraw from social contacts might naturally ensue.

In summary, then, this adolescent boy seemed to be confronted with intellectual demands imposed by his father and emotional demands implied by his social environment with which he was not equipped to cope. The development of his personality had been markedly influenced by a sense of parental rejection and of sibling rivalry. His characteristic behavior might be viewed as a vacillation between the repudiation of authority and social reality, on the one hand, and an infantile need to be accepted, on the other. Anxiety and guilt resulting from this conflict could find resolution in such somatic symptoms as he had. With his rather schizoid personality structure it would be conceivable for him to continue toward a more malignant form of withdrawal but the specificity of his complaints justified a more hopeful prognosis if treatment could be instituted for his interpersonal problems.

The present case has illustrated the value of psychodiagnostic exploration in some problems that are superficially of a somatic nature. It is true that the above analysis leaves unsettled the choice of the particular somatic complaint—abdominal pains—which first brought the patient to medical attention. To account for such details a much more exhaustive knowledge of the patient would be required and such understanding might even then not be forthcoming in the present state of psychosomatic knowledge. Descriptively, however, the problem of this adolescent boy is representative of many others which arise in the general hospital and which could most profitably be attacked by combined somatic and psychologic approaches.

Chapter 19

Amnesia as a Pattern of Reaction

IN THE HISTORY of psychopathology the study of hysteria and hypnosis in France during the nineteenth century marked an epoch. With the advent of psychoanalysis, interest in the more formal characteristics of dissociation and suggestibility gave way rather decidedly to the study of motivational dynamics. There thus developed a certain gap between the descriptive knowledge of structure in dissociated states and the psychodynamic formulations regarding etiology. It is therefore encouraging that during the past few years there have been timely signs of a revival of interest in hypnosis and hysteria coupled now, however, with a dynamic orientation.

The case which is reported in this chapter has many of the dramatic characteristics of the classical states of dissociation described in French psychopathology. Since, however, the emphasis of the study is upon psychodynamics, some of the problems that are posed for current research in this important area of psychopathology come rather clearly into focus.

SOCIAL AND PSYCHIATRIC HISTORY

The patient was a young man of 24. He had been adopted together with a twin brother at the age of 18 months from an orphanage where they had been left when less than a year old. His relationship to the twin brother had been problematic throughout the history. The brother was said always to have been stronger, larger, and generally more dominant. According to one report, he was born first. In any event, this brother was apparently favored from earliest years by virtue of physical characteristics and personality traits, and the adoptive father, especially, is supposed to have been very fond of him.

The school record of both boys was poor. The patient had difficulties throughout the course of his education, and the parents were rather disappointed in his poor achievement. The employment history showed much instability. In the few years that he had been working, he had had 16 jobs, the longest lasting five months. At times while working in other cities, he had misinformed his parents as to the nature and location of his job. His avocations included playing the piano and singing in the church choir, and—during preparatory school —wrestling. He was, in fact, for a time state champion wrestler at his level.

The adoption occurred when the parents were middle-aged—the mother 45, the father 58. They had had two children who died shortly after birth. They became interested in adopting a boy and when the orphanage informed them that twin boys were available, the parents decided to consider the proposal. The decision was finally reached to take both infants though, according to one report, it was the brother of the patient they really wanted. (It is of interest in this connection that the father was called John and that the patient's twin bore the same name.) It was not until they were about nine years old that the twins learned from the parents about the adoptive relationship.

The mother was the more dominant of the parents—a statement borne out by various incidents in the history as well as by the patient's own description. She controlled most situations in the home and managed the affairs of the children. Very rarely did the patient do anything without her intervention. When, for example, he was to be seen in the out-patient department, the mother insisted that she speak to the psychiatrist first.

The father was for many years secretary of an organization of churches. The home was naturally a very religious one in which churchgoing was a definite requirement. The patient was highly regarded because he unfailingly observed this practice.

The onset of the illness dated back about four and a half years although there were earlier indications of maladjustment. It was reported that the patient had walked in his sleep during childhood.

At the age of 11 both boys were seen at a child guidance clinic. They had been having difficulties in school work and were involved in minor thefts. The situation at that time was described by the agency as follows: Both boys were underweight and poorly developed physically. They were somewhat limited in mental ability, being rated as of low average intelligence, with the patient slightly lower than his brother. The patient's school achievement was not equal to his fifth-grade placement which was, however, within the limits of his measurable ability. In appearance the boys were much alike, but in personality they were very different. The patient seemed to be docile, easy-going, generous, and conforming, whereas his twin was noted to be more assertive, selfish, intractable, and sullen. There were suggestions of marked rivalry between the boys, the twin demonstrating his superiority in an aggressive fashion while the patient tended to side with the adoptive parents and to show up his brother in subtle ways. In the psychiatric interviews both boys were distractible and hyperactive. The patient, in particular, exhibited much show-off behavior and demonstrated a marked sense of inferiority. The adoptive parents were noted as being elderly persons of some culture and considerable wealth. They were both quite rigid, religious people who had extremely high standards of behavior and achievement and were therefore much disappointed by the delinquent and unscholarly practices of the twins. The parents considered it their primary duty to instil principles of morality, uprightness, and honesty in the children; but they often disagreed as to disciplinary measures, the father maintaining that the mother was too lenient. There seemed to be little evidence of real warmth in the home or understanding of the boys. Attempts to work with the parents proved futile since they refused to accept the boys' limitations or to lower their aspirations for them.

Shortly after this contact with the child guidance center the parents decided to send the boys away to school and reported that the twins were adjusting well there. Eight years later the mother telephoned repeatedly to get advice about the patient. He was reported by her to have been stealing and to have run away from home several times. Spells of unconsciousness were also mentioned. Since the boy was already under the care of a private psychiatrist, the mother was referred to this doctor whenever she called.

When the patient was 20, the illness had its frank onset. While working at a radio station, he appropriated a letter containing eight or nine dollars. When the theft was discovered, he was sent home. The mother insisted that he return the money personally and undertook to supervise this act herself. Plans were made for him to meet her at a prearranged place from which she would accompany him. He left home to keep his appointment but instead was next heard from in a city about 100 miles distant several days later. The manager of a hotel at which the patient had registered telephoned the parents that the boy was there and seemed to be suffering from an attack of amnesia. He had been sleeping for an inordinate number of hours and did not know his identity. This fugue-like episode was the first of many spells which occurred subsequently.

Five months after the first attack the patient joined the Coast Guard. While in the service his amnesic episodes recurred and he was accordingly discharged. He was admitted to the psychiatric ward of a local hospital and received electroshock treatment there the following year; but since his condition failed to improve, he became a voluntary patient at a state hospital for a short period. The following month he was seen as a psychiatric out-patient for one visit. A second series of shock treatments was later administered at the local hospital already mentioned. His condition now became worse. He displayed uncontrolled violence at times and ran away from home repeatedly. On one occasion he took the family car and returned three days later after abandoning it. He apparently arrived at the house late at night and, instead of arousing the family, procured a ladder, entered through an upstairs bedroom window, and hid in a clothes closet. When the parents awoke as a result of overhearing him, he made threats with a pistol which proved later to be a toy. In the meantime the neighbors, who had also been aroused by the patient's unusual behavior, became alarmed and called the police. He was taken to jail and readmitted to the state hospital. Six months later, at the age of 24, he was transferred as an in-patient to the hospital where the present study was made. The admission diagnosis was Psychoneurosis, Hysteria with Amnesia.

INTERVIEW

It may be useful to supplement the preceding picture with a short stenographically recorded interview between the psychologist and the patient. The conversation was originally intended to give the group before whom this case was presented a direct impression of the patient's personality—an advantage less inherent in the transcription—and to elicit for comparative purposes the patient's views upon some topics of importance in the history and in the test findings.

Examiner: Hello, Mr. W. As I told you yesterday, a group of psychologists and psychiatrists are having a conference here. We wanted to have a better idea of your problem so that we might discuss it more intelligently. Tell me, how long have you been here now?

Patient: I have been here a little over two months.

Examiner: Have you enjoyed your stay here?

Patient: Very much, sir.

Examiner: How have you been occupying your time?

Patient: I work in the library. I do bookkeeping and a few odd jobs.

Examiner: You go down there every day ordinarily?

Patient: Yes.

Examiner: What are you having in the way of treatment?

Patient: The doctor is doing some hypnosis.

Examiner: How long has this treatment been going on?

Patient: It has been going on for about three weeks.

Examiner: How does it affect you? Do you enjoy it or do you dislike it?

Patient: It doesn't bother me. I just go to sleep.

Examiner: Has it had any noticeable effect upon your condition?

Patient: A little.

Examiner: What would you say was wrong with you?

Patient: I have a case of amnesia.

Examiner: Could you talk just a little louder?

Patient: (Repeats answer.) I'll be walking along the street and I'll have a case of amnesia. In a week or ten days I'll not know what has happened to me or what has been going on since the attack. I go into it instantaneously and come out of it just as quickly.

Examiner: What does *amnesia* mean to you?

Patient: Loss of memory.

Examiner: That is, you don't remember what happened to you?

Patient: (Nods.)

Examiner: Sometimes in amnesia people go about doing their jobs and don't remember the past. What happens to you?

Patient: I don't know what happens to me. I guess I act normally. I've never found myself in jail under the circumstances. Only once did I find myself in jail. I went over to the post office and I never got back. I went to L— and when I came out of it I found myself in jail. I was told that I had U. S. mail on me.

Examiner: Could you give us an idea of the kind of fellow your twin brother is?

Patient: Well, I might be partial. He's larger than I am. We like the same things fundamentally. We never went out for the same sports. When we were small we played together—not against each other. When we played football, we never played opposite each other. We always played together.

Examiner: You say he's larger and has somewhat different taste in sports. Can you tell us anything else?

Patient: When I get mad I usually blow up. When he gets mad he usually pouts.

Examiner: Do you look very much alike?

Patient: We would look very much alike if we were the same size. We were when we were children.

Examiner: At what age would you say you became easily distinguishable? Was there anything that happened along about that time?

Patient: My brother has been a year ahead of me. He lost his teeth before I did, had the measles first, and so forth. I guess I had delayed action.

Examiner: Could you just give us a brief picture of your parents? What kind of people are your parents?

Patient: Again I'm probably partial. I have a very understanding mother and a very understanding father. They have always tried to treat us very nice.

Examiner: Is there anything that you might wish were different about your parents?

Patient: Well, if I wanted to do something they didn't think was exactly right, they would tell me. If I still wanted to go through with it, they would back me up. They would tell me their objections first.

Examiner: Well, now, I think that that's pretty much all we wanted to talk about. Thank you, Mr. W.

Patient: Glad to have helped.

PSYCHOLOGIC TEST RESULTS

To investigate personality structure and dynamics the Rorschach Method of Personality Diagnosis, the Thematic Apperception Test, the Picture-Frustration Study, an adaptation of the Goodenough Draw-A-Man Test, and the Photoscope (described below) were employed. The Rorschach method was considered valuable for its over-all picture of the problematic personality structure involved in this case. The Thematic Apperception Test was included to illuminate the motivational situation in general and the family relationships in particular. The Picture-Frustration Study was expected to clarify the role which habitual modes of responding to stress, with or without aggression, might have contributed to the illness. From the drawing test and the Photoscope information about the patient's psychosexual orientation—of interest in most cases of hysterical reaction type—was to be derived. To elicit the patient's opinions of himself as regards various aspects of personality and experience, the Minnesota Multiphasic Personality Inventory was administered. To evaluate his intellectual capacities in relation to his adjustment, the Wechsler-Bellevue Intelligence Scale was used. The findings from these various projective and nonprojective instruments will at first be reported separately and briefly. Occasional comparative points will be noted. Finally, an effort will be made to integrate the results of the tests with the data from the social and psychiatric history.

Throughout the various testing situations the patient proved highly cooperative. He carried out all instructions readily and without question though blocking and evasion occurred occasionally, possibly without his conscious awareness, especially during the projective procedures. In the capacity tests he seemed to be indifferent to failure and attempted to appear nonchalant. Several times he used odd phrases and mispronounced words in a mildly pedantic fashion. He expected the examiner to accept him as a pleasant, good-natured individual with certain weaknesses which were to be excused. On the whole, he appeared to enjoy the tests.

The patient was given intelligence tests on at least three occasions. At the age of 11, when he was being seen at the child guidance clinic, a Stanford-Binet was administered. He received an I. Q. of 89 and was judged to be of low average intelligence. When examined as a psychiatric out-patient, he earned an I. Q. of 106 on the Wechsler-Bellevue Scale. This test was again administered shortly after his current admission as an in-patient. The I. Q. obtained was 116. A trend toward improvement appears in these figures though, of course, there are hazards in comparing a Stanford-Binet I. Q. at the age of 11 with Wechsler-Bellevue results at 20. The assumption of an increase in poise since childhood and a decrease in the insecurity attendant upon sibling rivalry would help to account for the observed trend. The difference between the two Wechsler-Bellevue results is not remarkable, though here again some gain in security at the second testing situation should be considered. Currently he tested at the level of bright normal intelligence. Considered in terms of subtest pattern, it is of interest that the Verbal and Performance Scale ratings were practically the same on both recent examinations. His ability to organize and to plan ahead was particularly weak. He spontaneously maintained attention with difficulty though he could concentrate when the demand was externally imposed. This last-noted characteristic may be interpreted as a function of his extreme need to comply with social pressure.

The Minnesota Multiphasic Personality Inventory yielded a completely normal profile. "Objectively," i.e., in the terms of the inventory, he would need to be diagnosed as mentally well. More qualitatively, however, the results showed his evasiveness regarding his adjustment in the family. Since, however, the patient was so evasive, little beyond this fact itself could be learned from the inventory approach, and its use for obtaining a picture of the patient's self-estimate was curtailed.

The projective technics may now be considered. Because of its comprehensiveness, the Rorschach will be discussed first.* The patient was given three Rorschach tests—once while an out-patient, again when he entered as an in-patient, and, finally, about a month thereafter. Since the first examination was brief and inconclusive, the present interpretation is based chiefly upon the two later tests. The picture revealed was that of a normally intelligent individual who behaved in highly concrete terms, at times escaping into unessential details. The capacity to think abstractly and to organize concepts was definitely weak. (Whole responses, for example, were extremely infrequent. The results thus far were in good agreement with those of the conventional intelligence tests.) In social situations he was apt to be lacking in poise and in genuine participation. His relationship to other individuals was an anxious one. (Predominance of part over whole human responses and inadequate color distribution.) He was limited in his spontaneous expression of emotion though capable of a superficially good adjustment by overconventionality. Neurotic indications were present, the clearest evidences being the inferiority trends which consistently stood out (e.g., numerous vista responses) and the marked sense of inadequacy, possibly sexual, found especially in the repeated responses concerned with extremities of the body (fingers, thumbs, feet). No typically psychotic responses or patterns appeared in the various records.

A comparison of the two last administered Rorschach tests is of interest and is summarized in the accompanying table. As will be noted, the latter of the two examinations was about 30 per cent more productive. Of the 44 responses given in this second test, 27 were identical with those in the earlier one, and 17 were new. Nevertheless, the

* It should be noted that the method of scoring adopted for these records is based upon Beck rather than Klopfer and thus represents an exception to the practice in Parts II and III. See S. J. Beck, Rorschach's Test. Vol. I. New York: Grune and Stratton, 1944.

majority of the important test factors and ratios were remarkably consistent from the one to the other examination. (This interpretation preeminently involves the apperception type, the percentage of animal responses, the distribution of color responses, the experience balance, the high frequency of vista responses, and the ratio of whole to movement responses.) Moreover, taken as a whole each of the two records was essentially the same in import.

The Picture-Frustration Study highlighted again the overconventionality of the patient and his tendency to gloss over frustrating situations evasively. His Group Conformity Rating was extremely high and his typical response patterns were impunitive. He brought himself only with difficulty to a direct expression of aggression against the environment except when in so doing he managed to exact help from others in his weakness. These findings were obviously in good agreement with the evasiveness already noted in the Minnesota Multiphasic and with the social anxiety expressed in the Rorschach responses. The fact that the patient had proved to be readily hypnotizable could in part be attributed to the combination of compliance and evasiveness here revealed.

The adaptation of the Goodenough Draw-A-Man Test involved the drawing of, first, a man and, then, a woman. The patient's drawings have been reproduced and described as the second illustrative case for this test in Part II (p. 41). To recapitulate briefly: His productions portrayed a weak and ineffectual man, whose head was unusually small for his body, who had no hands and only crudely depicted feet. The woman was much larger and more completely elaborated in several respects. These results suggested a problem of sexual identification that underscored the historical information regarding the dominance of the patient's mother. It is, in fact, not unlikely that in these drawings he was unconsciously producing psychologic pictures of his parents which had by now become generalized to include all men and women. The hypothesis was further in order that he was possibly suffering from a sense of sexual inadequacy resulting from identification with a weak father-figure and subordination to an overdominant mother.

The evidence from the drawings recalled also the marked preoccupation with extremities of the body found in the Rorschach record—a cumulative result that would readily suggest to those with a Freudian bent the presence of "castration anxiety."

A Comparison of Some Scoring Categories in Two Rorschach Records

Scoring Category	9–12–46	10–19–46
R	32	44
Ap	D!Dd	D!(Dd)
Z	23	36.5
F+%	87	76
F%	56	73
A%	31	34
P	5	9
ΣC	2(1FC, 1CF)	2(1FC, 1CF)
M:ΣC	3:2	3:2
FV	5	6
S	2	4
W:M	1:3	2:3

From the Thematic Apperception Test further evidence regarding the patient's family adjustment was obtained. In general, his orientation toward his parents seemed to be characterized by pronounced ambivalence. While it appeared that, on the one hand, he resented the authority of his parents, on the other hand, he had a sense of indebtedness to them for everything they had done for him. He was accordingly guilt-ridden for such hostile impulses as he at times entertained toward them. As previously noted in connection with the Picture-Frustration Study and as again revealed in the present test findings, he attempted ordinarily to avoid any overt expression of aggression against others. Another consequence of his unstable relationship to the parents was his failure to have achieved independence from them. He still thought of himself as dependent upon older men though, at the same time, he rejected the father figure in the role of helper since too much pain was associated with such an acknowledgment. Hostility toward the mother was also clearly in evidence. He exhibited a need to escape from the control which both parents had exercised. These results were of special interest in the light of the interview, above reported, and the Minnesota Multiphasic Inventory, in both of which difficulties with the parents were denied. In the interview, for example, the parents were characterized by him as "very understanding." The TAT proved more deeply revealing.

The patient's problems in experiencing and expressing aggression may be illustrated by the story which he told for Card 3BM. This card shows the huddled form of a boy (or girl) crouched on the floor against a couch with his head bowed on his right arm; behind him on the floor lies an object which is often interpreted as a revolver or other weapon. The story told by the patient was as follows:

Could you tell me what that was? (Points to object on floor.) It's rather a vague object. Well, I guess we could put it by saying she's a young girl and she's rather tired. And she sat down on the floor and everything was so quiet and peaceful. And she laid her head across the end of the bed and fell asleep. [What led up to this?] Why she got tired? Well, she's probably done a pretty hard day's work. Maybe she's married and has small children. Usually children romp all over the house, and after doing the day's work and also taking care of the children, she's a pretty tired woman. Let's say her husband works at night and won't be home till late. And while waiting for him, she fell asleep. [How will it turn out?] Well, she'll sleep very peacefully until her husband comes home. When her husband opens up the lock on the door, she'll awaken. She'll cook him something to eat before he goes to bed. She'll tell him what she's done during the day, and he'll tell her what he's done.

Evasion of aggression was exhibited not only in the failure to identify the "weapon" but even more unmistakably in the content of the story. The girl is described as merely tired. Most subjects ascribe to the character an experience of sorrow, a crime, or a suicidal act.

Another important theme in the patient's stories—one that has been noted before in the Rorschach report—was found to be the striving to compensate for inferiority. The story told for 17 BM is a good example. The picture shows a naked man clinging to a rope in the act of climbing up or down. The patient narrated the following:

Well, this one's like a man that's sort of training—might be training for a boxing match, might be training for a wrestling match. He realizes he needs more strength in his shoulders and back. To accomplish that, he climbs the rope to the top of the gym. He climbs up and down that rope, up and down that rope. Finally, after much hard work with the rope and other things he gets more strength in his shoulders and back. He finally decides he's developed enough. He's confident of winning. It's a good meet that he's going into; it's a tough man he's going to oppose. But there's hope—there's plenty of hope. (Unusual vehemence here.) He must toughen himself for the ordeal. Finally after many weeks of training, after many weeks of exercise, the time comes for the meet. He was told right: his opponent was good. But he had something his opponent did not have. That was the knowledge that he was in fine physical condition. He had worked. Finally after a long, hard struggle he won. It was worth it. Because he not only proved to others but he proved to himself that he could do it. [What led up to this?] I think he was probably challenged—somebody probably told him he was scared of this man. Being a man of pride, he was determined himself that no one would call him a coward. So he took up this challenge. But he had to work. And work he did.

Not only was the general theme of compensation for inferiority here exhibited but the autobiographic relevance was underscored by the reference to wrestling. It will be recalled that the patient was at one time a champion wrestler. The indication was that his interest in that sport might have been compensatory in nature.

The final trend to be noted here concerns a moralistic and somewhat vapid attitude of optimism and hope for the future: a fair reward awaits him who tries and tries again despite discouraging obstacles. As will be readily recognized, this theme in a sense combines the evasion of aggression and the compensatory effort to overcome inferiority which have already been mentioned. The story which may serve for illustration was told for the blank card—the card which requires the subject not only to tell a story but first to imagine a picture as well. The patient's response was as follows:

You mean make up a picture in my mind? [Yes.] Let's say there's a high mountain. On top of this mountain you can find a beautiful view. A young man is standing on top of the mountain. And he throws his head up to the sky—throws it up toward the heavens. That's the picture. [And now the story?] This young man has been told by a friend that this was a hard mountain to climb. Yet when he got to the top, he would see something that would make the climb worth while—the view. When he got to the top, he looked over—it was a hard climb—and looked over and saw the view. And he raises his head and starts to think: "Life is sort of like this. Everybody must reach his goal. It's not an easy way— there are stumbling blocks, sometimes trouble. When you get up to the top and reach the goal, you look back and find that it was really worth while. The climb and struggle may be the setbacks for many, but it was worth it after all, because you have—he had something to look forward to." With this in his mind, he climbs down the mountain and follows his reasoning. The goal is near. [What was his goal?] I don't think that's unimportant—I mean important. I don't think that's really necessary.

The slip in the next to the last statement is noteworthy since it exemplified the patient's tendency to evade any realistic recognition of his problems.

Since the Photoscope, the final procedure to be discussed, is still in the process of experimental standardization, a brief introductory description of the method may be of value.* The approach is projective in nature and is designed to evaluate psychosexual interest and status. The detection of homosexual trends is one of its more particular objectives. The method employs a series of selected pictures ranging in subject matter from neutral designs and objects through heterosexual and suggestively homosexual content. The subject exposes the cards one at a time by means of a specially constructed apparatus (for which the test is named) which enables him to view the pictures in rotation and to repeat the performance at the end of the series. He is left by

* This technic was originated by the senior author and is being developed by him.

himself during the viewing of the pictures, the examiner having excused himself on some pretext, but the time spent on each card is automatically recorded. By means of a one-way screen and a concealed microphone, other significant behavior, including verbalizations, can be noted. After the pictures have been examined by the subject twice, the examiner re-enters the testing room and requests him to relax on a couch. Additional steps are then carried out in the following order: recall of the pictures, free association in connection with those remembered, report of any recent dream, and the construction of a story at will (in the fashion of the response to the blank card on the Thematic Apperception Test). Finally, the subject is seated at a small table and presented with miniature reproductions of the photoscope pictures in groups of five which he is asked to arrange in the order of his preference. Three sets of quantitative findings thus become available: the viewing times, which throw light upon the spontaneous or implicit interest of the subject in the various pictures; choice of pictures according to conscious preference; and number and choice of pictures recalled—in which "repression" may be disclosed. In more qualitative terms, the free associations and the reported dream and fantasy supply a context for the quantitative data.

In the viewing of the pictures the patient, according to the recorded viewing times, tended to reject active heterosexual subject matter. The time spent on pictures of this type was very brief—as brief, in fact, as the time given to neutral and presumably uninteresting designs. He was, on the other hand, more interested in pictures of suggestively homosexual content. The neutral objects were, on the average, attended to for the longest periods—a result again suggesting his well-known evasiveness. His conscious preferences could be understandingly reconciled with the preceding pattern. He showed highest preference for the neutral objects, delegated the "homosexual" pictures to an intermediate position, and the heterosexual ones, in general, to the least preferred. Even by the incomplete standards for interpretation which are at present available, the findings seemed significant since normal males consistently prefer the heterosexual to the "homosexual" pictures.

A question was thus again raised as to the heterosexual maturity of the patient.

The recall of the pictures was, in the large, not revealing since, having anticipated that he might be asked to describe or otherwise identify them, he remembered nearly all. However, some details in the recall process are illuminating. After the patient had been shown the miniature pictures in order to determine his conscious preferences, he commented spontaneously that he had missed two of them. He designated these pictures as "the dogs and the flowers." He began musing as to why he might have forgotten these pictures: "I thought the dogs were very cute, too—the mother looking at the baby dog. The flowers—I can't understand that—it was one of my favorites." On being asked whether he could offer any explanation for forgetting the flowers, he continued: "I think it had a hardness to it, and I don't like hardness in art. If it's supposed to be hard—all right; but if it isn't, I don't like it." The significance of these remarks was clarified by noting the sequence in which certain of the pictures were first seen by the patient and his description of them in his recall. In remembering the picture of a woman nursing a baby at her exposed breast, he had said, "Then there was a picture that reminded me of a statue—because of the hardness of the drawing—a hardness look—of a mother and a child. The child seemed to be sleeping." While this characterization of the picture as a statue was of interest in its agreement with his tendency to see statues rather than normally alive whole human figures in the Rorschach ink-blots, there was a particular interest in his characterization of it as having "a hardness look." It will be observed that he had made a similar comment in attempting to account for his having forgotten the picture of the flowers, but in that instance he went further and declared, "I don't like hardness in art." It may then be inferred that the picture of the mother nursing a baby and that of the flowers had for him an unpleasant hard quality in common. Some light may possibly be thrown upon the similarity which he saw in these two pictures by the fact that in the viewing series they immediately follow each other in the order: mother and baby, flowers. He could, then, readily have transposed to the second of the pictures a negative characterization which was for him inherent in the first. While he remembered the first, he repressed the second. In the light of the present analysis the forgetting of the other picture may also now be interpreted. The picture in question is that of the mother dog and puppy—a picture not dissimilar in general content to that of the mother and nursing baby. The hypothesis suggests itself that the picture of the dogs was forgotten because it became associated for him with the content *human mother and baby*. Thus the two pictures forgotten have collectively the characteristics of the picture to which he probably reacted most strongly and negatively though he did not for some reason forget it; i.e., the mother-and-baby situation in the picture of the dogs when combined with the "hardness look" of the flowers produces the picture of the human mother and child which he characterized as looking hard like a statue. The importance of this somewhat lengthy analysis lies in showing how the already noted evasiveness of the patient was functioning at a somewhat deeper level of personality as "repression" and how, more specifically, his aversion for his mother could have influenced not only his reaction to the mother-child picture but his general rejection of the heterosexual material in the Photoscope examination. The normality of his heterosexual interests was accordingly questioned.

The part of the procedure concerned with recent dreams merely elicited a denial of ever dreaming. The statement was taken as another indication of his tendency to repress and dissociate. His response to the request for a fantasy was more productive. The picture he described and the interpretation he made follow:

You have large mountains in the background—in the valley, a field of wheat. Just coming over the mountains is the sun. The breeze is blowing a bit and there is a ripple in the wheat.

Well, it reminds me very much of the sun—coming up—representing life—to give what the wheat needs—sunshine. The wind blowing lets the wheat move so that the sun can get at it in all directions. The sun is doing the wheat good—making it grow. All night it doesn't get light. The moon wasn't bright enough—didn't have the qualities. The wheat seems glad (laughs)—if you can say that—to see it. All of it reminds me of all life. The sun is something humans look forward to. The sun coming over the horizon is like human hopes—progress—like acccomplishing something instead of having a failure.

The preoccupation with distant views and mountain scenery exemplified here has been mentioned previously in reporting the Rorschach findings and in discussing the TAT. Beck, following a suggestion of Adler, has provided a basis for interpreting vista responses in the Rorschach which seems particularly appropriate in this case where the very brief Rorschach responses and the more detailed TAT stories were so definitely found to project the same preoccupations. Jointly these productions testified to the patient's deep-seated compensatory trends for sensed inferiority. He was continually comparing the near with the distant, himself with others, and presumably overstriving to make up for what he so painfully lacked. The quoted story regarding mountain-climbing from the regular TAT lends itself quite obviously to such an interpretation since in it the theme of compensation was explicitly stated. In the above example from the Photoscope his "optimism" and sexual passivity also entered. It was therefore inferred that while the rivalry with the brother and the attitudes of inferiority connected with his adoptive situation were perhaps less consciously manifest than they had been during his childhood and adolescence, he was still preoccupied with these same problems and functioned unconsciously in an orientation of inferiority-superiority.

In presenting the results of the several tests one by one an effort has been made to indicate in some degree the cumulative drift of the evidence. As has been repeatedly stated, the strength of psycho-diagnostic interpretations lies more in the convergence of many fragmentary and faltering leads, less in the indubitable statistical validity of an isolated finding. It may therefore now be helpful to bring out in summary the chief characteristics that the various technics have in common revealed.

The patient was clearly of normal intelligence though he suffered from a lack of conceptual and planning ability. He was distractible but could concentrate if so instructed externally. Evasiveness was an outstanding trait and revealed itself in various guises. He appeared not to face his problems realistically or to express his emotions with any degree of directness. Superficially he conformed to the demands of the environment, but his social relationships were anxious in nature. He glossed over frustrating situations without expressing aggression and resorted readily to the mechanism of repression as an escape from unpleasant experiences. However, the aggression which he failed to express openly played a prominent part in his unconscious adjustments. He actually experienced marked hostility against his parents and, presumably, other individuals in the environment whom he equated with them. At the same time guilt regarding such hostility was so strong that the ambitendent struggle was repressed. He also suffered from a marked sense of inferiority and exhibited various compensatory trends which were colored with moralistic optimism. A sexual maladjustment was indicated. His more general sense of inferiority included sexual inadequacy with possible homosexuality.

Psychodynamic Integration

An attempt will, in conclusion, be made to integrate the test results with the facts of the psychiatric and social history.

A first question arises regarding the possible contribution of constitutional factors. Since the patient was one of twins—who may or may not have been identical—knowledge of the brother's history and personality might be expected to throw light upon the present case. There was, unfortunately, not a great deal known about the brother though, as has already been pointed out, both boys presented problems of adjustment in their early school years and were referred to a child guidance clinic at the age of 11. While they appeared to differ in their symptomatic behavior and in personality at that time, both were maladjusted in their school work and in social relationships. Such recent history as is available substantiates these earlier indications. Whereas the patient was separated on medical grounds from the Coast Guard, the brother was dishonorably discharged from the Navy for repeated violations of discipline that are suggestive of psychopathic personality. The hypothesis may then be tentatively advanced that a common constitutional inadequacy was involved in the two cases and that the patient's maladjustment is in part so to be explained; but this explanation is definitely conjectural and of limited value since, in the first place, it is not known whether the boys were *identical* twins and, in the second, there is no clear basis for determining to what extent their common environment since infancy contributed to their common difficulties of adjustment.*

The relevant experiential factors are somewhat more tangible. However, the relationship of history to contemporary personality is never unequivocal. It is hazardous to point from history alone to determinants of present behavior. Biography may supply leads; projective and other test technics for studying present personality serve the important function of underscoring or confirming such leads. It is probably this corroborative service of the projective methods that should be regarded as their more important contribution though, of course, they also serve to bring out unsurmised factors that might otherwise have been overlooked.

Of the experiential factors here in question, the adoptive situation may first be discussed. Though the patient was not told about the adoption until his ninth year, it is inconceivable that the adoptive situation should not have communicated itself to him before that time. He had never known his natural parents and hence had a basis for anxiety. The situation was aggravated by the fact that he was adopted more or less as an "extra." Since his brother was wanted,

* The patient had at times been considered possibly epileptic and in this connection several electroencephalographic studies were made. The findings were, however, conflicting and inconclusive.

he came along in the bargain. The normal rivalry with his twin could thus have been enhanced.

A second and important related factor was this very rivalry with the twin brother. Twins, it may be assumed, are prone either to less or to more rivalry than ordinary siblings. When they are closely identified with each other, rivalry is reduced; when they are antagonistic, the basis for an extraordinary conflict is present. In this case rivalry was marked and from it, in part, was apparently bred the patient's deep sense of inferiority. Compensatory strivings of an unrealistic type were complementarily present. It is unnecessary, if not impossible, to decide whether a generalized orientation of inferiority or a more specific "castration anxiety" is to be regarded as primary.

The rigidly religious home also had its influence. The ecclesiastical occupation of the father coupled with the overprotective and domineering discipline of the mother doubtless figured in the moralistic and unrealistic optimism of the patient. He was presumably always trying to convince himself that the restrictions of the home were justified even though he did not basically accept them. The advanced age of the parents at the time of the adoption may be assumed to have intensified the lack of essential understanding between them and the children. The mother had persistently interfered in every attempt of the patient to achieve autonomy, occupationally or sexually, and had apparently had a particularly obstructive effect in his development to heterosexual maturity. The father in his role as the less dominant of the parents had offered the patient a weak model for masculine identification. The religious scruples combined with such a parental constellation could very readily have led to the sexual immaturity and possible homosexual orientation which have been described.

From the standpoint of personality structure, hypnotizability as a trait deserves consideration. Evasiveness was one of the patient's outstanding attributes. Superficial social conformity, self-deception, and repression were highly characteristic. His ambitendency regarding aggressiveness must also be considered. While, on the one hand, he was excessively submissive, as, for example, in the situation of hypnosis, on the other hand, as he said of himself, he broke out in violence if he let go at all. Ordinarily the aggressive conflict was repressed.

In the light of the foregoing analysis it becomes possible to formulate an hypothesis regarding the patient's hysterical episodes. It may be assumed that on the basis of a dissociable personality structure his fugues were produced as an escape from intolerable problems at home and within himself. It is significant that he had never had an amnesic attack while at home—a fact first noted in verifying the present hypothesis. The picture of his usual attacks involved two phases: (a) He became a rebel and a fugitive in order to separate himself from some unpleasant environmental situation, domestic or occupational. (b) Sometime in the course of this escape, dissociation set in as if to permit a further escape from the anxiety that his rebellious flight aroused and from the recognition of his conflicts. His unstable aggressive orientation thus expressed itself in the amnesic episodes.

Such a psychodynamic formulation, made possible by the psychiatric and social history in conjunction with the psychologic tests, provided a working basis for understanding and treating the patient.

Chapter 20

Uxoricide on an Unconscious Basis

THAT THE FIELD of criminology has many points of relationship to clinical psychology, psychoanalysis and psychiatry is
well known. There is, moreover, an intriguing analogy between
the methods employed by the detective as he tracks down clues and
attempts to establish identities and those of the psychodiagnostician
who similarly assembles various indications from the behavior of
the person in order to establish a basis for understanding any particular act or set of acts. While the police detective is ordinarily
confronted with the task of identifying the criminal after knowing
the crime, the clinical psychologist knows the nominal identity of
the patient with whom he deals but is concerned to establish the
identity of the forces in the personality, both conscious and unconscious, that give to the person in question the characteristics of his
individuality.

The case report which follows exemplifies the part which unconscious factors may occasionally play in the perpetration of crime.
Moreover, since various psychodiagnostic tests were employed for
studying the personality of the subject and could be correlated with
data from social history, interviews, and medical examinations, the
possible role of psychodiagnosis in cases of this sort is concretely
illustrated.

THE CRIME

The patient was a 48 year-old truckman. Early one morning in
October he appeared at the police station in the town of X and asked
for the lieutenant in charge. The lieutenant was absent so the patient
wandered about the station looking for the police surgeon and others
apparently known to him. He seemed to be preoccupied. Finally

he asked for help in transporting his children to a Home, quite casually explaining that their mother was dead and that he must have killed her. On questioning, he said that the children had been sent to bed early the night before, that he and his wife had retired, listened to the radio and read the paper. Shortly afterward, he had taken some pills that the doctor had left him for low-back pain. He awoke about 1:00 A.M., put on his shoes and walked about the kitchen and bedroom for about a quarter of an hour. He could think only of "bills, bills, bills" and felt that his mind was "twisted." He stopped at the bed, looked at his wife and began to attack her.

When the patient told this story to the police he gave it unhesitatingly and freely. He whimpered and sobbed without tears, from time to time laughing at serious remarks without particular reason. He appeared fascinated by his bloody shoes and displayed them. After the police took over the matter of their care, he showed no further concern about his children. He warned his oldest daughter not to go against her father by saying anything that would harm him. He showed no special reaction to another view of his wife's body; told the children to dress themselves and explained that they were going to an orphanage. He remained quite courteous and cooperative, evinced no emotion in discussing the crime, but showed progressive diminution in clarity about its details.

When interviewed several weeks later at the hospital, to which he was sent for psychiatric observation, the patient gave the following account. He awoke about 1:30 A.M., found that he had his shoes on, that he was on his wife's side of the bed with one foot on her face and was kicking her. He felt as if he were falling out of bed. He jumped out of bed and struck her in the face with his knuckles, trying to see if she would move. He saw a dim light in the kitchen, went to his side of the bed, lay down, then got up. His wife was breathing "hard like a river of water. I wondered what made her breathe like that. She didn't stop breathing so I pushed her head against the top of the bed. I knew there was something wrong. I sat on the side, then

got into my side, took my shoes off. Just before this I walked into
the kitchen—I don't know why—and came back. I had this in my
mind: 'I must have kicked her in the face.' I got a little nervous
and out of patience at her breathing like that. I had a nap. Something came over me; I grabbed a razor; I wanted to cut my wrist
or throat. I felt discouraged, thinking I had killed her. I woke
up again about 4 o'clock with the razor in my hand. I listened but
couldn't hear her breathe any more. I threw the razor on the bureau.
I lay down, didn't know what to do—there was so much on my
conscience. At 5 o'clock I got up, put on my clothes and went to
the police station."

It will be noted that the two foregoing accounts of the crime as
given by the patient can be easily reconciled if a state of semiconsciousness is assumed. The statement given at the police station
centered around the events just preceding the crime and the inception
of the attack at about 1:00 A.M. while the description given at
the hospital appears to cover the events of which he was conscious
when he "awoke" around 1:30. An interval of some 15 or 20
minutes remains unaccounted for and might represent a period of
amnesia.

This surmise is corroborated by the account of the crime later given
by the patient at his trial. His testimony, according to a local newspaper, follows: "'I put on my shoes and went into the bathroom. I
keeled over on the bed and when I awoke I discovered my wife was
bleeding.' . . . He said he was in a stupor, unconscious twenty minutes
and that when he came out of the coma he discovered his wife
bleeding, fatally injured. He was asked why he didn't get a doctor.
'I was so confused, I didn't think of it. There was nobody else in
the room as far as I know so I imagined I had killed my wife.' . . .
He could not remember telling the officers that he had struck his wife
in the face with his fist as hard as he could, or having admitted to
them that he had jumped on his wife's face with his shoes. 'My
mind was twisted. I was confused.'"

Medical and Psychiatric Investigations

Investigation at the hospital confirmed the reported history of back pain. This complaint was, moreover, found by x-ray examination to be symptomatic of marked arthritic changes in the lumbar arch. The symptoms manifested themselves after an attack of erysipelas which led to the patient's first and only hospitalization about eight months before the crime. Lumbar puncture findings were normal. No history indicating epilepsy was elicited nor did electroencephalography confirm this possibility. A normal picture in which alpha waves appeared in two rhythms of six and eleven per second, respectively, without distortion was found. This bimodality, in the light of the psychologic findings, suggested two more or less independent systems of reaction within the cortex. Interviews with sodium amytal were not elaborative.

The crux of the problem seemed to lie in the personality structure and personal history. The patient was at all times a quiet, unobtrusive individual, sociable and friendly. He adjusted extremely well to hospital routine and cooperated in all examinations and interviews. His tone of voice was always subdued, with little modulation. He showed an almost abnormal capacity for circumstantial detail. The general mood was slightly sombre and few affective reactions appeared even in the discussion of the crime. On the other hand, he could become enthusiastic over side issues, particularly sadistic equivalents like his promotion of cockfighting. Projection phenomena were absent. Intelligence appeared to be borderline. Judgment was fairly good, insight superficial. Essentially he was a cold, detached and egocentric person. He gave a detailed account of his life, of which many facts were corroborated by careful social service investigation.

The patient described himself as the youngest by nine years of the three offspring of a quiet, hard-working father—a teamster—and a vulgar, abusive mother. His first recollection concerned an argument between his parents over a red hair found by the mother on his father's coat. Immediately after the quarrel, while his mother was in the privy, he saw his father commit suicide by drinking poison. For years the patient carried the hair—which he believed was that of a horse—as proof of his father's innocence.

Throughout childhood his cruel and selfish brother and sister mistreated and starved him while taunting him for his physical inability to cope with them. He was always lonely and often hungry. With two years of schooling his formal education ceased. At ten he made good a threat to run away. Most of his youth was thereafter spent living from hand to mouth as he wandered over the countryside. In early manhood he enlisted for military duty and served overseas, but he somehow never applied for his bonus even when he needed money.

At the age of about 30 he settled in X and from then on was employed continuously with only one change of jobs. First he worked in a men's club; later as truckman for a dairy company. During this period his needs appeared to crystallize somewhat obsessively in two directions, viz., (1) to work; (2) to get adequate rest so as not to be too tired for further work. On his job he was industrious, business-like and careful of his employer's interests. In his relations with his associates he had a tendency to "get even," chiefly in fantasy, when mistreated.

Before marriage sexual gratification was obtained through casual contacts and without emotional involvement. On one occasion he and a companion "picked up" two sisters, and two years later there was a double wedding. The patient's marriage was "happy" and resulted in seven children of whom one died of poliomyelitis. He was a strict disciplinarian even as concerned his favorite daughter. He much disliked a sister-in-law who was a prostitute and resented her visits to the house. His wife managed the household efficiently but in the course of time, and especially following the birth of twins eight years after the marriage, she became bad-tempered and vulgar. When at this same period it became necessary for financial reasons to give up the family car, she began a series of reproaches which continued through the ensuing years.

About two weeks before the murder the patient surprised the

family by buying a car on terms. It was very old and in poor condition. His wife reproached him for this purchase in view of their economic difficulties, the money that had been spent during his recent illness with erysipelas, and the arrears in their debts, especially bills for milk. But, since they had the car, she decided she would learn to drive and practiced in the yard, damaging three of the tires. The patient concluded that he had better return the car and lose the down payment. His wife upbraided and nagged him for this decision. They did not speak to each other for several days at this time and considerable tension developed over the family finances, especially the disposition of his pay check. These strained relations existed, more or less, during the entire week before the murder.

Two days before the crime he suffered from a severe pain in the back. His wife showed little sympathy, complained that he would become an invalid and be a burden on her since she would have to take the responsibility for his care. The pain was so severe the next morning—preceding the night of the murder—that a physician was called. The patient had to stay away from work—a fact which gave him considerable anxiety though he knew he would lose no pay. The nagging over the car and the bills and over his illness continued. His wife visited her sister, whom the patient disliked, and was quite "mean" to the patient and the children. She became "hysterical" and when he tried to caress and console her, struck him several times. The patient was proud of the fact that he controlled himself at all times. When they finally went to bed, he dreamed of taking the car back, and about bills. The crime occurred as described above. He expressed himself as at a loss regarding its motivation.

PSYCHOLOGIC STUDIES

The patient was seen on eight different occasions for psychologic tests which lasted in all over a period of about 14 hours. Examinations were administered to ascertain intellectual capacities and personality functioning.

It appeared from various intelligence scales that the patient was of borderline or dull-normal intelligence. His ability in tests of conceptual thinking was found to be of a very low order but no pathologic defects, such as occur in schizophrenia or organic psychoses, could be detected. The Wells Memory Test* showed him to be above the level expected from his general intelligence results.

Of greater consequence were those procedures aimed at the determination of psychodynamic trends. The Rorschach method confirmed the findings in the intellectual sphere already mentioned. It added certain information regarding his highly methodical and detailed approach to the ink-blot stimuli—a result which raised a question of obsessional tendencies. No unusual affective disturbance was found with the exception of one or two responses indicative of uncontrolled emotionality. It is significant also that the only movement response he produced concerned the form of a woman apperceived by him with one arm akimbo and with only her torso showing. By her posture, he explained, she seemed to be saying defiantly, "What is this all about?" In addition to the hostility thus revealed several responses showed latent anxiety. The test as a whole did not point to psychosis though more specific psychiatric diagnosis could not be reliably made.

The Thematic Apperception Test yielded stories of considerable interest. One outstanding and recurrent thema was an attitude of being rejected, probably by the mother or wife. Even more striking was a group of related factors centering in concern about strength and manliness—factors of rest, extreme self-control, a strict moral code, physical prowess and deeply rooted aggressive tendencies. Lack of strength often turned up in the stories to present the danger of deep discouragement verging on suicide.

The Kent-Rosanoff Word Association Test gave the patient a group contact rating that placed him just outside the range of normality. Critical words, (shoes, wife, kill) interpolated in the series, yielded

* See footnote for p. 272.

responses which were not unusual either in content or in reaction time. Most of the associations were given in 1–2 seconds. Two delayed responses were: *hand-flat* (15 sec.) and *dream-dreamed* (15 sec.). These delays suggested blocking in reference to the murder. The longest delay, together with some tittering and muttering, occurred on the item *cheese-Dutch* (35 sec.) and was apparently due to emotional factors the nature of which could not at the time be determined. The conclusion seemed warranted that the patient was in good contact with reality and responded without hesitation to words very directly concerned with the murder, but he unconsciously inhibited associations less obviously referring to the crime.

An attempt to hypnotize the patient proved unsuccessful but this result may, of course, have been due to his apprehensiveness of revealing things that could have been to his disadvantage.

In brief, then, the psychologic investigation revealed an individual of approximately dull-normal intelligence who appeared to have more capacity for dealing with concrete than with abstract material. His memory was found to be above the expected level for his intelligence. Projective technics brought to the fore a strong sense of being rejected, deep aggressive tendencies, and some obsessional rigidity. His associations were on the surface well controlled and showed no guilt with respect to the crime, but they seemed more revealing at an unconscious level. He did not prove to be hypnotizable.

Coordination and Interpretation of the Several Findings

The data from the various sources having thus been presented, it now becomes possible to show how they coalesced into a unified view of the case.

Despite the report of the semiconscious condition in which the crime was committed, the neurologic and physical examinations failed to provide support for any important organic determinants, including epilepsy. Such physical illness as existed can hardly be held accountable for the murder. The significance of his illness must have been psychodynamic rather than physical—a matter of the patient's reaction to his indisposition.

Psychodynamically the pivotal point seems to lie in the patient's unconscious concern regarding manliness, virility, or—if a Freudian designation is preferred—"castration anxiety." In the present formulation any of these alternative expressions can be used with equivalent import, and if occasionally a term which is less to the liking of the reader than one of the alternatives should be employed, it is hoped that he will merely substitute the corresponding notion. The only essential idea is that a deep imperative need with its roots in the earliest childhood experiences of the patient compelled him to the crime in order to preserve his sense of vital power. Whether this sense is referred to by such more neutral terms as power, manliness and virility or whether it is thought of as more strictly sexual, and hence related to castration anxiety, affects the argument but slightly.

The father's suicide at the instigation of a jealous wife when the patient was four years old—the height of the Oedipus complex—left him with a great threat to his own life where women were concerned. Women for him represented possible death. He was not only identified with his father; he also loved him. Hence he kept for years the red hair which served as proof of the father's unjust death and the guilt of his mother. That his mother was in the privy at the time of the suicide may have intensified the sexual aspects of the experience for him. Her mistreatment of him reinforced his fears. Hence at the early age of ten, when he was verging once more on the Oedipus complex (of puberty), he ran away from home and supported himself from then on. That he carried through such an unusual scheme of life for a boy of this age is strong proof of his great anxieties regarding his mother.

The identification with and love of the father requires further consideration. Fearing and hating the mother, identified with and loving the father, the boy was in danger of homosexuality. Homosexuality, however, represented the further peril that to be an apt object for a man's love, he would have to be emasculated. He was thus in an intolerable dilemma—both men and women represented possible castration for him. There was only one solution—repression and a reaction formation in which the importance of physical strength and rest, together with a strict moral code, played the chief roles.

In his struggle for strength the automobile assumed special importance. He acquired a car shortly after his arrival in X and used it very largely as an adjunct to his sexual prowess. With it he could pick up girls—among them his future wife. He owned an automobile continuously until eight years after his marriage. At that date, which may well be regarded as a turning-point in his life, several significant events simultaneously occurred. For one thing, he lost his job at the men's club where he had worked for nearly ten years; in the second place, his wife gave birth to twins and, according to the patient, became from then on irritable, profane and nagging; thirdly, and perhaps because of the two preceding strains upon his finances, he found it necessary to sell his automobile. The solution for this three-fold setback was found in a single stroke—he obtained a new job as truckman for a dairy company. In this way he once more found himself in a paying position and behind the wheel of an automobile. Moreover, since his new employer treated him as a father would a son, he was not merely regaining a car, with all that it might mean to him as regards manly power, but he was also reinforcing his identification with his father. (His father, it will be recalled, had been a teamster.) By emphasizing his relationship with his father surrogate, he could compensate for his wife's growing callousness. An alternative view is that his budding friendship with his father surrogate may have reawakened the buried hostility toward his wife (mother surrogate) so that he began to regard her as vulgar and irritable if he did not actually provoke her to assume such a role. In either case this new adjustment in his job as truckman was adequate for a number of years until one day about eight months before the murder he bumped his nose on the handle of the truck door and by subsequent infection developed erysipelas. He was hospitalized for two or three weeks as a result and was out of work for about two months. The importance of this illness was manifold. By being thrown out of work for so long a time his confidence in himself as a man was distinctly shaken, particularly since he had bungled in the use of the truck and been injured in a place which is an easy unconscious substitute for the penis. To make matters worse, when he returned to his job it was thought best for him to serve as helper on the truck instead of driver.

From this point on a combination of difficulties involving an automobile and some phase of physical illness played a prominent part and worked together to impress upon him his growing loss of manly power (castration anxiety).

Having been deposed as truck-driver he decided about two weeks before the crime to surprise the family by buying an automobile. His wife dwelt upon the practical problems created by this new drain on their limited resources. All their arguments over the car, including the fuss about her attempts at learning to drive, served to reinforce his insecurity. That he found it impossible to please her no mattter what he did regarding the car, and that she was ruining it by her driving, had an indubitable significance for his unconscious attitudes— she was threatening him at every step. When, on the day of the murder, he finally made up his mind that he would take the car back the next day, there must already have been prepared within him an enormous reservoir of aggressive tension against her. It is possible that the acute attack of arthritis in the lower back, which assailed him about two days before the crime and while the arguments over the car prevailed, had a psychologic foundation in the earlier association of the accident to his nose, the erysipelas and his deposition as truck-driver. It will be recalled that his arthritis actually first developed at the time of these events. Now that he was having renewed difficulties as the driver of an automobile of his own, physical illness reasserted itself. Little wonder, then, that he protested so strongly against staying out of work at this time even though he knew in advance that he would not lose any salary. To him absence from work was far more important in its psychologic than in its financial significance. Hence, when his wife viewed his arthritis unsympathetically and told him he would probably become an invalid for life, she was unwittingly sowing the seeds of her own destruction. For, more and more, she was forcing him into the dangerous position which his identification with his father had from his fourth year of life represented for him. She was herself at the same time increasingly assuming the role of his hated mother.

On the evening of the murder, with the arguments about his illness and the purchase of the car still in the air, they listened to the Betty-Lou radio program (patient's favorite) and read in the newspaper just before retiring about an automobile accident on a nearby highway cut-off in which someone was killed. At this point his unconscious plight must have become sharply focused: his wife had interpreted his illness as the beginning of invalidism, i.e., powerlessness; the car (power symbol) which he had bought and his wife had nearly destroyed was to be returned; the radio program was one in which a man "becomes" a (little) girl, i.e., emasculated; the newspaper account involved once more an automobile but with the significant addition of a fatal accident occurring on a road designated as a *cut-off*. Accordingly he dreamed of taking the car back and of bills—both of which ideas signified his impotence. It is assumed that he was now acutely confronted with the fate of his father in its unconscious sexual equivalent—the fate of castration. His contemplation of suicide with the razor vividly supports this view. But to save himself from just such a fate may be supposed to have been one of his deepest unconscious needs since that early moment when the father with whom he was identified resorted to suicide as an escape from *his* wife's aggression. In this light the uxoricide was an act of unconscious self-defense against intolerable castration anxiety.

PSYCHIATRIC DIAGNOSIS AND DISPOSITION OF THE CASE

Thus far motivational history alone has been considered. The problem of the personality structure at the time of the murder still remains. As has already been pointed out, the possible diagnosis of epilepsy finds little support from the history of the patient or from neurologic studies. At no time was clear evidence of psychosis found. As differentiated from any clear break with reality, the dominant picture appears rather to have been that of a definitely unusual personality structure characterized by highly formalized and rigid attitudes. Perfectionism and obsessional tendencies, combined with a cold emotional detachment, were salient traits. Such a personality picture is not uncommonly found among chronic arthritics.

The role of this personality in the precipitation of the crime may be represented as follows. As long as this rigid structure could be maintained without serious danger of disruption, the patient was able to give every appearance of normality. He could exercise self-control and be proud of it. When, however, he was finally threatened by an unprecedented combination of circumstances, the intense latent anxiety which it was the function of this personality structure to guard broke through, perhaps during the lowered resistance of semiconsciousness, and released the unmitigated hostility of the crime. In the light of such a view the patient was diagnosed as "Without Psychosis, Psychopathic Personality with Pathological Emotionality."

While it is thus possible to understand his behavior as not representing a preconceived or deliberate deed, legally he was not adjudged insane in the technical sense of being unaware of the nature and consequences of his act. Moreover, in such a personality structure, with the age and intelligence of the patient being what they were, there seemed to be little hope of producing any essential modification. But without such alteration one could have had no assurance that under similar psychologic conditions he would not repeat his behavior. From the standpoint of protecting society, the sentence of life imprisonment which he received would therefore appear to have been justified.

CORROBORATION BY FOLLOW-UP

The patient having been sentenced, it became possible to visit him and attempt to verify the interpretation of the case. One could now obtain further information under conditions where he would have less to gain by concealment. Deliberation over a definite hypothesis had, moreover, suggested questions that would rather specifically test the psychodynamic formulation. The psychologist accordingly interviewed the patient for several hours in prison after about eight months of the sentence had been served.

The very first words the patient spoke after spontaneously recognizing the examiner were, "Isn't it terrible that I should have to be here just because my wife happened to fall down and hit her head against a cedar chest?" He was encouraged to explain this unexpected remark. In consequence, the following somewhat new version of the crime was given.

While he was in bed on the evening of the crime with the low-back pain already mentioned, he and his two older daughters listened to the Betty-Lou radio program. After a time his wife requested that he send the children to bed, appealing to him because she knew that his word carried greater weight with them. When the children had gone to their room to undress, he and his wife discussed the newspaper account of the automobile accident. The girls now returned on their way to the bathroom and stopped at their father's bed to chat. They were dressed only in panties. The mother, appearing from the kitchen and seeing them, flew into a rage and called them obscene names.

"Imagine her having such ideas," he interrupted himself, "when they were only 10 and 11 years old." Asked why his wife might have taken this attitude, he explained that the oldest girl was his favorite child, and that though she was only 11, she acted like 14 in some ways. "Of course," he added, "she was getting a little developed." Pointing to his breasts, he suited the action to the words. "My wife had been at the children for about two weeks (the length of time during which the arguments over the car went on) to wear more clothes when passing through the bedroom to the bathroom."

The mother rushed at the girls to punish them; they escaped to their own room through the door. As she was about to follow, the patient, sick as he was, jumped out of bed and covered their retreat by standing in the doorway. His wife, blocked by him, started to force her way through. He took hold of her and, insisting that she was getting too excited for her own good and should go to bed, helped her undress—"but without hurting her," he added. Having secured her in bed he proceeded to get in himself. As soon as he had put out the light, she jumped out of bed and again made for the children's room. The patient followed and his wife, in trying to avoid him, tripped over the rug, fell, and bumped her head against the edge of the cedar chest. She seemed unconscious so he picked her up and carried her to the bed. As he let her body descend, his own became limp. He lay down and, falling asleep, dreamt about the "kids," bills, and the car. At 1 o'clock he awoke and went to the bathroom. The door was ajar and he bumped his head as he entered. He became confused and returned to bed. He lay down again with his shoes on. Some sort of spell now overcame him and when he awoke around 1:30 (he could see the clock, he explained), he found that he had been kicking his wife in the face. At 5 o'clock he decided to go to the police station.

However fabricated in other respects, especially as regards the possible accidental contribution to his wife's death, one aspect of this account is apparently unimpeachable—the sexual jealousy of the wife. Here for the first time clearly emerges the crucially precipitating motive of the crime. Up to now the prevailing circumstances at the time of the crime—the dispute over the car and the disagreements about his illness—have been symbolically interpreted as "castration" threats. This new light perfectly completes the previous interpretation by supplying the one factor needed to make the present situation agree fully with the original one in which the castration anxiety of the patient had been crystallized—the father's suicide at the instigation of the mother's sexual jealousy.

Asked about the razor which he had formerly said he held in his hand on the night of the crime with the thought of using it to cut his throat or wrist, the patient could recall no such plan of suicide. He added, nevertheless, that there was a razor in the bedroom—on the bureau where it always lay. This razor had formerly belonged to his father-in-law, from whom his wife inherited it. She used to cut her toenails with this razor and had, in fact, done so around noon on the day of the crime. On the assumption that his original story about the razor had now undergone repression, one may note that the razor which belonged to his *wife's father* and was used by her for cutting her toenails (suggestive of castration) would be a natural weapon for his contemplated self-destruction on the pattern of his own father's suicide. That he did not carry out the plan—and instead repressed the memory of it—bespeaks the essential function of the father's suicide in setting the stage to prevent just such a fate for himself and replacing it with the outwardly directed aggression as a defense.

In order to probe further into the significance of the baffling longest-delayed association of the Word Association Test—"cheese-Dutch"—the patient was casually asked whether he knew any unusual meaning of the word "cheese." (It should perhaps be indicated that the psychologist had discovered in attempting to track down this association that "cheese" had a sexual connotation not previously known to him: cheese = smegma.) The examiner said that he had heard this word used in some peculiar sense lately; he wondered if the patient could help out in its interpretation. The patient's first reply was that the word meant "a dairy product." He used to deliver such things when he worked as a truck-driver, he suggested. Soon, however, he added that perhaps something about a woman—some bad meaning of the term—had been meant. He then mentioned a song which he had learned when he was in the army: "Maggie's drawers were full of cheese." He recited several verses. Later in the conversation, without any relationship to the word "cheese" being indicated, the patient was asked about the nationality of his various relatives, among them his wife, father and mother. (An hypothesis regarding the association *Dutch* was here being tested.) It turned out that one of these—and only one—was of *Dutch* extraction: his mother.

One may then venture to interpret the most-delayed word association as follows: the word "cheese" first brought up a sexual association in terms of the obscene song he had learned in the army and this perhaps set off a further association involving his mother. He naturally blocked, lengthening the response time. He searched in embarrassment—as shown by some observed tittering and muttering—for a way out of his dilemma and lighted finally upon the seemingly harmless word "Dutch" which in one of its meanings would give the innocuous phrase "Dutch cheese"—something to eat. However, he was betrayed by his unconscious because the word "Dutch" (rather than such alternatives as Swiss or American, for instance) occurred not only because it signified a kind of cheese but also because it had reference to his mother—the very association he was attempting to inhibit. This interpretation, obviously speculative, is, however, in agreement with the view that in killing his wife he was actually responding in terms of a sexual complex involving his mother.

CONCLUSION AND SUMMARY

From the standpoint of psychiatric diagnosis the patient was difficult to characterize. The state of his consciousness at the time of the murder could not be accurately described but that the act represented an eruption of great suddenness and violence out of an extremely rigid personality structure can scarcely be doubted. For statistical purposes he was diagnosed "Without Psychosis, Psychopathic Personality with Pathological Emotionality."

Psychodynamically the uxoricide appeared to have been essentially a defense against possible "castration" by the wife. The anxiety was traceable to frustrating childhood experiences in which the suicide of the patient's father, resulting from the mother's sexual jealousy, was the most traumatic moment. That one speaks here more properly of castration anxiety than of death fear, although the original childhood situation involved the actual death of the father, becomes clear when it is recognized that the patient's wife confronted him not with the prospect of physical extinction but with the loss of manliness or virility —the psychical equivalent of physical death.

The conclusions reached in the analysis of this case were the result of close cooperation between psychiatric and medical investigators, social service workers, physiologist and psychologists. Thus the psychiatric history and the social service investigation provided the personal data about the patient's relationship to his parents and his subsequent experiences with his wife. The physical examination and medical history confirmed the story of illnesses he suffered shortly before and during the crime, though these had to be evaluated in the light of their psychologic meaning for him. The psychologic studies at many points supported and supplemented the psychodynamics arrived at by the other methods as, for example, in showing the great importance of physical strength and rest to him, his sense of being rejected by women, and his deeply repressed aggressiveness.

Part V

THE FUTURE

Chapter 21

Psychodiagnosis as a Science

DURING the second quarter of the present century psychology has emerged as a profession. In this development the clinical aspects of the science have naturally taken the leading part. Problems of psychodiagnosis and of selection and, to a lesser extent, those of counseling and psychotherapy were emphasized during World War II and are currently finding broad application in Veterans Administration facilities, through the support of the U. S. Public Health Service, and in numerous outlets at universities and community agencies. The demand for clinical psychologists has correspondingly increased and the salaries in this field of work equal where they do not exceed some of the best paid positions in the academic setting. There is, in other words, a distinct boom in psychology as a profession or, more particularly, in clinical psychology.

This change of the times has obviously had a very desirable effect upon the immediate practical fortunes of the psychologist. However, the new order has brought with it a number of problems concerned, for example, with the relationships of the psychologist to the psychiatrist and social worker, and with the training of the clinical psychologist in combined university and practicum arrangements.

Not least among these emerging problems is that related to the scientific and theoretical foundations of clinical psychology. While psychodiagnosis and psychotherapy are distinctly matters of art as much as of science, the development of the latter aspect is basic to the continued soundness of the former. That the issue requires consideration is recognized by all serious workers in the clinical area. Whether more academically oriented psychologists are aware of the problem or not, it is of significance to them also. One writer (5, p. 210) in the latter group warns the growing profession that the practices of the clinician if they come to dominate psychology may do it in. Says he: "It is the systematic psychological structure which has made possible the clinical field and other applications. Pure science must come before application. If the systematic structure in psychology ceases to grow, it is doubtful if adequate application can be made beyond the present limits of the psychological system. Are we killing the goose that laid the golden eggs?" The note of caution in this statement that calls upon us to emphasize ultimate rather than immediate goals cannot be ignored. Whether, however, the goose in the parable has been properly identified is a question that requires clarification.

To illustrate first the present gap between clinical practice and personality theory, it need only be recalled how considerable a part of the current research in clinical psychology deals with such matters as diagnostic differentiations in the psychiatric sense or with the selection of individuals for one or another vocational role. While there can be no doubt about the practical value of such objectives, it is worth noting that in the former case—that of psychiatric diagnosis—the labors of the clinical psychologist rest in the long run upon an unstable foundation. In numerous quarters the need for abandoning or radically revising present psychiatric classification has been stressed. Similarly, tools of selection, however excellent, contribute relatively little to systematic science. While the statement is admittedly hazardous, it is at least not beyond credence that the best practical tools will emerge from improved theoretical understanding—the test being derived from the experiment. Tests which are constructed in the absence of, or in isolation from, psychologic theory are apt soon to become outmoded.

It might then be countered that the clinical psychologist would be well advised to build his psychodiagnostic tests and counseling procedures upon the theories of academic psychology. While to a limited extent this advice is valid, it raises the question mentioned earlier—the identity of the goose to be credited with laying the golden eggs. What, in actual fact, is the theoretical foundation upon which clinical psychology rests? And, further, upon what such foundation can it hope to prosper?

Examination of the history of psychology reveals that the theories of the academic psychologist and the practices of the clinical psychologist have, for the most part, developed independently of each other. On occasion, to be sure, the one field has fertilized the other and there has been a fruitful consummation. Thus, for example, the studies in word association initiated by Francis Galton on a more or less clinical basis led to certain systematic formulations at the hands of Wundt and his students, then made possible the verification of some aspects of Freudian theory by Jung and his colleagues, and finally emerged as a psychodiagnostic test. Many such instances would, however, be difficult to find. It would in all probability be easier to discover examples of the influence of medicine and literature upon clinical psychology. Consequently the formulations of the systematic psychologist are apt to have little relevance to the problems with which the psychiatrist and social worker are confronted. The methods and concepts employed by the clinical psychologist have likewise profited but little from the theories of general psychology. The unfortunate fact is that the psychologist working in the university setting has typically concerned himself with certain general laws of behavior in which segments or isolated functions of the so-called average human being have been viewed in their relationships to one another. The individual as such in his personal idiosyncrasies as these appear in the work of the clinical psychologist—and in that of the psychiatrist and the social worker—has been almost completely ignored.

In justification for such an omission there has, of course, been the assumption that an understanding of the general laws of behavior should make it possible to infer any necessary knowledge about the particular individual. It has been further indicated that the individual as such is never the proper concern of science which, by definition, deals in generalization. But, as G. W. Allport and others have maintained, these assumptions overlook the fact that the definition of science is a matter, not of tradition or of revelation, but of convenience in relation to the problems confronting man. Systematization in psychology is, similarly, not coercive but optional to a very large degree. The choice of data to be observed and of concepts to describe them is a very real one, representing, in fact, one of the chief responsibilities of a young science like psychology.

It is therefore a matter of note that there are today numerous signs pointing to the individual as the unit of study and intended to close the hiatus between general laws and personal behavior. It becomes more and more a matter of doubt whether one can deduce from general laws of segmental behavior the structure and function of individuals. If one is to learn about the individual it seems probable that one will need to begin with him in all his inner intricacies as the unit of observation and conceptualization—an enterprise that must include not only the practical work of the clinical psychologist but the efforts of the laboratory worker as well.

In the growing professional consciousness of the clinical psychologist, and especially if he has a psychodynamic orientation, there is thus a certain unrest as to the designation of his field as "applied." Since historically there is no clear relationship of dependence between academic psychology and the practical work of the clinician, considerable doubt exists as to just what is being applied. There is less doubt regarding the objects to which the application is being made—the mental patient, the vocational advisee or the job applicant. Clinical psychology as *applied* thus becomes a psychology which is relevant to the problems of everyday life without at the same time being a psychology grounded upon the systematic foundations of academic science. The goose in the parable turns out to have been somewhat misidentified.

Such a bald statement of the case is obviously false to many of the subtle interrelationships between academic theory and clinical practice as these have developed during the past century. What may, however, be reasonably inferred is that the dichotomy of *applied* and *pure* psychology is misleading where personality is concerned. In other words, clinical psychology unfortunately has not in any real sense represented or been able to represent the application of pure psychology. To solve the implied problem it would seem that the clinical worker has need to recognize the theoretical implications of his tools and of his concepts; the academic psychologist may reasonably be expected to reorient some of his efforts toward the study of the total individual. Should such developments occur, clinical psychology would become not merely a field of dubious application but in considerable measure the content of systematic psychology.

The center of gravity in psychology would thus be shifted from the older experimental concern with the generalized average man to the study of the structure and organization of the individual person. The earlier role of the clinical psychologist, according to which he was cast as a psychometrician who dealt with the measurement of intelligence, would give way to one in which he would function as a psychodiagnostician in the fullest sense—with as much interest in research as in practice. The university psychologist would similarly turn from the investigation of relationships between behavior segments to a study of functions intrinsic to the individual. Such a reorientation could transform the opportunistic danger of the present practical boom in clinical psychology into a lasting scientific advance.

Signs of such a liaison are already on the horizon and the concepts and methods for implementing the advance are beginning to crystallize (14, 15, 17). Among the issues that insistently here demand inquiry three major ones may be cited: (1) The systematic reconciliation of *clinical, experimental* and *statistical* modes of observation; the aptness of the projective technics in such an effort. (2) The significance of *normality* and *norms* in mental health and adjustment; the needed availability of data from so-called normal persons as a basis for interpreting the so-called abnormal. (3) The relationships of the various *levels* of personality—opinion (self-evaluative), overt (directly observed), and implicit (autistically projective); the validity of measurements and predictions of behavior in this perspective.

Progress in settling such issues must mean the coalescence of clinical practice with experimental discipline, and each degree of success will to the same extent fortify the art of psychodiagnosis with the necessary science.

GENERAL BIBLIOGRAPHY

*1. Buros, O. K. (Editor) The 1938 Mental Measurements Yearbook. New Brunswick: Rutgers University Press, 1938.

*2. Buros, O. K. (Editor) The 1940 Mental Measurements Yearbook. Highland Park, New Jersey: The Mental Measurements Yearbook, 1940. (Another edition of *The Mental Measurements Yearbook* is in press.)

3. Burton, A., and Harris, R. E. (Editors) Case Histories in Clinical and Abnormal Psychology. New York: Harpers, 1947.

4. Darley, J. G. Testing and Counseling in the High-School Guidance Program. Chicago: Science Research Associates, 1943.

5. Fernberger, S. W. The future of psychology, or the goose that laid the golden eggs. *Am. Psychologist*, 1947, 2, 209–210.

6. Greene, E. B. Measurements of Human Behavior. New York: Odyssey Press, 1941.

*7. Hildreth, G. A Bibliography of Mental Tests and Rating Scales. New York: Psychological Corporation, 1939.

*8. Hildreth, G. A Bibliography of Mental Tests and Rating Scales. 1945 Supplement. New York: Psychological Corporation, 1945.

9. Hunt, W. A. The future of diagnostic testing in clinical psychology. *J. clin. Psychol.*, 1946, 2, 311–317.

10. Murray, H. A., et al. Explorations in Personality. New York: Oxford University Press, 1938.

11. Mursell, J. L. Psychological Testing. New York: Longmans, Green, 1947.

*12. Pennington, L. A., and Berg, I. A. (Editors) Introduction to Clinical Psychology. New York: Ronald Press, 1948.

13. Richards, T. W. Modern Clinical Psychology. New York: McGraw-Hill, 1946.

*14. Rosenzweig, S. Investigating and appraising personality. Chap. 18 in *Methods of Psychology*, ed. by T. G. Andrews. New York: John Wiley & Sons, 1948.

15. Rosenzweig, S. Norms and the individual in the psychologist's perspective. In *Second International Symposium of Feelings and Emotions*, ed. by M. Reymert. In press.

* Asterisk indicates that the reference in question includes a fairly extensive bibliography related to its subject matter.

16. Rosenzweig, S., Bundas, L. E., Lumry, K., and Davidson, H. W. An elementary syllabus of psychological tests. *J. Psychol.*, 1944, 18, 9–40.

17. Rosenzweig, S., Roe, A., MacKinnon, D. W., Snyder, W. U., Combs, A. W., Zubin, J. and Klein, G. S. Clinical practice and personality theory: a symposium. *J. abnorm. soc. Psychol.* 1949, 44, in press.

18. Shaffer, L. F. Clinical psychology and psychiatry. *J. consult. Psychol.*, 1947, 11, 5–11.

19. Thorne, F. C. The clinical method in science. *Am. Psychologist*, 1947, 2, 159–166.

*20. Wells, F. L. Mental Tests in Clinical Practice. New York: World Book, 1927.

Index

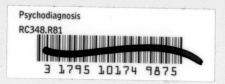